HYDROLOGY FOR ENGINEERS

McGraw-Hill Civil Engineering Series

HARMER E. DAVIS, *Consulting Engineer*

HYDROLOGY FOR ENGINEERS

RAY K. LINSLEY, JR.
Professor of Hydraulic Engineering
Stanford University

MAX A. KOHLER
Chief Research Hydrologist
United States Weather Bureau

JOSEPH L. H. PAULHUS
Staff Hydrologist
United States Weather Bureau

McGRAW-HILL BOOK COMPANY, INC.
New York   Toronto   London
1958

THE MAPLE PRESS COMPANY, YORK, PA.

To the memory of

MERRILL BERNARD

*friend and colleague
whose enthusiasm was a source
of inspiration to the authors*

PREFACE

The publication in 1949 of "Applied Hydrology" was well received, and that book has found extensive use as a text in schools of engineering. No single book can meet all needs, and "Hydrology for Engineers" has been written specifically to serve as an elementary text. The emphasis throughout is on quantitative methods of arriving at answers to hydrologic problems. The handbook approach, as exemplified by the many empirical formulas widely used in the early days of hydrology, has been avoided.

"Hydrology for Engineers" is not a mere condensation of "Applied Hydrology." While there is much similarity in the organization, the text has been completely rewritten. Where appropriate, new methods and concepts developed since 1949 have been included. The experience of the authors in teaching hydrology over several years has been utilized as a basis for selecting topics to be included and methods of presentation.

The student should find hydrology an interesting subject but one much different from most of his engineering courses. The natural phenomena with which hydrology is concerned do not lend themselves to rigorous analyses such as are possible in engineering mechanics. There is, therefore, a greater variety of methods, more latitude for judgment, and a seeming lack of accuracy in problem solutions. Actually, the accuracy of sound hydrologic solutions compares favorably with other types of engineering computations. Uncertainties in engineering are frequently hidden by use of factors of safety, rigidly standardized working procedures, and conservative assumptions regarding properties of materials.

The authors gratefully acknowledge the splendid cooperation of their many friends and colleagues whose helpful suggestions have added much to this text. Special appreciation goes to Walter T. Wilson and David Hershfield of the U.S. Weather Bureau for review and comments on frequency analysis, to Professor Stanley N. Davis of Stanford University for his helpful review of the chapter on groundwater, and to T. J. Nordenson of the Weather Bureau for many suggestions. Professor J. B. Franzini of Stanford reviewed the entire manuscript, and many of his worthwhile suggestions are incorporated in the final text. Miss Dianne Linsley prepared the final manuscript.

Ray K. Linsley, Jr.
Max A. Kohler
Joseph L. H. Paulhus

CONTENTS

SYMBOLS AND ABBREVIATIONS

SYMBOLS

A area
a coefficient
B width
b coefficient
C Chézy coefficient
C runoff coefficient
C electrical capacitance
C_p synthetic unit-hydrograph coefficient of peak
C_t synthetic unit-hydrograph coefficient of lag
c coefficient
c_s sediment concentration
D depth
D degree days
d diameter
d coefficient
E evaporation
E erosion
E voltage
E_T evapotranspiration
e vapor pressure
e base of Napierian logarithms
e_a atmospheric vapor pressure
e_s saturation vapor pressure
F fall
F force
F total infiltration
f relative humidity
$f(\ )$ function of
f_c final infiltration capacity
f_i infiltration rate
f_0 initial infiltration capacity
f_p infiltration capacity
G safe yield of a groundwater basin
G_i bed-load transport
g gage height
g acceleration of gravity
H_v heat of vaporization
h height, head
I inflow
I antecedent-precipitation index
i rainfall intensity
i electric current

i_s supply rate (rainfall less retention)
J probability of occurrence
j portion of streambed subject to shear
K Muskingum storage constant
K frequency factor
K compaction coefficient
K_b base-flow recession constant
K_d direct-runoff recession constant
K_p coefficient of permeability
K_r recession coefficient
K_w conductivity
k coefficient
L length
L_c distance from outlet to center of a basin
L_o length of overland flow
M snowmelt
M_i suspended sediment transport
m coefficient or exponent
m rank
N normal precipitation
N number
n Manning roughness coefficient
n coefficient or exponent
n number
O outflow
O_g subsurface seepage
P probability of nonoccurrence
P precipitation
p pressure
p porosity
pF   logarithm of capillary potential in centimeters of water
Q volume of discharge or runoff
Q_b net long-wave radiation
Q_e energy used for evaporation
Q_g groundwater-flow volume
Q_h sensible-heat transfer
Q_n net radiant energy
Q_r reflected short-wave radiation
Q_s volume of surface streamflow
Q_s short-wave radiation
Q_v advected energy
Q_θ change in energy storage
q discharge rate
q_b base-flow discharge
q_d direct-runoff discharge
q_e equilibrium flow rate
q_h specific humidity
q_p peak discharge
q_s sediment discharge rate
R hydraulic radius
R Bowen's ratio

R resistance

R_g gas constant

r radius

S storage

S volume of surface retention

S_c storage constant of an aquifer

S_g groundwater storage

S_s surface storage

s slope

s_b slope of channel bottom

s_o slope of overland flow plane

s_r $dg/u\ dt$

T temperature

T transmissibility

T time base of unit hydrograph

T_L lag time

T_d dewpoint temperature

T_r return period or recurrence interval

T_w wet-bulb temperature

t time

t_c time of concentration

t_e time to equilibrium

t_p basin lag

t_R duration of rain

t_r unit duration of rain for synthetic unit hydrograph

U unit-hydrograph ordinate

u wave celerity

u a factor in well hydraulics

V_e volume of surface detention at equilibrium

V_0 volume of surface detention when $i = 0$

v velocity

v_g horizontal velocity of sediment particles

v_s settling velocity

W infiltration index

W_p precipitable water

$W(u)$ well function of u

w specific weight

w_g specific weight of sediment

w_m ultimate specific weight of sediment deposits

X a variable

$\bar{X}$ the mean of X

X_f the mode of X

x distance

x a constant or exponent

Y a variable

Y a vertical distance

$\bar{Y}$ the mean of Y

y a vertical distance

y a reduced variate in frequency analysis

y_n a statistical factor in frequency analysis

Z drawdown in a well

z a vertical distance
α evaporation portion of advected energy
β constant
Δ slope of vapor pressure vs. temperature curve
Δ an increment
ϵ mixing coefficient
θ an angle
Λ total potential
μ absolute viscosity
ν kinematic viscosity
ξ ratio of average sediment load to bottom concentration
γ Bowen's ratio coefficient
π 3.1416 . . .
ρ density
Σ summation
σ standard deviation
τ shear
τ_0 shear at channel bed
τ_c critical shear
Υ du Boys' coefficient
Φ infiltration index
χ $v_s/\sqrt{gDs}$
ψ capillary potential

ABBREVIATIONS

acre-ft   acre-foot
atm   atmosphere
Btu   British thermal unit
cal   calories
$C°$ centigrade degrees
cu   cubic
cfs   cubic feet per second
csm   cubic feet per second per square mile
cm   centimeters
$F°$ Fahrenheit degrees
Fig.   Figure
ft   feet
fps   feet per second
g   gram
gpd   gallons per day
gpm   gallons per minute
hr   hour
Hg   mercury (chemical symbol)
in.   inches
$\log_e$ logarithm to base e
$\log_{10}$ logarithm to base 10
ly   Langley
mb   millibar
m   meter

mi	mile
min	minute
mgd	million gallons per day
mo	month
mph	miles per hour
msl	mean sea level
oz	ounce
ppm	parts per million
pt	pint
sec	seconds
sfd	second-foot-day
sfm	second-foot-minute
sq	square
yr	year

1

INTRODUCTION

Hydrology is that branch of physical geography which is concerned with the origin, distribution, and properties of the waters of the earth. Engineering hydrology includes those segments of the very broad field of hydrology pertinent to the design and operation of engineering projects for the control and use of water. The boundaries between hydrology and other earth sciences such as meteorology, oceanography, and geology are indistinct, and no good purpose is served by attempting to define them rigidly. Likewise, the distinctions between engineering hydrology and other branches of applied hydrology are vague. Indeed, the engineer owes much of his present knowledge of hydrology to agriculturists, foresters, meteorologists, geologists, and others in a variety of fields.

1-1. The hydrologic cycle. The concept of the *hydrologic cycle* is a useful, if somewhat academic, point from which to begin the study of hydrology. This cycle (Fig. 1-1) is visualized as beginning with the evaporation of water from the oceans. The resulting vapor is transported by moving air masses. Under the proper conditions, the vapor is condensed to form clouds, which in turn may result in precipitation. The precipitation which falls upon land is dispersed in several ways. The greater part is temporarily retained in the soil near where it falls and is ultimately returned to the atmosphere by evaporation and transpiration by plants. A portion of the water finds its way over and through the surface soil to stream channels, while other water penetrates farther into the ground to become part of the earth's groundwater supply. Under the influence of gravity, both surface streamflow and groundwater move toward lower elevations and may eventually discharge into the ocean. However, substantial quantities of surface and underground water are returned to the atmosphere by evaporation and transpiration before reaching the oceans.

This description of the hydrologic cycle and the schematic diagram of Fig. 1-1 are enormously oversimplified. For example, some water which enters surface streams may percolate to the groundwater, while in other cases groundwater is a source of surface streamflow. Some precipitation may remain on the ground as snow for many months before melting releases the water to the streams or groundwater. The hydrologic cycle is a convenient means for a rough delineation of the scope of hydrology as that portion between precipitation on the land and the return of this water to the atmosphere or the ocean. The hydrologic cycle serves also to emphasize the four basic phases of interest to the hydrologist: precipitation, evaporation and transpiration, surface streamflow, and groundwater. These topics are the subject of much more detailed discussion later in this text.

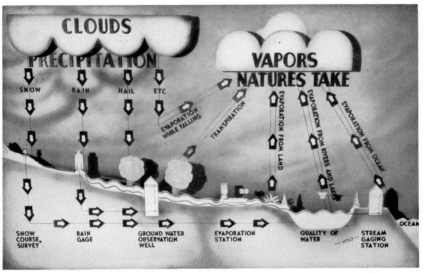

FIG. 1-1. The hydrologic cycle. (*Courtesy of U.S. Geological Survey.*)

If the discussion of the hydrologic cycle gives any impression of a continuous mechanism through which water moves steadily at a constant rate, this impression should be dispelled at once. The movement of water through the various phases of the cycle is most erratic, both in time and area. On occasion, nature seems to work overtime to provide torrential rains which tax surface-channel capacities to the utmost. At other times it seems that the machinery of the cycle has stopped completely and, with it, precipitation and streamflow. In adjacent areas the variations in the cycle may be quite different. It is precisely these extremes of flood and drought that are often of most interest to the engineering hydrologist, for many of our hydraulic engineering projects are designed to protect against the ill effect of extremes. The reasons for these climatic extremes are found in the science of meteorology and should be understood, in broad detail at least, by the hydrologist.   This aspect of hydrology is discussed in the following chapter.

The hydrologist is interested in more than obtaining a qualitative understanding of the hydrologic cycle and measuring the quantities of water in transit in this cycle.   He must be able to deal quantitatively with the interrelations between the various factors so that he can accurately predict the influence of man-made works on these relationships. He must also concern himself with the frequency with which the various extremes of the cycle may occur, for this is the basis of economic analysis which is, or should be, the final determinant for all hydraulic projects. The final chapters of this text deal with these quantitative problems.

1-2. History.   The first hydraulic project has been lost in the mists of prehistory.   Perhaps some prehistoric man found that a pile of rocks across a stream would raise the water level sufficiently to overflow the land which was the source of his wild food plants and thus water them during a drought.   Whatever the early history of hydraulics, abundant evidence exists to show that the builders understood little hydrology. Abandoned irrigation projects the world over, including Indian works in the southwest United States dating from about A.D. 1100, are believed to be evidence of developments inadequate to sustain a permanent civilization.

Early Greek and Roman writings indicate that these people could accept the oceans as the ultimate source of all water but they could not visualize precipitation equaling or exceeding streamflow.   Typical of the ideas of the time was a view that sea water moved underground to the base of the mountains.   There a natural still desalted the water and the vapor rose through conduits to the mountain tops where it condensed and escaped at the source springs of the streams.   Leonardo da Vinci (ca. A.D. 1500) seems to have been one of the first to recognize the hydrologic cycle as we accept it today, but Perreault of France offered the first recorded proof about A.D. 1650.   Using crude instruments, he measured the flow of the Seine River and found it to be only one-sixth of the precipitation.   About A.D. 1700 the English astronomer Halley confirmed that oceanic evaporation was an adequate source of moisture for precipitation.

Precipitation was measured in India as early as the fourth century B.C., but satisfactory methods for measuring streamflow were a much later development.   Frontinus, water commissioner of Rome in A.D. 97, based estimates of flow on cross-sectional area alone without regard to velocity.   In the United States, organized measurement of precipitation started under the Surgeon General of the Army in 1819, was transferred to the Signal Corps in 1870, and finally to a newly organized U.S. Weather Bureau in 1891.   Scattered streamflow measurements were made on the

Mississippi River as early as 1848, but a systematic program was not started until 1888 when the U.S. Geological Survey undertook this work. It is not surprising, therefore, that little quantitative work in hydrology was done before the early years of the twentieth century, when men such as Horton, Mead, and Sherman began to explore the field. The great expansion of activity in flood control, irrigation, soil conservation, and related fields which began about 1930 gave the first real impetus to organized research in hydrology, as the need for more precise design data became evident. Most of our present-day concepts of hydrology date since 1930. Hydrology is, therefore, a young science with many important problems only imperfectly understood and much research still ahead.

1-3. Hydrology in engineering. Hydrology is used in engineering mainly in connection with the design and operation of hydraulic structures. What flood flows may be expected at a spillway or highway culvert or in a city drainage system? What reservoir capacity is required to assure adequate water for irrigation or municipal water supply during droughts? What effect will reservoirs, levees, and other control works exert on flood flows in a stream? These are typical of the questions which the hydrologist is expected to answer.

Large organizations such as Federal and state water agencies can maintain staffs of hydrologic specialists to analyze their problems, but smaller offices often have insufficient hydrologic work for full-time specialists. Hence, many civil engineers are called upon for occasional hydrologic studies. It is probable that these civil engineers deal with a larger number of projects (without regard to size) than do the specialists, although in respect to annual dollar volume the situation may be reversed. In any event, it seems that knowledge of the fundamentals of hydrology is an essential part of the civil engineer's training.

1-4. The subject matter of hydrology. Hydrology deals with many topics. The subject matter as presented in this book can be broadly classified into two phases: data collection and methods of analysis and application. Chapters 2 to 6 deal with the basic data of hydrology. Adequate basic data are essential to any science, and hydrology is no exception. In fact, the complex features of the natural processes involved in hydrologic phenomena make it difficult to treat many hydrologic processes by rigorous deductive reasoning. One cannot always start with a basic physical law and from this determine the hydrologic result to be expected. Rather, it is necessary to start with a mass of observed facts, analyze these facts statistically, and from this analysis establish the systematic pattern that governs these events. Thus, without adequate historical data for the particular problem area, the hydrologist is in a difficult position. The collection of hydrologic data has been the life work of many hydrologists and is a primary function of the U.S. Geological Survey and the U.S. Weather Bureau. It is important, therefore, that the student learn how these data are collected and published, the limitations on their accuracy, and the proper methods of interpretation and adjustment.

Generally, each hydrologic problem is unique in that it deals with a distinct set of physical conditions within a specific river basin. Hence, the quantitative conclusions of one analysis are often not directly transferable to another problem. However, the general solution for most problems can be developed from the application of a few relatively standard procedures. Chapters 6 to 12 describe these procedures and explain how they are utilized to solve specific phases of a hydrologic problem. Chapter 13 summarizes the preceding material by describing how the various steps are combined in the solution of typical engineering problems.

BIBLIOGRAPHY

Hydrology Handbook, *ASCE Manual* 28, 1949.

Johnstone, Don, and W. P. Cross: "Elements of Applied Hydrology," Ronald, New York, 1949.

Linsley, R. K., M. A. Kohler, and J. L. H. Paulhus: "Applied Hydrology," McGraw-Hill, New York, 1949.

Mead, D. W.: "Hydrology," 1st ed., McGraw-Hill, New York, 1919 (revised by H. W. Mead, 2d ed., 1950).

Meinzer, O. E. (ed.): "Hydrology," Vol. IX, Physics of the Earth Series, McGraw-Hill, New York, 1942 (reprinted Dover Publications, New York, 1949).

Meyer, A. F.: "Elements of Hydrology," 2d ed., Wiley, New York, 1928.

Wisler, C. O., and E. F. Brater: "Hydrology," Wiley, New York, 1949.

PROBLEMS

1-1. List the agencies in your state which have responsibilities of a hydrologic nature. What is the special problem of each agency?

1-2. Repeat Prob. 1-1 for Federal agencies.

1-3. List the major hydraulic projects in your area. What specific hydrologic problems did each project involve?

2

WEATHER AND HYDROLOGY

The hydrologic characteristics of a region are determined largely by its climate and its geological structure. Among the climatic factors that establish the hydrologic features of a region are the amount and distribution of precipitation; the occurrence of snow and ice; and the effects of wind, temperature, and humidity on evaporation and snowmelt. Consequently, the design and operation of hydraulic projects involve meteorological considerations. Hydrologic problems in which meteorology plays an important role include determination of probable maximum precipitation and optimum snowmelt conditions for spillway design, forecasts of precipitation and snowmelt for reservoir operation, and determination of probable maximum winds over water surfaces for evaluating resulting waves in connection with the design of dams and levees. Obviously, the hydrologist should have some understanding of the meteorological processes determining a regional climate. The general features of climatology are discussed in this chapter. Because of its special importance in hydrology, precipitation is treated separately and in more detail in Chap. 3.

THE GENERAL CIRCULATION

2-1. Thermal circulation. If the earth were a nonrotating sphere, a purely thermal circulation (Fig. 2-1) would result. The equator receives more solar radiation than the higher latitudes. Equatorial air, being warmer, is lighter and tends to rise. As it rises, it is replaced by cooler air from higher latitudes. The only way the air from the higher latitudes can be replaced is

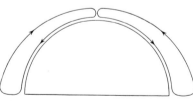

FIG. 2-1. Simple thermal circulation on nonrotating earth (Northern Hemisphere).

from above—by the poleward flow of air rising from the equator. The true circulation differs from that of Fig. 2-1 because of the earth's rotation and the effects of land and sea distribution and land forms.

2-2. Factors modifying the thermal circulation. The earth rotates from west to east, and a point at the equator moves at about 1500 fps while one at 60° lat. moves at one-half this speed. From the principle of conservation of angular momentum, it follows that a parcel of air at rest relative to the earth's surface at the equator would attain a theoretical eastward velocity of 2250 fps (relative to the earth's surface) if moved northward to 60° lat. Conversely, if a parcel of air at the North Pole were moved southward to 60° lat., it would reach a theoretical westward velocity of 2250 fps. However, wind speeds of this magnitude are never observed in nature because of friction. The force that would

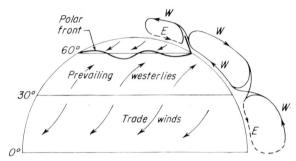

FIG. 2-2. General circulation of Northern Hemisphere.

be required to produce these changes in velocity is known as the *Coriolis force*. This apparent force always acts to the right in the Northern Hemisphere and to the left in the Southern Hemisphere.

The observed pattern of the general circulation in the Northern Hemisphere is shown in Fig. 2-2. Unfortunately, the physical reasons for this circulation are only partly known. The rising equatorial air acquires an eastward component as it moves northward. At about 30° lat., it tends to subside because of cooling. The subsiding air splits into two currents, one moving southward as the northeast *trade winds* and the second continuing northward and eastward.

In the polar cell, loss of heat in the lower layers results in subsidence, the subsiding air spreading southward and westward. As it moves southward the air is warmed, and at about 60° lat. it rises and returns poleward as a southwesterly current aloft.

In the middle cell the southwesterly current in the lower layers meets the southern edge of the polar cell and is forced upward over the colder westward-moving air. This circulation would result in an accumulation of air in the polar cell were it not for outbreaks of excess polar air southward.

The idealized circulation of Fig. 2-2 implies belts of low pressure (surface) at the equator and at about 60° lat. where warmer air is rising.

Similarly, high pressure would be expected at about 30° lat. and at the poles. This pressure pattern (Fig. 2-3) is greatly distorted by the effects of water and land masses. These effects are the results of differences in the specific heats, reflectivity, and mixing properties of water and land and of the existence of barriers to air flow. Heat gains and

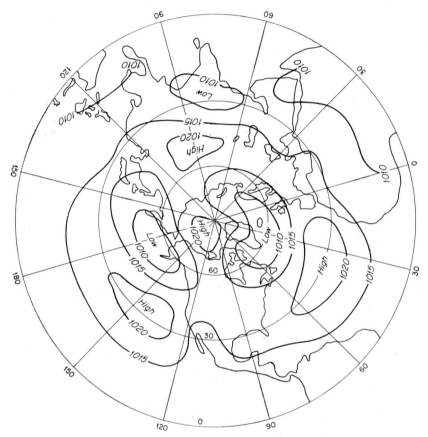

FIG. 2-3. Mean-pressure pattern of the Northern Hemisphere.

losses are distributed through relatively great depths in large bodies of water by mixing, while land is affected only near the surface. Consequently, land-surface temperatures are far less equable than those of the surface of large bodies of water. This condition is further emphasized by the lower specific heat of the soil and its higher albedo, especially in winter when snow cover reflects most of the incident radiation back to space. In winter there is a tendency for the accumulation of cold dense air over land masses and warm air over the oceans. In summer, the situation is reversed.

2-3. Migratory systems.   The semipermanent features of the general, or mean, circulation (Fig. 2-3) are statistical and at any time may be distorted or displaced by transitory, or migratory, systems.   Both semipermanent and transitory features are classified as cyclones or anticyclones.   A *cyclone* is a more or less circular area of low atmospheric pressure in which the winds blow counterclockwise in the Northern Hemisphere.   *Tropical cyclones* form at low latitudes and may develop into violent *hurricanes* or *typhoons* with winds exceeding 75 mph over areas as large as 200 mi in diameter.   *Extratropical cyclones* form along *fronts*, the boundaries between warm and cold air masses.   Such cyclones are usually larger than tropical cyclones and may produce precipitation over thousands of square miles.   An *anticyclone* is an area of relatively high pressure in which the winds tend to blow spirally outward in a clockwise direction in the Northern Hemisphere.   Details on the general circulation and on the structure of cyclones and anticyclones can be found in meteorological textbooks.

TEMPERATURE

2-4. Measurement of temperature.   In order to measure air temperature properly, the thermometers must be placed where air circulation is relatively unobstructed and yet they must be protected from the direct rays of the sun and from precipitation.   In the United States thermometers are placed in white, louvered, wooden boxes, called *instrument shelters* (Fig. 2-4), through which the air can move readily.   The shelter location must be typical of the area for which the measured temperatures are to be representative.   Because of marked vertical temperature gradients just above the soil surface, the shelters should be about the same height above the ground for the recorded temperatures to be comparable.   In the United States shelters are set about 4½ ft above the ground.

There are about 6000 stations in the United States for which the Weather Bureau compiles temperature records.   Except for a few hundred stations equipped or staffed to obtain continuous or hourly temperatures, most make a daily observation consisting of the current, maximum, and minimum temperatures.   The *minimum thermometer*, of the alcohol-in-glass type, has an index which remains at the lowest temperature occurring since its last setting.   The *maximum thermometer* has a constriction near the bulb which prevents the mercury from returning to the bulb as the temperature falls and thus registers the highest temperature since its last setting.   The *thermograph*, with either a bimetallic strip or a metal tube filled with alcohol or mercury for its thermometric element, makes an autographic record on a ruled chart wrapped around a clock-driven cylinder.   Electrical-resistance thermometers, thermocouples, gas-bulb thermometers, and other types of instruments are used for special purposes.

2-5. Terminology. A knowledge of terminology and methods of computation is required in order to avoid misuse of published temperature

FIG. 2-4. Instrument shelter with maximum and minimum thermometers and psychrometer. (*U.S. Weather Bureau.*)

data. The terms *average, mean,* and *normal* are all arithmetic means. The first two are used interchangeably, but the *normal,* generally used as a standard of comparison, is the average value for a particular date, month, season, or year over a specific 30-yr period (1921 to 1950 as of 1958). Plans call for recomputing the 30-yr normals every decade, dropping off the first 10 yr and adding the most recent 10 yr.

The *mean daily temperature* is the average of the daily maximum and minimum temperatures. In the United States, this yields a value usually less than a degree above the true daily average. Once-daily temperature observations are usually made about 7 A.M. or 5 P.M. Temperatures are published as of the date of the reading even though the maximum or minimum may have occurred on the preceding day. Mean temperatures computed from evening readings tend to be slightly higher than those from midnight readings. Morning readings yield mean temperatures with a negative bias, but the difference is less than that for evening readings.[1]

The *normal daily temperature* is the average daily mean temperature for a given date computed for a specific 30-yr period. The *daily range* in temperature is the difference between the highest and lowest temperatures recorded on a particular day. The *mean monthly temperature* is the average of the mean monthly maximum and minimum temperatures. The *mean annual temperature* is the average of the monthly means for the year.

The *degree day* is a departure of one degree for one day in the mean daily temperature from a specified base temperature. For snowmelt computations, the number of degree days for a day is equal to the mean daily temperature minus the base temperature, all negative differences being taken as zero. The number of degree days in a month or other time interval is the total of the daily values. Published degree-day values are for heating purposes and are based on departures below 65°F.

2-6. Lapse rates. The *lapse rate*, or vertical temperature gradient, is the rate of change of temperature with height in the free atmosphere. The mean lapse rate is a decrease of about 3.6 F° per 1000 ft increase in height. The greatest variations in lapse rate are found in the layer of air just above the land surface. The earth radiates heat energy to space at a relatively constant rate which is a function of its absolute temperature. Incoming radiation at night is less than the outgoing, and the temperature of the earth's surface and of the air immediately above it decreases. This surface cooling sometimes leads to an increase of temperature with altitude, or *temperature inversion*, in the surface layer. This condition usually occurs on still, clear nights because there is little turbulent mixing of air and because outgoing radiation is unhampered by clouds. Temperature inversions are also observed at higher levels when warm air currents overrun colder air.

In the daytime there is a tendency for steep lapse rates because of the relatively high temperatures of the air near the ground. This daytime heating usually destroys a surface radiation inversion by early forenoon. As the heating continues, the lapse rate in the lower layers of the air steepens until it may reach the *dry-adiabatic* lapse rate (5.4 F° per 1000

[1] W. F. Rumbaugh, The Effect of Time of Observation on the Mean Temperature, *Monthly Weather Rev.*, Vol. 62, pp. 375–376, October, 1934.

ft) which is the rate of temperature change of unsaturated air resulting from expansion or compression as the air rises (lowering pressure) or descends (increasing pressure) without heat being added or removed.

Air having a dry-adiabatic lapse rate mixes readily, whereas a temperature inversion indicates a stable condition in which warm lighter air overlies cold denser air. Under optimum surface heating conditions the air near the ground may be heated sufficiently so that the lapse rate in the lowest layers becomes *super-adiabatic*, i.e., exceeding 5.4 F° per 1000 ft. This is an unstable condition since any parcel of air lifted dry-adiabatically remains warmer and lighter than the surrounding air and thus has a tendency to continue rising.

If a parcel of saturated air is lifted adiabatically, its temperature will decrease and its water vapor will condense, releasing latent heat of vaporization. This heat reduces the cooling rate of the ascending air. Hence, the *saturated-adiabatic lapse rate* is less than the dry-adiabatic, being about 3.0 F° per 1000 ft in the lower layers. At very low temperatures or at high altitudes there is little difference between the two lapse rates because of the very small amounts of water vapor available.

If the moisture in the rising air is precipitated as it is condensed, the temperature of the air will decrease at the *pseudo-adiabatic lapse rate* which differs very little from the saturated-adiabatic. Actually, the process is not strictly adiabatic as heat is carried away by the falling precipitation. A layer of saturated air having a saturated- or pseudo-adiabatic lapse rate is said to be in neutral equilibrium. If its lapse rate is less than the saturated- or pseudo-adiabatic, the air is stable; if greater, unstable.

2-7. Geographic distribution of temperature. In general, temperature tends to be highest at low latitudes and to decrease poleward. However, this trend is greatly distorted by the influence of land and water masses, topography, and vegetation. In the interior of large islands and continents, temperatures are higher in summer and lower in winter than on coasts at corresponding latitudes. Temperatures at high elevations are lower than at low levels, and southern slopes have warmer temperatures than northern slopes. The average rate of decrease of surface air temperature with height is usually between 3 and 5 F° per 1000 ft. Forested areas have higher daily minimum and lower daily maximum temperatures than do barren areas. The mean temperature in a forested area may be 2 to 4 F° lower than that in comparable open country, the difference being greater in the summer.

The heat from a large city, which may roughly equal one-third of the solar radiation reaching it, produces local distortions[1] in the temperature

---

[1] F. S. Duckworth and J. S. Sandberg, The Effect of Cities upon Horizontal and Vertical Temperature Gradients, *Bull. Am. Meteorol. Soc.*, Vol. 35, pp. 198–207, May, 1954.

pattern so that temperatures recorded in cities may not represent the surrounding region. The mean annual temperature of cities averages about 2 F° higher than that of the surrounding region, most of the difference resulting from higher daily minima in the cities. Any comparison of city and country temperatures must allow for differences in exposure of thermometers. In cities the instrument shelters are often located on roofs. On still, clear nights, when radiational cooling is particularly effective, the temperature on the ground may be as much as 15 F° lower than that at an elevation of 100 ft. A slight gradient in the opposite direction is observed on windy or cloudy nights. Daytime maxima tend to be lower at rooftop level than at the ground. In general, the average temperature from roof exposures is slightly lower than that on the ground.

2-8. Time variations of temperature. In continental regions the warmest and coldest points of the annual temperature cycle lag behind the solstices by about one month. In the United States, January is usually the coldest month and July the warmest. At oceanic stations the lag is nearer two months, and the temperature difference between warmest and coldest months is much less.

The daily variation of temperature lags slightly behind the daily variation of solar radiation. The temperature begins to rise shortly after sunrise, reaches a peak 1 to 3 hr (about $\frac{1}{2}$ hr at oceanic stations) after the sun has reached its highest altitude, and falls through the night to a minimum about sunrise. The daily range of temperature is affected by the state of the sky. On cloudy days the maximum temperature is lower because of reduced insolation, and the minimum is higher because of reduced outgoing radiation. The daily range is also smaller over oceans.

HUMIDITY

2-9. Properties of water vapor. The process by which liquid water is converted into vapor is called *vaporization* or *evaporation*. Molecules of water having sufficient kinetic energy to overcome the attractive forces tending to hold them within the body of liquid water are projected through the water surface. Since kinetic energy increases and surface tension decreases as temperature rises, the rate of evaporation increases with temperature. Most atmospheric vapor is the product of evaporation from water surfaces. Molecules may leave a snow or ice surface in the same manner as they leave a liquid. The process whereby a solid is transformed directly to the vapor state, and vice versa, is called *sublimation*.

In any mixture of gases, each gas exerts a *partial pressure* independent of the other gases. The partial pressure exerted by water vapor is called *vapor pressure*. If all the water vapor in a closed container of moist air with an initial total pressure p were removed, the final pressure

p' of the dry air alone would be less than p. The vapor pressure e would be the difference between the pressure of the moist air and that of the dry air, or $p - p'$.

Practically speaking, the maximum amount of water vapor that can exist in any given space is a function of temperature and is independent of the coexistence of other gases. When the maximum amount of water vapor for a given temperature is contained in a given space, the space is said to be *saturated*. The more common expression "the air is saturated" is not strictly correct. The pressure exerted by the vapor in a saturated space is called the *saturation vapor pressure*, which, for all practical purposes, is the maximum vapor pressure possible at a given temperature (Appendix B).

The process by which vapor changes to the liquid or solid state is called *condensation*. In a space in contact with a water surface, condensation and vaporization always go on simultaneously. If the space is not saturated, the rate of vaporization will exceed the rate of condensation, resulting in a net evaporation.[1] If the space is saturated, the rates of vaporization and condensation balance, provided that the water and air temperatures are the same.

Since the saturation vapor pressure over ice is less than that over water at the same temperature, the introduction of ice into a space saturated with respect to liquid water at the same or higher temperature will result in condensation of the vapor on the ice. This is an important factor in the production of heavy rain.

Vaporization removes heat from the liquid being vaporized, while condensation adds heat. The *latent heat of vaporization* is the amount of heat absorbed by a unit mass of a substance, without change in temperature, while passing from the liquid to the vapor state. The change from vapor to the liquid state releases an equivalent amount of heat known as the *latent heat of condensation*.

The heat of vaporization of water H_v (cal/g) varies with temperature but may be determined accurately up to 40°C by

$$H_v = 597.3 - 0.56T \tag{2-1}$$

where T is the temperature in degrees centigrade.

The *latent heat of fusion* for water is the amount of heat required to convert one gram of ice to liquid water at the same temperature. When 1 g of liquid water at 0°C freezes into ice at the same temperature, the latent heat of fusion (79.7 cal/g) is liberated.

The *latent heat of sublimation* for water is the amount of heat required to convert one gram of ice into vapor at the same temperature without passing through the intermediate liquid state. It is equal to the sum of

---

[1] In hydrology, net evaporation is termed simply "evaporation."

the latent heat of vaporization and the latent heat of fusion. At 0°C, it is about 677 cal/g. Direct condensation of vapor into ice at the same temperature liberates an equivalent amount of heat.

The *specific gravity* of water vapor is 0.622 that of dry air at the same temperature and pressure. The density of water vapor ρ_v in grams per cubic centimeter is

$$\rho_v = 0.622 \frac{e}{R_g T} \tag{2-2}$$

where T is the absolute temperature (C°) and R_g, the gas constant, equals 2.87×10^3 when the vapor pressure e is in millibars.[1]

The density of dry air ρ_d in grams per cubic centimeter is

$$\rho_d = \frac{p_d}{R_g T} \tag{2-3}$$

where p_d is the pressure in millibars.

The density of moist air is equal to the mass of water vapor plus the mass of dry air in a unit volume of the mixture. If p_a is the total pressure of the moist air, $p_a - e$ will be the partial pressure of the dry air alone. Adding Eqs. (2-2) and (2-3) and substituting $p_a - e$ for p_d,

$$\rho_a = \frac{p_a}{R_g T} \left(1 - 0.378 \frac{e}{p_a} \right) \tag{2-4}$$

This equation shows that moist air is lighter than dry air.

2-10. Terminology. There are many expressions used for indicating the moisture content of the atmosphere. Each serves special purposes, and only those expressions common to hydrologic uses are discussed here. *Vapor pressure e* in millibars can be computed from the empirical psychrometric equation

$$e = e_s - 0.000367 p_a (T - T_w) \left(1 + \frac{T_w - 32}{1571} \right) \tag{2-5}$$

where T and T_w are the dry- and wet-bulb temperatures (°F), respectively, and e_s is the saturation vapor pressure in millibars corresponding to T_w.

The *relative humidity f* is the percentage ratio of the actual to the saturation vapor pressure and is therefore a ratio of the amount of moisture in a given space to the amount the space could contain if saturated.

$$f = 100 \frac{e}{e_s} \tag{2-6}$$

---

[1] The millibar is the standard unit of pressure in meteorology. It is equivalent to a force of 1000 dynes/sq cm, 0.0143 psi, or 0.0295 in. of mercury. Mean-sea-level air pressure is 1013 millibars.

The *dewpoint* T_d is the temperature at which the air becomes saturated when cooled under constant pressure and with constant water-vapor content. It is thus the temperature having a saturation vapor pressure e_s equal to the existing vapor pressure e.

The *specific humidity* q_h, usually expressed in grams per kilogram, is the mass of water vapor per unit mass of moist air.

$$q_h = 622 \frac{e}{p_a - 0.378e} \approx 622 \frac{e}{p_a} \qquad (2\text{-}7)$$

where p_a is the total pressure (millibars) of the air.

The total amount of water vapor in a layer of air is often expressed as the depth of *precipitable water* W_p, in inches, even though there is no natural process capable of precipitating the entire moisture content of the layer. The amount of precipitable water in any air column of considerable height is computed[1] by increments of pressure from

$$W_p = \Sigma 0.0004 q_h \, \Delta p_a \qquad (2\text{-}8)$$

where the pressure p_a is in millibars and q_h, in grams per kilogram, is the average of the specific humidities at the top and bottom of each layer. Figure 2-5 gives the depth of precipitable water in a column of saturated air with its base at the 1000-millibar level and its top anywhere up to 200 millibars. Tables for computing[2] precipitable water and charts[3] of mean precipitable water in the atmosphere over the United States are available.

2-11. Measurement of humidity. In general, official measurements of humidity in the surface layers of the atmosphere are made with a *psychrometer*, which consists of two thermometers, one with its bulb covered by a jacket of clean muslin saturated with water. The thermometers are ventilated by whirling or by use of a fan. Because of the cooling effect of evaporation, the moistened, or *wet-bulb*, thermometer reads lower than the dry, the difference in degrees being known as the *wet-bulb depression*. The air temperature and wet-bulb depression are used to obtain various expressions of humidity by reference to special tables.[4] Condensed psychrometric tables are included in Appendix B.

The *hair hygrometer* makes use of the fact that length of hair varies with relative humidity. The changes are transmitted to a pointer indi-

---

[1] S. Solot, Computation of Depth of Precipitable Water in a Column of Air, *Monthly Weather Rev.*, Vol. 67, pp. 100–103, April, 1939.

[2] Tables of Precipitable Water, *U.S. Weather Bur. Tech. Paper* 14, 1951.

[3] Mean Precipitable Water in the United States, *U.S. Weather Bur. Tech. Paper* 10, 1949.

[4] "Psychrometric Tables," W.B. 235, U.S. Weather Bureau, 1941.

· Hygrometric and Psychrometric Tables, Sec. VII in "Smithsonian Meteorological Tables," rev., 6th ed., pp. 347–372, Smithsonian Institution, Washington, D.C., 1951.

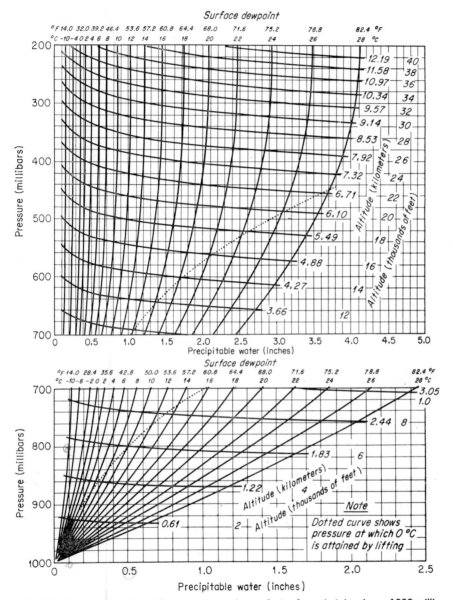

FIG. 2-5. Depths of precipitable water in a column of air of any height above 1000 milli-bars as a function of dewpoint, assuming saturation and pseudo-adiabatic lapse rate. (*U.S. Weather Bureau.*)

cating the relative humidity on a graduated scale.   The *hair hygrograph* is a hair hygrometer operating a pen marking a trace on a chart wrapped around a revolving drum.   The *hygrothermograph*, combining the features of both the hair hygrograph and the thermograph, records both relative humidity and temperature on one chart.   A *dewpoint hygrometer*, which measures dewpoint directly and is used mostly for laboratory purposes, consists of a highly polished metal vessel containing a suitable liquid which is cooled by any of several methods.   The temperature of the liquid at the time condensation begins to occur on the exterior of the metal vessel is the dewpoint.   The *spectroscopic hygrometer*[1] measures the selective absorption of light in certain bands of the spectrum by water vapor.   With the sun as a light source, it has been used to measure total atmospheric moisture.[2]

Measurement of humidity is one of the least accurate instrumental procedures in meteorology.   The standard psychrometer invites many observational errors.   The two thermometers double the chance of misreading.   At low temperatures, misreading by a few tenths of a degree can lead to absurd results.   Also, there is always the chance that the readings are not made when the wet-bulb is at its lowest temperature.   In addition, there are errors with a positive bias resulting from insufficient ventilation, dirty or too thick muslin, and impure water.

Any instrument using a hair element is subject to appreciable error. The hair expands with increasing temperature, and its response to changes in humidity is very slow, the lag increasing with decreasing temperature until it becomes almost infinite at about $-40°F$.   This can lead to significant error in upper-air soundings where large ranges in temperature and sharp variations of humidity with altitude are observed.   Consequently, sounding instruments are now equipped with electrical hygrometers.[3]

2-12. Geographic distribution of humidity.   Atmospheric moisture tends to decrease with increasing latitude, but relative humidity, being an inverse function of temperature, tends to increase.   Atmospheric moisture is greatest over oceans and decreases with distance inland.   It also decreases with elevation and is greater over vegetation than over barren soil.

2-13. Time variations in humidity.   Like temperature, atmospheric moisture is at a maximum in summer and at a minimum in winter.

[1] L. W. Foskett, N. B. Foster, W. R. Thickstun, and R. C. Wood, Infrared Absorption Hygrometer, *Monthly Weather Rev.*, Vol. 81, pp. 267–277, May, 1953.

[2] N. B. Foster and L. W. Foskett, A Spectrophotometer for the Determination of the Water Vapor in a Vertical Column of the Atmosphere, *J. Opt. Soc. Am.*, Vol. 35, pp. 601–610, September, 1945.

[3] V. B. Morris, Jr., and F. Sobel, Some Experiments on the Speed of Response of the Electric Hygrometer, *Bull. Am. Meteorol. Soc.*, Vol. 35, pp. 226–229, May, 1954.

Relative humidity, however, varies in reverse. The diurnal variation of atmospheric moisture is normally small, except where land and sea breezes bring air of differing characteristics. Near the ground surface, condensation of dew at night and reevaporation during the day may result in a minimum moisture content near sunrise and a maximum by noon. Relative humidity, of course, behaves in a manner opposite to that of temperature, being at a maximum in the early morning and at a minimum in the afternoon.

WIND

Wind, which is air in motion, is a very influential factor in several hydrometeorological processes. Moisture and heat are readily transferred to and from air, which tends to adopt the thermal and moisture conditions of the surfaces with which it is in contact. Thus, stagnant air in contact with a water surface eventually assumes the vapor pressure of the surface so that no evaporation takes place. Similarly, stagnant air over a snow or ice surface eventually assumes the temperature and vapor pressure of the surface so that melting by convection and condensation ceases. Consequently, wind exerts considerable influence in evaporative and snowmelt processes. It is also important in the production of precipitation, since it is only through sustained inflow of moist air into a storm that precipitation can be maintained.

2-14. Measurement. Wind has both speed and direction. The *wind direction* is the direction *from* which it is blowing. Direction is usually expressed in terms of 16 compass points (N, NNE, NE, ENE, etc.) for surface winds, and for winds aloft in degrees from north, measured clockwise. Wind speed is usually given in miles per hour, meters per second, or knots (1 m/sec = 2.2 mph and 1 knot = $1\frac{1}{7}$ mph, approximately).

Wind speed is measured by instruments called *anemometers*, of which there are several types. The *three-* or *four-cup anemometer* with a vertical axis of rotation is most commonly used for official observations. It tends to register too high a mean speed in a variable wind because the cups accelerate faster than they lose speed. Vertical currents (turbulence) tend to rotate the cups and cause overregistration of horizontal speeds. Most cup anemometers will not record speeds below 1 or 2 mph because of starting friction. Less common is the *propeller anemometer* with a horizontal axis of rotation. *Pressure-tube anemometers*, of which the Dines is the best known, operate on the Pitot-tube principle.

While wind speed varies greatly with height above the ground, no standard anemometer level has been adopted. Differences in wind speed resulting from differences in anemometer height, which may range anywhere from thirty to several hundred feet above the ground, usually exceed the errors from instrumental deficiencies. However, approximate adjustment can be made for differences in height [Eq. (2-9)].

2-15. Geographic variation of wind.   Because of its location in the general circulation, the United States has prevailing westerly winds. However, the winds are generally variable since most of the country is affected by migratory pressure systems.   The upper-air winds tend to increase with latitude, but this tendency is not noticeable near the surface. In winter there is a tendency for surface winds to blow from the colder interior of land masses toward the warmer oceans (Sec. 2-2).   Conversely, in summer the winds tend to blow from the cooler bodies of water toward the warmer land.   Similarly, diurnal land and sea breezes may result from temperature contrasts between land and water.

On mountain ridges and summits wind speeds (30 ft or more above the ground) are higher than in the free air at corresponding elevations because of the convergence of the air forced by the orographic barriers.   On lee slopes and in sheltered valleys wind speeds are light.   Wind direction is greatly influenced by orientation of orographic barriers.   With a weak pressure system, diurnal variation of wind direction may occur in mountain regions, the winds blowing upslope in the daytime and downslope at night.

Wind speeds are reduced and directions deflected in the lower layers of the atmosphere because of friction produced by trees, buildings, and other obstacles.   These effects become negligible above about 2000 ft, and this lower layer is referred to as the *friction layer*.   Over land the surface wind speed averages about 40 per cent of that just above the friction layer, and at sea about 70 per cent.   The relationship between wind speed at anemometer height and that at some higher level in the friction layer may be expressed by the empirical formula

$$\frac{v}{v_0} = \left(\frac{z}{z_0}\right)^k \tag{2-9}$$

where v is the wind speed at height z above the ground, v_0 is the wind speed at anemometer level z_0, and k is often taken as $\frac{1}{7}$.

2-16. Time variation of winds.   Wind speeds are highest and most variable in winter, whereas middle and late summer is the calmest period of the year.   In winter westerly winds prevail over the United States up to at least 20,000 ft, except near the Gulf of Mexico where there is a tendency for southeasterly winds up to about 5000 ft.   In summer, while there is still a tendency for prevailing westerly winds, there is generally more variation of direction with altitude.   In the plains west of the Mississippi River there is a tendency for southerly winds up to about 5000 ft, and on the Pacific Coast the lower winds are frequently from the northwest.

The diurnal variation of wind is significant only near the ground and is most pronounced during the summer.   Surface wind speed is usually at a minimum about sunrise and increases to a maximum in early afternoon. At about 2000 ft above the ground, the maximum occurs at night and the minimum in the daytime.[1]

BIBLIOGRAPHY

Benton, G. S., R. T. Blackburn, and V. O. Snead: The Role of the Atmosphere in the Hydrologic Cycle, *Trans. Am. Geophys. Union*, Vol. 31, pp. 61–73, February, 1950.

Bernard, M.: The Primary Role of Meteorology in Flood Flow Estimating, *Trans. ASCE*, Vol. 109, pp. 311–382, 1944.

Bernard, M.: The Role of Hydrometeorology in Planning the Water Economy of the West, *Trans. Am. Geophys. Union*, Vol. 30, pp. 263–271, April, 1949.

Byers, H. R.: "General Meteorology," pp. 215–234, McGraw-Hill, New York, 1944.

Fletcher, R. D.: Hydrometeorology in the United States, in T. F. Malone (ed.), "Compendium of Meteorology," pp. 1033–1047, American Meteorological Society, Boston, 1951.

Landsberg, H.: Climatology, Sec. XII, in F. A. Berry, Jr., E. Bollay, and N. R. Beers (eds.), "Handbook of Meteorology," pp. 937–973, McGraw-Hill, New York, 1945.

Landsberg, H.: "Physical Climatology," Pennsylvania State University, University Park, Pa., 1941.

Linsley, R. K.: The Hydrologic Cycle and Its Relation to Meteorology, in T. F. Malone (ed.), "Compendium of Meteorology," pp. 1048–1054, American Meteorological Society, Boston, 1951.

McClendon, E. W.: The Role of Meteorology in Projects of the Corps of Engineers in the Missouri River Basin, *Bull. Am. Meteorol. Soc.*, Vol. 31, pp. 238–243, September, 1950.

Middleton, W. E. K., and A. F. Spilhaus: "Meteorological Instruments," 3d ed. rev., pp. 57–117, 135–196, University of Toronto Press, Toronto, 1953.

Rossby, C. G.: The Scientific Basis of Modern Meteorology, in "Climate and Man," *U.S. Dept. Agr. Yearbook*, pp. 599–655, 1941.

Thiessen, A. H.: Weather Glossary, *U.S. Weather Bur. Publ.* 1445, 1945.

Willett, H. C.: "Descriptive Meteorology," Academic Press, Inc., New York, 1944.

DATA SOURCES

The main sources of data on temperature, humidity, and wind are the monthly bulletins entitled *Climatological Data* published by the U.S. Weather Bureau. The *Climatic Summary of the United States* summarizes monthly and annual data from the beginning of record to 1950. *Monthly Weather Review* contains maps summarizing the weather of the previous month for the country. A summary of normals and extremes may be found in "Normal Weather for the United States" (by J. B. Kincer, U.S. Weather Bureau, 1943) and "Climate and Man" (*U.S. Dept. Agr. Yearbook*, 1941). Special summaries are available as follows:

Humidity

Maximum Persisting Dewpoints in Western United States, *U.S. Weather Bur. Tech. Paper* 5, 1948.

Mean Precipitable Water in the United States, *U.S. Weather Bur. Tech. Paper* 10, 1949.

---

[1] G. Hellman, Über de Bewegung der Luft in den untersten Schichten der Atmosphäre, *Meteorol. Z.*, Vol. 34, pp. 272–285, 1917.

Wind

"Airway Meteorological Atlas for the United States," U.S. Weather Bureau, 1941.
"Normal Surface Wind Data for the United States," U.S. Weather Bureau, 1942.

PROBLEMS

2-1. Show why the theoretical eastward velocity (constant angular momentum) of air at rest relative to the earth's surface at the equator would be 2250 fps if the parcel were displaced to 60° N. lat.

2-2. How many degree days above 32°F are there in a day with a minimum temperature of 28°F and a maximum of 48°F?

2-3. A parcel of moist air at 50°F initially at 1000 ft mean sea level is forced to pass over a mountain ridge at 8000 ft mean sea level and then descends to its original elevation. Assuming that a lift of 2000 ft produces saturation and precipitation, what is the final temperature of the parcel?

2-4. What is the heat of vaporization, in calories per gram, for water at 20°C?

2-5. What is the density, in grams per cubic centimeter, of (*a*) dry air at 35°C and a pressure of 1000 millibars and (*b*) moist air at the same temperature and pressure with 70 per cent relative humidity?

2-6. Assuming dry- and wet-bulb temperatures of 75 and 63°F, respectively, and using the psychrometric tables of Appendix B, determine (*a*) dewpoint temperature, (*b*) relative humidity, (*c*) saturation vapor pressure, and (*d*) actual vapor pressure.

2-7. A radio sounding in saturated air shows temperatures of 18.1, 13.8, and 8.6°C at the 900, 800, and 700-millibar levels, respectively. Compute the precipitable water in the layer between 900 and 700 millibars and compare these results with those obtained from Fig. 2-5. (The temperature of 18.1°C at the 900-millibar level reduces pseudo-adiabatically to 22.0°C at 1000 millibars.)

2-8. A snowmelt formula requires wind speed 50 ft above the ground. What is the estimated speed at this level if an anemometer 30 ft above the ground indicates 15 mph?

2-9. A pilot-balloon observation shows wind speed of 60 mph at 1000 ft above the ground. What is the probable wind speed at 20 ft above the ground?

2-10. Compute the weight (lb/cu ft) of dry air under standard atmosphere conditions at sea level (Appendix B). What would the weight be if the temperature were increased 20 F° at constant pressure?

2-11. How many calories of heat are required to evaporate 50 gal of water at 100°F? How many pounds of ice at 20°F would the same amount of heat melt?

2-12. The wind speed at 10 ft above the ground is 20 mph. Plot the probable velocity profile to a height of 500 ft.

2-13. How many calories per square foot are required (*a*) to melt a 1-ft layer of ice of 90 per cent density at 25°F and (*b*) to evaporate the resulting melt water without raising its temperature above 32°F?

3

PRECIPITATION

To the hydrologist, *precipitation* is the general term for all forms of moisture emanating from the clouds and falling to the ground. From the time of its formation in the atmosphere until it reaches the ground, precipitation is of more interest to the meteorologist than to the hydrologist. However, once it reaches the ground, it becomes a basic element of hydrology.

3-1. Formation and types of precipitation. While water vapor in the atmosphere is a necessary factor in the formation of precipitation, it is by no means the only requirement. Moisture is always present in the atmosphere, even on cloudless days. For precipitation to occur, some mechanism is required to cool the air sufficiently to cause condensation and droplet growth. Condensation nuclei are also necessary, but they are usually present in the atmosphere in adequate quantities. The large-scale cooling needed for significant amounts of precipitation is achieved by lifting the air. Precipitation is often typed according to the factor responsible for the lifting. Thus, *cyclonic precipitation* results from the lifting of air converging into a low-pressure area, or cyclone. Most general storms in plains regions are of this type. *Convective precipitation* is caused by the natural rising of warmer, lighter air in colder, denser surroundings. The difference in temperature may result from unequal heating at the surface, unequal cooling at the top of the air layer, or mechanical lifting when the air is forced to pass over a denser, colder air mass or over a mountain barrier. Convective precipitation is spotty, and its intensity may range from light showers to cloudbursts. *Orographic precipitation* results from mechanical lifting over mountain barriers. In rugged terrain the orographic influence is so marked that storm precipitation patterns tend to resemble that of mean annual precipitation. In nature, the effects of these various types of cooling are often interrelated, and the resulting precipitation cannot be identified as being of any one type.

3-2. Forms of precipitation. In the middle latitudes precipitation occurs in many forms, depending on the existing meteorological conditions. *Drizzle* consists of waterdrops under 0.02-in. diameter, and its intensity is usually less than 0.04 in./hr. *Rain* consists of drops usually greater than 0.02-in. diameter. Drops greater than 0.25-in. diameter tend to break up as they fall through the air, so that 0.25 in. may be accepted as a practical upper limit of raindrop size. *Glaze* is the ice coating formed when drizzle or rain freezes as it comes in contact with cold objects at the ground. *Sleet* is frozen raindrops cooled to the ice stage while falling through air at subfreezing temperatures. *Snow* is precipitation in the form of ice crystals resulting from sublimation, i.e., from water vapor directly to ice. A *snowflake* is made up of a number of ice crystals fused together. *Hail* is precipitation in the form of balls or lumps of ice over 0.2-in. diameter formed by alternate freezing and melting as they are carried up and down in highly turbulent air currents. Single hailstones weighing over a pound have been observed.

3-3. Artificially induced precipitation. In spite of the great interest in artifically induced precipitation since World War II, this controversial subject is not discussed herein because it more properly belongs in the field of meteorology. References are listed in the bibliography for those who would like to learn more about it.

MEASUREMENT OF PRECIPITATION

A variety of instruments and techniques have been developed for gathering information on various phases of precipitation. Instruments for measuring amount and intensity of precipitation are the most important. Other instruments include devices for measuring raindrop-size distribution and for determining the time of beginning and ending of precipitation. This text describes briefly the gages and observational techniques for making official measurements of precipitation amount and intensity in the United States. Details on these gages and those in common use in other countries and information on the use of radar for measuring precipitation can be obtained from the references listed in the bibliography.

All forms of precipitation are measured on the basis of the vertical depth of water that would accumulate on a level surface if the precipitation remained where it fell. In the United States precipitation is measured in inches and hundredths. An amount less than 0.005 in. is recorded as a *trace*.

3-4. Precipitation gages. Any open receptacle with vertical sides is a convenient rain gage, but because of varying wind and splash effects the measurements would not be comparable unless the receptacles were of the same size[1] and shape and similarly exposed. The standard gage[2] (Fig. 3-1) of the U.S. Weather Bureau has a collector (receiver) of 8-in. diameter. Rain passes from the collector into a cylindrical measuring tube inside the overflow can. The measuring tube has a cross-sectional area one-tenth that of the collector so that 0.1-in. rainfall will fill the

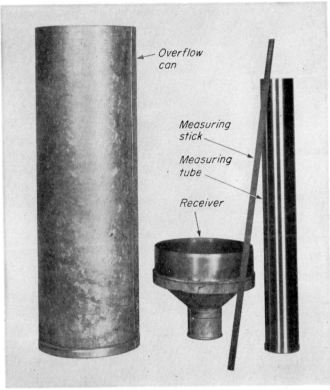

FIG. 3-1. Standard 8-in. precipitation gage. (U.S. Weather Bureau.)

tube to a depth of 1 in. With a measuring stick marked in tenths of an inch, rainfall can be measured to the nearest 0.01 in. The collector and tube are removed when snow is expected. The snow caught in the outer container, or overflow can, is melted, poured into the measuring tube, and measured.

The two main types of recording gages in common use in the United

[1] F. A. Huff, Comparison between Standard and Small Orifice Raingages, *Trans. Am. Geophys. Union*, Vol. 36, pp. 689–694, August, 1955.

[2] Instructions for Climatological Observers, *U.S. Weather Bur. Circ. B*, 10th ed., pp. 19–32, rev. October, 1955.

States are the U.S. Weather Bureau's *tipping-bucket gage* (Fig. 3-2) and the *weighing-type gage* (Fig. 3-3). The former is used at some Weather Bureau first-order stations and is equipped with a remote recorder located inside the office. The 12-in. collector funnels the rain into a two-compartment tipping bucket. One-hundredth inch of rain will fill one compartment and overbalance it so that it tips, emptying into a reservoir and moving the second compartment of the bucket into place beneath the funnel. As the bucket is tipped by each 0.01 in. of rain, it actuates an electrical circuit causing a pen to mark on a revolving drum. Unfortunately, this type of gage is not suitable for measuring snow without heating the collector.

FIG. 3-2. Tipping-bucket rain gage. (*U.S. Weather Bureau.*)

The *weighing-type gage* weighs the rain or snow which falls into a bucket set on a platform of a spring or lever balance. The increasing weight of the bucket and its contents is recorded on the chart held by a clock-driven drum. The record thus shows the accumulation of precipitation.

Storage gages are used in mountainous regions where much of the precipitation falls as snow and where frequent servicing is impracticable. Weighing-type storage gages operate from 1 to 2 months without servicing, and some nonrecording storage gages are designed to operate for an entire season without attention. Since storage gages are located in heavy-snowfall areas, the collectors are usually in the form of an inverted frustum of a cone to prevent wet snow from clinging to the inside walls and clogging the orifice. Of course, the orifice should be above the maximum snow depth expected. The *standpipe-type gage* (Fig. 3-4) used by the U.S. Weather Bureau is made from 12-in. thin-walled pipe in 5-ft sections, so that any height in multiples of 5 ft is possible. Storage gages are customarily charged with a calcium chloride solution (antifreeze) to liquefy the snow and prevent damage to the gage. Interim measurements of the gage catch are made by stick or tape, while the initial charge and final measurement of the seasonal catch are made by weighing the contents. Losses due to evaporation of the gage contents are practically eliminated by a thin film of oil.[1]

FIG. 3-3. Weighing-type precipitation gage—12-in. dual traverse. (*Friez Instrument* Co.)

Precipitation measurements are subject to various errors,[2] most being individually small but with a general tendency to yield measurements

[1] E. L. Hamilton and L. A. Andrews, Control of Evaporation from Rain Gages by Oil, *Bull. Am. Meteorol. Soc.*, Vol. 34, pp. 202–204, May, 1953.

[2] R. E. Horton, Measurement of Rainfall and Snow, *Monthly Weather Rev.*, Vol. 47, pp. 294–295, May, 1919.

that are too low. Except for mistakes in reading the scale of the gage, observational errors are usually small but cumulative; e.g., light amounts may be neglected, and extended immersion of the measuring stick may result in water creeping up the stick. Errors in scale reading, although large, are usually random and compensating. Instrumental errors may be quite large and are cumulative. The water displaced by the measuring stick increases the reading about 1 per cent. Dents in the collector rim may change its receiving area. It is estimated that 0.01 in. of each rain measured with a gage initially dry is required to moisten the funnel and inside surfaces. This loss could easily amount to 1 in./yr in some areas. Another loss results from raindrop splash from the collector, but no estimate of its magnitude is available.

In rainfall of 5 to 6 in./hr the bucket of a tipping-bucket gage tips every 6 to 7 sec. About 0.3 sec is required to complete the tip, during which some water is still pouring into the already filled bucket. The recorded rate may be 5 per cent too low.[1] However, the water, which is all caught in the gage reservoir, is measured independently of the recorder count, and the difference is pro-rated through the period of excessive rainfall.

FIG. 3-4. Standpipe-type precipitation storage gage equipped with Alter shield. (*U.S. Weather Bureau.*)

Of all the errors the most serious is the deficiency of measurements due to wind. The vertical acceleration of air forced upward over a gage imparts an upward acceleration to precipitation about to enter and results in deficient catch. The deficiency is greater for snow and apparently[2] may be in the order of 60 per cent of the true snowfall for winds of 30 mph at orifice level (Fig. 3-5). Equipping gages with windshields increases the catch by about 20 per cent in open areas. Various types

[1] D. A. Parsons, Calibration of a Weather Bureau Tipping-bucket Rain Gage, *Monthly Weather Rev.*, Vol. 69, p. 205, July, 1941.

[2] W. T. Wilson, Discussion of paper Precipitation at Barrow, Alaska, Greater Than Recorded, *Trans. Am. Geophys. Union*, Vol. 35, pp. 206–207, April, 1954.

of shields[1] have been used, but the Alter shield (Fig. 3-4) has been adopted as standard by the U.S. Weather Bureau. Its open construction provides less opportunity than solid shields for the building up of snow on it, and the flexible design allows wind movement to aid in keeping the shield free from accumulated snow. Artificial windshields cannot overcome the effects of inherently poor gage exposure. Roof installations and

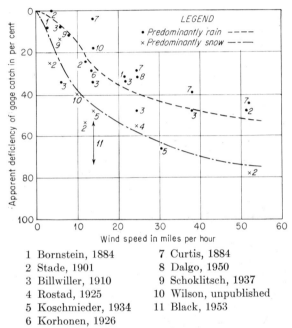

FIG. 3-5. Apparent effect of wind speed on the catch of precipitation gages. (After Wilson.)

1 Bornstein, 1884	7 Curtis, 1884
2 Stade, 1901	8 Dalgo, 1950
3 Billwiller, 1910	9 Schoklitsch, 1937
4 Rostad, 1925	10 Wilson, unpublished
5 Koschmieder, 1934	11 Black, 1953
6 Korhonen, 1926	

windswept slopes should be avoided. The best site is on level ground with bushes or trees serving as a windbreak, provided that these are not so close as to reduce the gage catch.

When rain is falling vertically, a gage inclined 10° from the vertical will catch 1.5 per cent less than it should. If a gage on level ground is inclined slightly toward the wind, it will catch more than the true amount. Some investigators[2] feel that gages should be perpendicular to land slopes. However, the area of a basin is its projection on a horizontal plane, and measurements from tilted gages must be reduced by multiplying by the cosine of the angle of inclination. Considering the variability of land

[1] See Bibliography at end of chapter.

[2] E. L. Hamilton, Rainfall Sampling on Rugged Terrain, *U.S. Dept. Agr. Tech. Bull.* 1096, 1954.

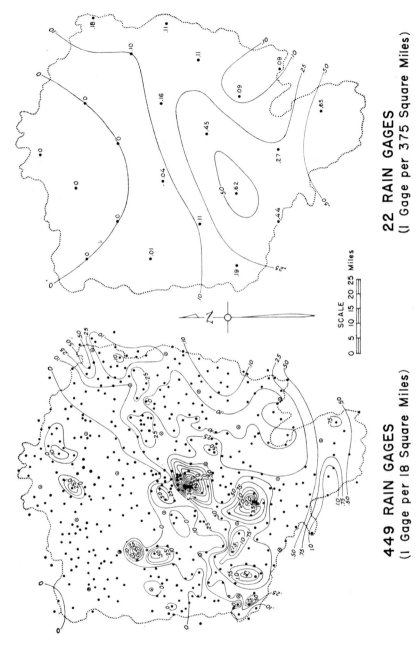

22 RAIN GAGES
(1 Gage per 375 Square Miles)

449 RAIN GAGES
(1 Gage per 18 Square Miles)

SCALE
0 5 10 15 20 25 Miles

FIG. 3-6. Isohyetal maps of the storm of Aug. 3, 1939, in the Muskingum Basin, Ohio, showing effect of network density on apparent storm pattern. (U.S. Weather Bureau.)

slope, aspect, and wind direction, it is virtually impossible to install a network of tilted gages for general purposes. Practically speaking, no gage has been designed which will give reliable measurements on steep slopes experiencing high winds, and such sites should be avoided. All U.S. Weather Bureau precipitation records are obtained from vertical gages.

3-5. The precipitation-gage network. The U.S. Weather Bureau networks consist of about 3500 recording and 11,000 nonrecording gages

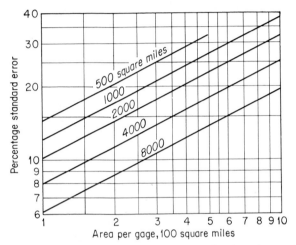

FIG. 3-7. Standard error of precipitation averages as a function of network density and area for the Muskingum Basin. (*U.S. Weather Bureau.*)

of various types at about 13,000 stations, or one station per 230 sq mi, on an average. The catchment area of the standard 8-in. gage is about 1/80,000,000 sq mi. The degree of extrapolation from gage catch to computed average depth over a large area is obvious.

The uses for which precipitation data are intended should determine network density. A relatively sparse network of stations would suffice for studies of large general storms or for determining annual averages over large areas of level terrain. A very dense network is required to determine the rainfall pattern in thunderstorms. The probability that a storm center will be recorded by a gage varies with network density (Fig. 3-6). A network should be so planned as to yield a representative picture of the areal distribution of precipitation. There should be no concentration of gages in heavy rainfall areas at the expense of dry areas, or vice versa. Unfortunately, cost of installing and maintaining a network and accessibility of the gage site to an observer are always important considerations.

The error of rainfall averages computed from networks of various densities has been investigated. Figure 3-7, based on an analysis[1] of rainfall in the Muskingum Basin, Ohio, shows the standard error of rainfall averages as a function of network density and area. Figure 3-8 is based on a similar study[2] on a 220-sq mi area near Wilmington, Ohio, and shows the average error of average rainfall as a function of network density and amount of storm precipitation. These figures are examples

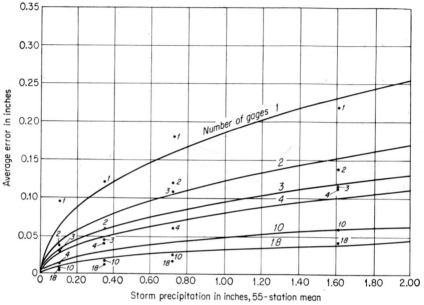

FIG. 3-8. Average error of precipitation averages as a function of network density and true precipitation for a 220-sq mi area near Wilmington, Ohio.

and would not necessarily apply under other topographic or climatic conditions.

INTERPRETATION OF PRECIPITATION DATA

In order to avoid erroneous conclusions it is important to give the proper interpretation to precipitation data, which often cannot be accepted at face value. For example, a mean annual precipitation value for a station may have little significance if the gage site has been changed significantly during the period for which the average is computed. Also, there are several ways of computing average precipitation over an area, each of which may give a different answer.

[1] Thunderstorm Rainfall, *Hydrometeorol. Rept.* 5, pp. 234–259, U.S. Weather Bureau in cooperation with Corps of Engineers, 1947.

[2] R. K. Linsley and M. A. Kohler, Variations in Storm Rainfall over Small Areas, *Trans. Am. Geophys. Union*, Vol. 32, pp. 245–250, April, 1951.

3-6. Estimating missing precipitation data. Many precipitation stations have short breaks in their records because of absences of the observer or because of instrumental failures. It is often necessary to estimate this missing record. In the procedure[1] used by the U.S. Weather Bureau, precipitation is estimated from that observed at three stations as close to and as evenly spaced around the station with the missing record as possible. If the normal annual precipitation at each of the index stations is within 10 per cent of that for the station with the missing record, a simple arithmetic average of the precipitation at the index stations provides the estimated amount.

If the normal annual precipitation at any of the index stations differs from that at the station in question by more than 10 per cent, the *normal-ratio method* is used. In this method, the amounts at the index stations are weighted by the ratios of the normal-annual-precipitation values. That is, precipitation at Station X, P_X, is

$$P_X = \frac{1}{3}\left(\frac{N_X}{N_A}P_A + \frac{N_X}{N_B}P_B + \frac{N_X}{N_C}P_C\right) \tag{3-1}$$

in which N is the normal annual precipitation.

3-7. Double-mass analysis. Changes in gage location, exposure, instrumentation, or observational procedure may cause a relative change in the precipitation catch. Frequently these changes are not disclosed in the published records. Current U.S. Weather Bureau practice calls for a new station identification whenever the gage location is changed by as much as 5 mi and/or 100 ft in elevation.

Double-mass analysis[2] tests the consistency of the record at a station by comparing its accumulated annual or seasonal precipitation with the concurrent accumulated values of mean precipitation for a group of surrounding stations. In Fig. 3-9, for example, a change in slope about 1923 indicates a change in the precipitation regime at Hermit. A change due to meteorological causes would not cause a change in slope as all base stations would be similarly affected. The station history for Hermit discloses a change in gage location in 1923. To make the record prior to

---

[1] J. L. H. Paulhus and M. A. Kohler, Interpolation of Missing Precipitation Records, *Monthly Weather Rev.*, Vol. 80, pp. 129–133, August, 1952.

J. E. McDonald, A Note on the Precision of Estimation of Missing Precipitation Data, *Trans. Am. Geophys. Union*, Vol. 38, pp. 657–661, October, 1957.

[2] J. B. Kincer, Determination of Dependability of Rainfall Records by Comparison with Nearby Records, *Trans. Am. Geophys. Union*, Vol. 19, Part 1, pp. 533–538, 1938.

C. F. Merriam, Progress Report on the Analysis of Rainfall Data, *Trans. Am. Geophys. Union*, Vol. 19, Part 1, pp. 529–532, 1938.

M. A. Kohler, Double-mass Analysis for Testing the Consistency of Records and for Making Required Adjustments, *Bull. Am. Meteorol. Soc.*, Vol. 30, pp. 188–189, May, 1949.

1923 comparable with that for the more recent location, it should be adjusted by the ratio of the slopes of the two segments of the double-mass curve (0.95/1.12). The consistency of the record for each of the base stations should be tested, and those showing inconsistent records should be dropped before other stations are tested or adjusted.

Considerable caution should be exercised in applying the double-mass technique. The plotted points always deviate about a mean line, and

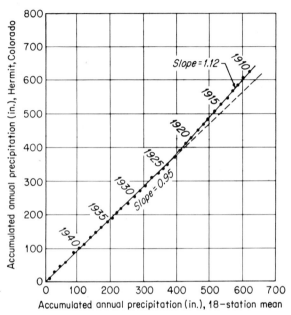

FIG. 3-9. Adjustment of precipitation data for Hermit, Colorado, by double-mass curve.

changes in slope should be accepted only when marked or substantiated by other evidence. A procedure has been devised[1] to evaluate the significance of any slope change in terms of the probability of getting such a change purely by chance. However, the procedure itself is subject to some error, its results are not altogether conclusive, and its application is somewhat cumbersome.

3-8. Average precipitation over area. The average depth of precipitation over a specific area, either on a storm, seasonal, or annual basis, is required in many types of hydrologic problems. The simplest method of obtaining the average depth is to average arithmetically the gaged amounts in the area. This method yields good estimates in flat

[1] L. L. Weiss and W. T. Wilson, Evaluation of Significance of Slope Changes in Double-mass Curves, *Trans. Am. Geophys. Union,* Vol. 34, pp. 893–896, December, 1953.

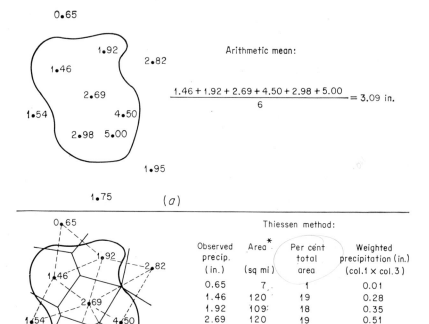

Arithmetic mean:

$$\frac{1.46 + 1.92 + 2.69 + 4.50 + 2.98 + 5.00}{6} = 3.09 \text{ in.}$$

(a)

Thiessen method:

Observed precip. (in.)	Area* (sq mi)	Per cent total area	Weighted precipitation (in.) (col.1 × col.3)
0.65	7	1	0.01
1.46	120	19	0.28
1.92	109	18	0.35
2.69	120	19	0.51
1.54	20	3	0.05
2.98	92	15	0.45
5.00	82	13	0.65
4.50	76	12	0.54
	626	100	2.84

Average = 2.84 in.

*Area of corresponding polygon within basin boundary

(b)

Isohyetal method:

Isohyet (in.)	Area* enclosed (sq mi)	Net area (sq mi)	Avg. precip. (in.)	Precipitation volume (col.3 × col.4)
5	13	13	5.3	69
4	90	77	4.6	354
3	206	116	3.5	406
2	402	196	2.5	490
1	595	193	1.5	290
<1	626	31	0.8	25
				.1634

Average = 1634 ÷ 626 = 2.61 in.

*Within basin boundary

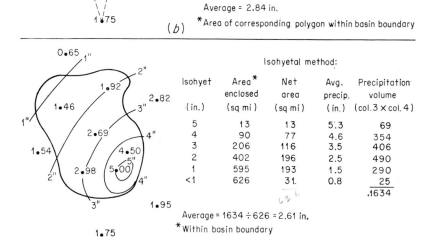

(c)

FIG. 3-10. Areal averaging of precipitation by (a) arithmetical method, (b) Thiessen method, and (c) isohyetal method.

country if the gages are uniformly distributed and the individual gage catches do not vary widely from the mean. These limitations can be partially overcome if topographic influences and areal representativity are considered in the selection of gage sites.[1]

The *Thiessen method*[2] attempts to allow for nonuniform distribution of gages by providing a weighting factor for each gage. The stations are plotted on a map, and connecting lines are drawn (Fig. 3-10b). Perpendicular bisectors of these connecting lines form polygons around each station. The sides of each polygon are the boundaries of the effective area assumed for the station. The area of each polygon is determined by planimetry and is expressed as a percentage of the total area. Weighted average rainfall for the total area is computed by multiplying the precipitation at each station by its assigned percentage of area and totaling. The results are usually more accurate than those obtained by simple arithmetical averaging.[3] The greatest limitation of the Thiessen method is its inflexibility, a new Thiessen diagram being required every time there is a change in the gage network. Also, the method makes no attempt to allow for orographic influences. Actually, the method simply assumes linear variation of precipitation between stations and assigns each segment of area to the nearest station.

The most accurate method of averaging precipitation over an area is the *isohyetal method*. Station locations and amounts are plotted on a suitable map, and contours of equal precipitation[4] (*isohyets*) are then drawn (Fig. 3-10c). The average precipitation for an area is computed by weighting the average precipitation between successive isohyets (usually taken as the average of the two isohyetal values) by the area between isohyets, totaling these products, and dividing by the total area.

The isohyetal method permits the use and interpretation of all available data and is well adapted to display and discussion. In constructing an isohyetal map the analyst can make full use of his knowledge of orographic effects and storm morphology, and in this case the final map should represent a more realistic precipitation pattern than could be obtained from the gaged amounts alone. The accuracy of the isohyetal method is highly dependent upon the skill of the analyst. If

[1] H. G. Wilm, A. Z. Nelson, and H. C. Storey, An Analysis of Precipitation Measurements on Mountain Watersheds, *Monthly Weather Rev.*, Vol. 67, pp. 163–172, May, 1939.

[2] A. H. Thiessen, Precipitation for Large Areas, *Monthly Weather Rev.*, Vol. 39, pp. 1082–1084, July, 1911.

[3] R. E. Horton, Accuracy of Areal Rainfall Estimates, *Monthly Weather Rev.*, Vol. 51, pp. 348–353, July, 1923.

[4] W. G. Reed and J. B. Kincer, The Preparation of Precipitation Charts, *Monthly Weather Rev.*, Vol. 45, pp. 233–235, May, 1917.

linear interpolation between stations is used, the results will be essentially the same as those obtained with the Thiessen method. Moreover, an improper analysis may lead to serious error.

3-9. Depth-area-duration analysis. Various hydrologic problems require an analysis of time as well as areal distribution of storm precipitation. Basically, depth-area-duration analysis of a storm is performed to determine the maximum amounts of precipitation within various dura-

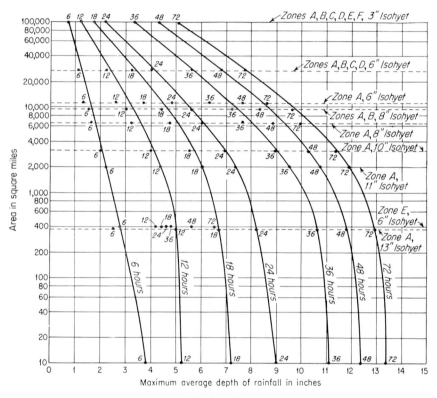

Explanation

"Zones A, B, 8″ Isohyet" refers to maximum depth-duration values computed for the area within the 8″ isohyet in Zones A and B. Plotted points represent maximum average depth of rainfall, over the area designated, within the number of hours indicated by figures beside points. Depths for 10-sq mi area are maximum station rainfall.

FIG. 3-11. Maximum depth-area-duration curves for the storm of Jan. 18 to 21, 1935, centered near Bolivar, Tennessee, and Hernando, Mississippi. (*After U.S. Corps of Engineers.*)

tions over areas of various sizes. The method[1] discussed here is somewhat arbitrary but has been standardized by the Federal agencies so that results will be comparable. For a storm with a single major center, the isohyets are taken as boundaries of individual areas. The average storm precipitation within each isohyet is computed as described in Sec. 3-8. The storm total is distributed through successive increments of time (usually 6 hr) in accordance with the distribution recorded at nearby stations.[2] When this has been done for each isohyet, data are available showing the time distribution of average rainfall over areas of various sizes. From these data, the maximum rainfall for various durations (6, 12, 18 hr, etc.) can be selected for each size of area. These maxima are plotted (Fig. 3-11), and an enveloping depth-area curve is drawn for each duration. Storms with multiple centers are divided into zones for analysis.

VARIATIONS IN PRECIPITATION

3-10. Geographic variations. In general, precipitation is heaviest at the equator and decreases with increasing latitude. However, the irregularity and orientation of the isohyets on the mean annual precipitation map of the United States (Fig. 3-12) indicate that the geographic distribution of precipitation depends on more effective factors than distance from the equator. A study[3] of maximum rainstorms in the United States indicated heaviest intensities at about 30°N.

The main source of moisture for precipitation is evaporation from the surface of large bodies of water. Therefore, precipitation tends to be heavier near coastlines. This characteristic is shown by the isohyets of Fig. 3-12, especially northward of the Gulf of Mexico. Although distorted by orography, a similar variation is observed in the Far Western states.

Since lifting of air masses accounts for almost all precipitation, amounts and frequency are generally greater on the windward side of mountain barriers. Conversely, since downslope motion of air results in decreased relative humidity, the lee sides of barriers usually experience relatively light precipitation. However, the continued rise of air immediately

---

[1] Manual for Depth-Area-Duration Analysis of Storm Precipitation. *U.S. Weather Bur. Coop. Studies Tech. Paper* 1, 1946.

R. K. Linsley, M. A. Kohler, and J. L. H. Paulhus, "Applied Hydrology," pp. 79–90, McGraw-Hill, New York, 1949.

[2] A. L. Shands and G. N. Brancato, Applied Meteorology: Mass Curves of Rainfall, *U.S. Weather Bur. Hydrometeorol. Tech. Paper* 4, 1947.

[3] R. A. McCormick, Latitudinal Variation of Maximum Observed United States Rainfall East of the Rocky Mountains, *Trans. Am. Geophys. Union*, Vol. 30, pp. 215–220, April, 1949.

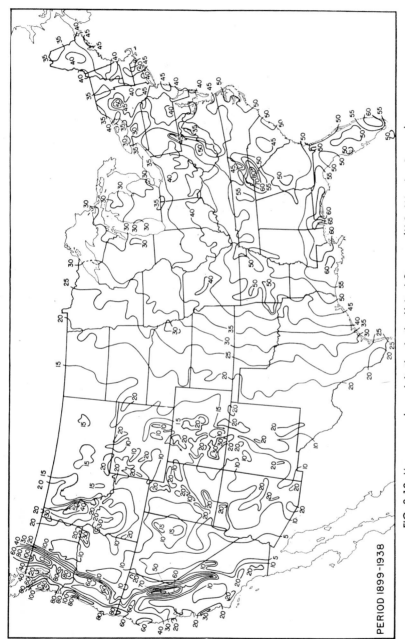

FIG. 3-12. Mean annual precipitation in the United States. (U.S. Weather Bureau.)

39

downwind from the ridge and the slanting fall of the precipitation produce heavy amounts on the lee slopes near the crest.

The variation of precipitation with elevation and other topographic factors has been investigated[1] with somewhat varying conclusions.

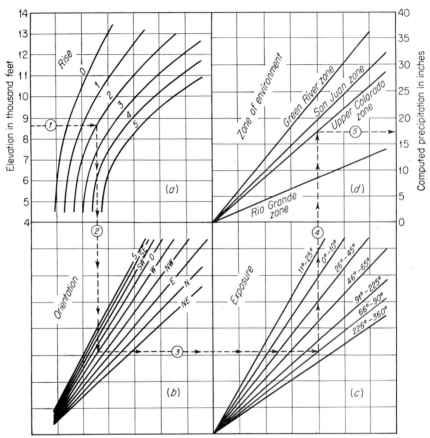

FIG. 3-13. Relation between average October–April precipitation and topographic parameters for western Colorado. (*After Spreen.*)

Perhaps the most detailed study of orographic influences on precipitation is that by Spreen, who correlated mean seasonal precipitation with elevation, slope, orientation, and exposure for western Colorado (Fig. 3-13). The parameters of the relation are (1) elevation of the precipita-

[1] J. I. Burns, Small-scale Topographic Effects on Precipitation Distribution in San Dimas Experimental Forest, *Trans. Am. Geophys. Union*, Vol. 34, pp. 761–768, October, 1953.

W. C. Spreen, Determination of the Effect of Topography upon Precipitation, *Trans. Am. Geophys. Union*, Vol. 28, pp. 285–290, April, 1947.

tion station (in 1000 ft) above mean sea level; (2) *rise*, difference in elevation (in 1000 ft) between station and highest point within a 5-mi radius; (3) *exposure*, the sum (in degrees) of those sectors of a 20-mi-radius circle about the station not containing a barrier 1000 ft or more

TABLE 3-1. World's Greatest Observed Point Rainfalls
(After Jennings[*])

Duration	Depth, in.	Station	Date
1 min.	1.23	Unionville, Md.	July 4, 1956
8 min.	4.96	Füssen, Bavaria	May 25, 1920
15 min.	7.80	Plumb Point, Jamaica	May 12, 1916
20 min.	8.10	Curtea de Arges, Rumania	July 7, 1889
42 min.	12.00	Holt, Mo.	June 22, 1947
2 hr, 10 min.	19.00	Rockport, W. Va.	July 18, 1889
2 hr, 45 min.	22.00	D'Hanis, Texas (17 mi NW)	May 31, 1935
4 hr, 30 min.	30.8+	Smethport, Pa.	July 18, 1942
15 hr.	34.50	Smethport, Pa.	July 17–18, 1942
18 hr.	36.40	Thrall, Texas	Sept. 9, 1921
24 hr.	45.99	Baguio, Philippine I.,	July 14–15, 1911
39 hr.	62.39	Baguio, Philippine I.,	July 14–16, 1911
2 days.	65.79	Funkiko, Formosa	July 19–20, 1913
2 days, 15 hr.	79.12	Baguio, Philippine, I.,	July 14–17, 1911
3 days.	81.54	Funkiko, Formosa	July 18–20, 1913
4 days.	101.84	Cherrapunji, India	June 12–15, 1876
5 days.	114.50	Silver Hill Plantation, Jamaica	Nov. 5–9, 1909
6 days.	122.50	Silver Hill Plantation, Jamaica	Nov. 5–10, 1909
7 days.	131.15	Cherrapunji, India	June 24–30, 1931
8 days.	135.05	Cherrapunji, India	June 24–July 1, 1931
15 days.	188.88	Cherrapunji, India	June 24–July 8, 1931
31 days.	366.14	Cherrapunji, India	July, 1861
2 mo.	502.63	Cherrapunji, India	June–July, 1861
3 mo.	644.44	Cherrapunji, India	May–July, 1861
4 mo.	737.70	Cherrapunji, India	April–July, 1861
5 mo.	803.62	Cherrapunji, India	April–Aug., 1861
6 mo.	884.03	Cherrapunji, India	April–Sept., 1861
11 mo.	905.12	Cherrapunji, India	Jan.–Nov., 1861
1 yr.	1041.78	Cherrapunji, India	Aug., 1860–July, 1861
2 yr.	1605.05	Cherrapunji, India	1860–1861

[*] A. H. Jennings, World's Greatest Observed Point Rainfalls, *Monthly Weather Rev.*, Vol. 78, pp. 4–5, January, 1950.

above the station elevation; and (4) *orientation*, the direction to eight points of the compass of the greatest exposure defined above. While elevation alone accounted for only 30 per cent of the variation in precipitation, the five parameters together accounted for 85 per cent. Relations of this type are very useful for constructing isohyetal maps in rugged areas having sparse data.

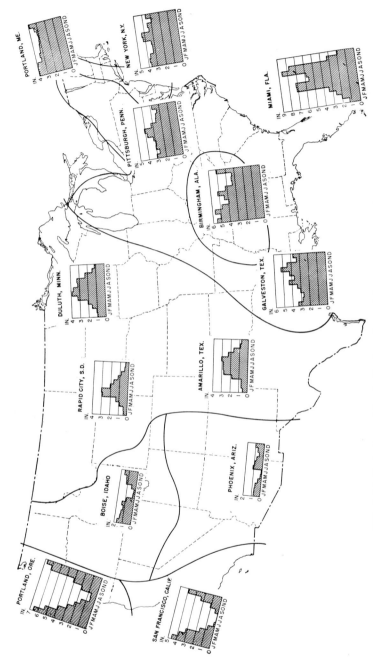

FIG. 3-14. Typical monthly distribution of precipitation in various climatic regions.

3-11. Time variations. While portions of a precipitation record may suggest an increasing or decreasing trend, there is usually a tendency to return to the mean; abnormally wet periods tend to be balanced by dry periods. The regularity of these fluctuations has been repeatedly investigated. More than 100 apparent cycles, ranging in period from 1 to 744 yr, have been reported.[1] The bibliography lists several reports on attempts to detect these variations from the analysis of tree rings and geological formations or to associate them with fluctuations in sunspots

TABLE 3-2. Maximum Recorded Rainfalls at Five Major U.S. Cities
(After Shands and Ammerman)

Station	Duration					
	Minutes			Hours		
	5	15	30	1	6	24
New York, N.Y............	0.75	1.63	2.34	2.48	4.09	9.40
	8/12/56	7/10/05	8/12/26	8/12/26	10/9/03	10/8/03
St. Louis, Mo.............	0.60	1.39	2.56	3.47	3.72	8.78
	7/9/42	8/8/23	8/8/23	7/23/33	7/23/33	8/15/46
New Orleans, La..........	0.90	1.89	2.38	3.66	7.95	14.01
	3/27/46	3/27/46	9/30/05	4/9/20	4/15/27	4/15/27
Denver, Colo.............	0.91	1.54	1.72	2.20	2.91	6.53
	7/14/12	7/14/12	7/14/12	8/23/21	8/23/21	5/21/76
San Francisco, Calif........	0.33	0.65	0.83	1.07	1.70	4.67
	1/25/26	11/4/18	3/4/12	3/4/12	1/12/14	1/29/81

and solar radiation. However, with the exception of diurnal and seasonal variations, no persistent regular cycles of any appreciable magnitude have been conclusively demonstrated.[2]

The seasonal distribution of precipitation varies widely within the United States. Figure 3-14 shows typical seasonal distribution graphs for stations in the precipitation regions defined by Kendrew.[3]

3-12. Record rainfalls. Table 3-1 lists the world's greatest observed point rainfalls. The predominance of U.S. stations for durations under 24 hr should not be interpreted as a tendency for heavier short-duration rainfall in the United States. The large number of recording rain gages

[1] Sir Napier Shaw, "Manual of Meteorology," 2d ed., Vol. 2, pp. 320–325, Cambridge, London, 1942.

[2] H. Landsberg, Climatology, Sec. XII, in F. A. Berry, Jr., E. Bollay, and N. R. Beers (eds.), "Handbook of Meteorology," p. 964, McGraw-Hill, New York, 1945.

[3] W. G. Kendrew, "The Climate of the Continents," 4th ed., p. 434, Oxford, New York, 1953.

enhances the probability of measuring localized rainfalls such as thunder-storms and cloudbursts. If the values of Table 3-1 were plotted on logarithmic paper, they would define an enveloping curve closely approximating a straight line.

The maximum rainfalls of record[1] for durations up to 24 hr at five major U.S. cities are given in Table 3-2. Table 3-3 lists maximum

TABLE 3-3. Maximum Depth-Area-Duration Data for the United States
(Average precipitation in inches)

Area, sq mi	Duration, hr						
	6	12	18	24	36	48	72
10	24.7a	29.8b	35.0b	36.5b	37.6b	37.6b	37.6b
100	19.6b	26.2b	30.7b	31.9b	32.9b	32.9b	35.2c
200	17.9b	24.3b	28.7b	29.7b	30.7b	31.9c	34.5c
500	15.4b	21.4b	25.6b	26.6b	27.6b	30.3c	33.6c
1,000	13.4b	18.8b	22.9b	24.0b	25.6d	28.8c	32.2c
2,000	11.2b	15.7b	19.5b	20.6b	23.1d	26.3c	29.5c
5,000	8.1bj	11.1b	14.1b	15.0b	18.7d	20.7d	24.4d
10,000	5.7j	7.9k	10.1e	12.1e	15.1d	17.4d	21.3d
20,000	4.0j	6.0k	7.9e	9.6e	11.6d	13.8d	17.6d
50,000	2.5eh	4.2g	5.3e	6.3e	7.9e	8.9e	11.5f
100,000	1.7h	2.5ih	3.5e	4.3e	5.6e	6.6f	8.9f

Storm	Date	Location of center
a	July 17–18, 1942	Smethport, Pa.
b	Sept. 8–10, 1921	Thrall, Texas
c	Aug. 6–9, 1940	Miller Island, La.
d	June 27–July 1, 1899	Hearne, Texas
e	March 13–15, 1929	Elba, Ala.
f	July 5–10, 1916	Bonifay, Fla.
g	April 15–18, 1900	Eutaw, Ala.
h	May 22–26, 1908	Chattanooga, Okla.
i	Nov. 19–22, 1934	Millry, Ala.
j	June 27–July 4, 1936	Bebe, Texas
k	April 12–16, 1927	Jefferson Parish, La.

depth-area-duration data for the United States and the storms producing them. They represent the enveloping values for over 400 of the country's major storms analyzed by the Corps of Engineers in cooperation with the U.S. Weather Bureau.

[1] A. L. Shands and D. Ammerman, Maximum Recorded United States Point Rainfall for 5 Minutes to 24 Hours at 207 First Order Stations, *U.S. Weather Bur. Tech. Paper* 2, 1947.

SNOW PACK AND SNOWFALL

3-13. Measurement. Measurement of the depth of accumulated snow on the ground is a regular function of all Weather Bureau observers. Where the accumulation is not large, the measurements are made with a yardstick or rain-gage measuring stick. In regions where large accumulations are the rule, permanent *snow stakes*, graduated in inches, are normally used. Such stakes should be installed where they will be least affected by blowing or drifting snow.

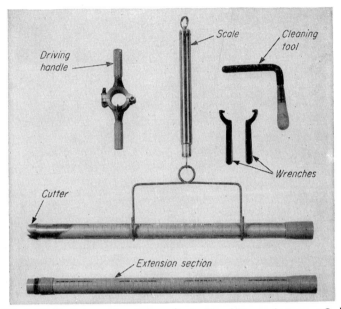

FIG. 3-15. Mt. Rose snow sampler. (*Leupold and Stevens Instrument* Co.)

The hydrologist is usually more interested in the water equivalent of the snow pack than in its depth. The *water equivalent* of the snow pack, i.e., the depth of water that would result from melting, depends on snow density as well as on depth. *Snow density*, the ratio between the volume of melt water from a sample of snow and the initial volume of the sample, has been observed to vary from 0.004 for freshly fallen snow at high latitudes to 0.91 for compacted snow in glaciers. An average density of 0.10 for freshly fallen snow is often assumed. In regions of heavy snow accumulation, densities of 0.4 to 0.6 are common by the time the spring thaws begin.

Measurements of water equivalent are usually made by sampling with a snow tube of the type shown in Fig. 3-15. The tube is driven vertically into the snow pack, sections of tubing being added as required.

The cutting edge on the leading section is designed to penetrate ice layers when the tube is rotated. When the bottom of the snow pack is reached, the snow depth is determined from the graduations on the tube. The tube and its contents are then withdrawn and weighed to determine the water equivalent. For convenience most tubes have a diameter such that 1 oz is equivalent to 1 in. of water.

Because of the highly variable snow pack resulting from drifting and nonuniform melting, 3 to 10 measurements are made at intervals of 10 to 50 ft along an established line, or *snow course*. Courses are selected at sites free from extensive wind effects and lateral drainage of melt water. Even then the measurement for each course is considered to be only an index to areal snow pack. Monthly or semimonthly snow surveys are made in late winter and early spring at over 1000 courses in the Western mountain region by the U.S. Soil Conservation Service and cooperating agencies. The U.S. Geological Survey and cooperators make similar surveys at over 500 courses in the Northeastern states. Twice-weekly observations of water equivalent are made at all first-order U.S. Weather Bureau stations, but these data are not published on a current basis.

Snow is usually composed of ice crystals and liquid water; the amount of liquid water is referred to as the *water content* of the snow. The *quality of snow*, i.e., the percentage by weight which is ice, can be determined by a calorimetric process.[1] Snow is inserted into a thermos bottle containing hot water. The quality can be computed from initial and final temperatures and weights (or volumes) of the water and melted snow. The water content in per cent of the water equivalent is 100 minus the quality. Most evaluations of quality made to date indicate values of 90 per cent or more, but values as low as 50 per cent have been obtained at times of rapid melting.

3-14. Variations. The mean annual snowfall for the United States is shown in the map (Fig. 3-16). This map may be considerably in error in mountainous regions because of the paucity of measurements at high elevations. As should be expected, there is a gradual increase of snowfall with latitude and elevation. In the Sierra Nevada and Cascade Range annual snowfalls of 400 in. are not uncommon. In general, maximum annual snowfall occurs at slightly higher elevations than maximum annual precipitation.

Maps of mean depth of snow on the ground or mean water equivalent for specific dates are not available. Snow depths would, of course, be much lower than annual snowfall amounts because of compaction of old

[1] M. Bernard and W. T. Wilson, A New Technique for the Determination of the Heat Necessary to Melt Snow, *Trans. Am. Geophys. Union*, Vol. 22, Part 1, pp. 178–181, 1941.

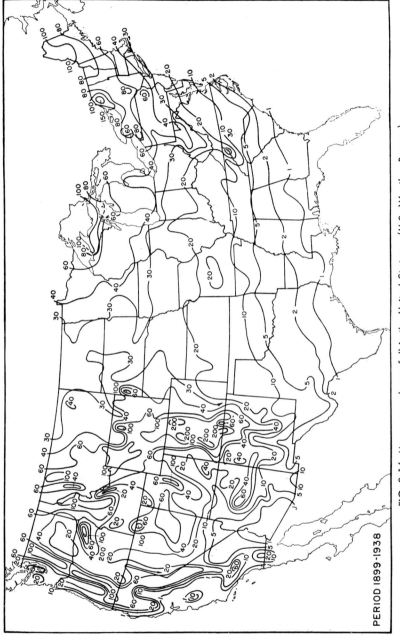

FIG. 3-16. Mean annual snowfall in the United States. (U.S. Weather Bureau.)

PERIOD 1899-1938

47

snow, evaporation, and melting. Snow depth usually builds up rapidly early in the season and then remains relatively constant as compaction of old snow compensates for new falls. Maximum depths on the ground are usually less than one-half the annual snowfall at high elevations and are still less at lower elevations where intermittent melting occurs. Similarly, the maximum water equivalent approaches 10 per cent of the annual snowfall at high elevations and is much less at lower elevations. The mean water equivalent at the beginning of the melting season is a good index to the mean annual precipitation.[1]

Because of drifting, considerable variation in snow depth and water equivalent may be observed within short distances. This variation can be intensified by differences in melting rates, which are generally greater on south slopes and in areas without forest cover. Nevertheless, there is a consistency in the distribution pattern from year to year as many important factors affecting melting—slope, aspect, elevation, forest cover, wind currents, etc.—normally undergo little change.

BIBLIOGRAPHY

Precipitation Forms and Formation

Byers, H. R.: "General Meteorology," pp. 489–507, McGraw-Hill, New York, 1944.
Petterssen, S.: "Weather Analysis and Forecasting," pp. 37–47, McGraw-Hill, New York, 1940.

Artificial Induction of Precipitation

Dufour, L., F. Hall, F. H. Ludlam, and E. J. Smith: Artificial Control of Clouds and Hydrometeors, *World Meteorol. Organization Tech. Note* 13, 1955.
Final Report of the Advisory Committee on Weather Control, Vols. 1 and 2, 1957.
Houghton, H. G.: An Appraisal of Cloud Seeding as a Means of Increasing Precipitation, *Bull. Am. Meteorol. Soc.*, Vol. 32, pp. 39–46, February, 1951.

Measurement of Precipitation

Hiatt, W. E., and R. W. Schloemer: How We Measure the Variations in Precipitation, from "Water," *U.S. Dept. Agr. Yearbook*, pp. 129–133, 1955.
Kadel, B. C.: Measurement of Precipitation *U.S. Weather Bur. Circ. E*, 4th ed., rev., 1936.
Kurtyka, J. C.: "Precipitation Measurements Study," State Water Survey Division, Urbana, Ill., 1953.
Marshall, J. S., R. C. Langille, and W. McK. Palmer: Measurement of Rainfall by Radar, *Am. Meteorol. Soc. J.*, Vol. 4, pp. 186–192, December, 1947.
Middleton, W. E. K., and A. F. Spilhaus: "Meteorological Instruments " 3d ed., rev., pp. 118–131, University of Toronto Press, Toronto, 1953.
Stout G. E., and J. C. Neill: Utility of Radar in Measuring Areal Rainfall, *Bull. Am. Meteorol. Soc.*, Vol. 34, pp. 21–27, January, 1953.

[1] J. L. H. Paulhus, C. E. Erickson, and J. T. Riedel, Estimation of Mean Annual Precipitation from Snow-survey Data, *Trans. Am. Geophys. Union*, Vol. 33, pp. 763–767, October, 1952.

Depth-Area Relations

Fletcher, R. D.: A Relation between Maximum Observed Point and Areal Rainfall Values, *Trans. Am. Geophys. Union*, Vol. 31, pp. 344–348, June, 1950.

Huff, F. A., and G. E. Stout: Area-Depth Studies for Thunderstorm Rainfall in Illinois, *Trans. Am. Geophys. Union*, Vol. 33, pp. 495–498, August, 1952.

Sanderson, E. E., and Don Johnstone: Accuracy of Determination of Annual Precipitation over a Given Area, *Trans. Am. Geophys. Union*, Vol. 34, pp. 49–57, February, 1953.

Wind Shields

Alter, J. C.: Shielded Storage Precipitation Gages, *Monthly Weather Rev.*, Vol. 65, pp. 262–265, July, 1937.

Brooks, C. F.: Further Experience with Shielded Precipitation Gages on Blue Hill and Mt. Washington, *Trans. Am. Geophys. Union*, Vol. 21, Part 2, pp. 482–485, 1940.

Warnick, C. C.: Experiments with Wind Shields for Precipitation Gages, *Trans. Am. Geophys. Union*, Vol. 34, pp. 379–388, June, 1953.

Wilson, W. T.: Analysis of Winter Precipitation in the Cooperative Snow Investigations, *Monthly Weather Rev.*, Vol. 82, pp. 183–199, July, 1954.

Precipitation Cycles

Glock, W. S.: "Tree Growth and Rainfall; A Study of Correlation and Methods," Smithsonian Institution, Washington, D.C., 1950.

Haurwitz, B.: Relation between Solar Activity and the Lower Atmosphere, *Trans. Am. Geophys. Union*, Vol. 27, pp. 161–163, April, 1946.

Schulman, E.: Centuries-long Tree Indices of Precipitation in the Southwest, *Bull. Am. Meteorol. Soc.*, Vol. 23, pp. 148–161, 204–217, May, 1942.

Tannehill I. R.: "Drought," Princeton University Press, Princeton, N.J., 1947.

Tannehill, I. R.: Is Weather Subject to Cycles?, in "Water," *U.S. Dept. Agr. Yearbook*, pp. 84–90, 1955.

SOURCES OF DATA

The main source of precipitation data is *Climatological Data* published monthly by the U.S. Weather Bureau and containing the daily records of rainfall. Hourly rainfall intensities are found in *Hydrologic Bulletin* (1940–1948), *Climatological Data* (1948–1951), and *Hourly Precipitation Data* (1951–   ). Weekly and monthly maps of precipitation over the United States are found in *Weekly Weather and Crop Bulletin* and *Monthly Weather Review*. The *Climatic Summary for the United States* summarizes monthly and annual data from beginning of record to 1950.

The *Water Bulletin* of the International Boundary and Water Commission contains data for the Rio Grande Basin, and *Precipitation in the Tennessee River Basin* published by the Tennessee Valley Authority summarizes data in their service area. Many states and local groups publish data summaries which contain information on precipitation.

Results of snow surveys in California are published by the State Department of Water Resources in *Water Conditions in California*. Elsewhere in the West, snow-survey data are published by the U.S. Soil Conservation Service in bulletins called *Federal-State Cooperative Snow Surveys and Water-supply Forecasts*. In the East snow-survey data are available as follows:

"New York Cooperative Snow Survey," U.S. Geological Survey.

"Snow Cover Surveys by Eastern Snow Conference," U.S. Weather Bureau.

"Snow and Ice Measurements, Susquehanna River Watershed," Federal-State Forecasting Service, Weather Bureau Office, Harrisburg, Pa.

Special summaries and data on normals and extremes of precipitation and snow may be found in:

Atlas of Climatic Types in the United States 1900–39, *U.S. Dept. Agr. Misc. Publ.* 421, 1941.

"Climate and Man," *U.S. Dept. Agr. Yearbook*, 1941.

Maps of Seasonal Precipitation and Tables of Normals, *U.S. Weather Bureau Misc. Publ.* 1353, 1942.

Kincer, J. B.: "Normal Weather for the United States," U.S. Weather Bureau, 1943.

McDonald, W. F.: "Average Precipitation in the United States," U.S. Weather Bureau, 1944.

Shands, A. L., and D. Ammerman: Maximum Recorded U.S. Point Rainfall, *U.S. Weather Bur. Tech. Paper* 2, 1947.

Maximum station precipitation for 1, 2, 3, 6, 12, and 24 Hours, *U.S. Weather Bur. Tech. Paper* 15, Parts 1 to 15, 1951–1955.

Maximum 24-hour Precipitation in the United States, *U.S. Weather Bur. Tech. Paper* 16, 1952.

Rainfall Intensities for Local Drainage Design in the United States, *U.S. Weather Bur. Tech. Paper* 24, Part 1, 1953, Part 2, 1954.

Rainfall Intensity-Duration-Frequency Curves, *U.S. Weather Bur. Paper* 25, 1955.

Rainfall Intensities for Local Drainage Design in Western United States, *U.S. Weather Bur. Tech. Paper* 28, 1956.

Storm Rainfall in the United States, *U.S. Corps of Engineers.*

PROBLEMS

3-1. Assuming rain falling vertically, express the catch of a gage inclined 20° from the vertical in terms of a percentage of the catch for the same gage installed vertically.

3-2. Precipitation Station X was inoperative for part of a month during which a storm occurred. The storm totals at three surrounding stations, A, B, and C, were, respectively, 4.20, 3.50, and 4.80 in. The normal annual precipitation amounts at Stations X, A, B, and C are, respectively, 38.50, 44.10, 36.80, and 47.20 in. Estimate the storm precipitation for Station X.

3-3. The annual precipitation at Station X and the average annual precipitation at 25 surrounding stations are as shown in the table on page 51.

(a) Determine the consistency of the record at Station X.

(b) In what year is a change in regime indicated?

(c) Compute the mean annual precipitation for Station X at its present site for the entire 36-yr period, first, without adjustment and, secondly, with the data adjusted for the change in regime.

3-4. The average annual precipitation for the four subbasins constituting a large river basin is 39.70, 44.20, 33.40, and 28.90 in. The areas are 360, 275, 420, and 650 sq mi, respectively. What is the average annual precipitation for the area as a whole?

3-5. Construct maximum depth-area-duration curves for the United States from the data of Table 3-3. Tabulate maximum values for areas of 50, 7500, and 30,000 sq mi for durations of 6, 12, 18, 24, 36, 48, and 72 hr.

3-6. Plot the 25-station average precipitation of Prob. 3-3 as a time series. Also plot 5-yr moving averages and accumulated annual departures from the 36-yr mean. Are there any apparent cycles or time trends? Discuss.

Year	Annual precipitation		Year	Annual precipitation	
	Sta. X	25-station average		Sta. X	25-station average
1956	7.4	10.4	1938	8.8	14.2
1955	7.3	9.0	1937	6.8	9.2
1954	12.2	15.2	1936	11.1	13.1
1953	11.6	11.7	1935	8.6	9.3
1952	8.2	11.2	1934	9.7	9.9
1951	11.3	13.8	1933	11.2	11.2
1950	7.2	9.3	1932	19.0	14.2
1949	12.0	14.6	1931	12.6	11.1
1948	9.0	9.2	1930	10.8	10.7
1947	8.5	11.4	1929	12.7	10.8
1946	8.8	11.1	1928	17.2	11.9
1945	8.0	9.7	1927	15.3	13.8
1944	11.2	10.4	1926	12.0	9.0
1943	11.6	13.1	1925	12.6	12.3
1942	8.1	9.1	1924	12.9	11.1
1941	10.6	9.2	1923	12.1	12.4
1940	9.5	9.1	1922	11.9	11.0
1939	11.2	12.3	1921	16.3	13.5

3-7. Repeat Prob. 3-6 for some station in your immediate vicinity, using data from the *Climatic Summary of the United States* or other source.

3-8. Compute the mean annual precipitation for some river basin selected by your instructor. Use the arithmetic average, Thiessen network, and isohyetal map and compare the three values. Which do you feel is most accurate? How consistent are the answers determined by each method among members of your class?

3-9. Repeat Prob. 3-8 using rainfall from some storm selected by your instructor. Obtain the precipitation data from *Climatological Data*.

3-10. Plot a graph showing the monthly distribution of normal precipitation for a station in your area. Explain briefly the climatological factors causing the observed distribution.

3-11. Plot the data of Table 3-1 on logarithmic paper and determine the equation of the enveloping straight line. Use duration in hours.

3-12. Write an equation for the calorimetric determination of snow quality.

4

STREAMFLOW

Most data used by hydrologists serve other purposes in meteorology, climatology, or other earth sciences. Streamflow data are gathered primarily by hydrologists and used mainly for hydrologic studies. More significant to the engineering hydrologist, however, is the fact that streamflow is the dependent variable in most studies, since engineering hydrology is concerned mainly with estimating rates or volumes of flow or the changes in these values resulting from man-made causes.

WATER STAGE

4-1. Staff gages. *River stage* is the elevation of the water surface at a specified station above some arbitrary zero datum. The zero elevation is sometimes taken as mean sea level but more often it is set slightly below the point of zero flow in the stream. Because it is difficult to make a direct and continuous measurement of the rate of flow in a stream but relatively simple to obtain a continuous record of water-surface elevation, the primary field data gathered at a streamflow measurement station are river stage. Stage data are transformed to flow data by methods discussed in the subsequent sections.

The simplest way to measure river stage is by means of a *staff gage*, a scale set so that a portion of it is immersed in the water at all times. The gage may consist of a single vertical scale attached to a bridge pier, piling, wharf, or other structure that extends into the low-water channel of the stream (Fig. 4-1a). If no suitable structure exists in a location which is accessible at all stages a *sectional staff gage* (Fig. 4-1b) may be used. Short sections of staff are mounted on available structures or on specially constructed supports in such a way that one section is always accessible. An alternative to the sectional staff is an *inclined staff gage* (Fig. 4-1c) which is placed on the slope of the stream bank and graduated so that the scale reads directly in vertical depth.

The gage scale may consist of marks painted on an existing structure or on a wooden plank attached to the support. Painted scales are usually

graduated in feet and tenths.   Markings are often in the pattern used
on stadia rods for visibility.   Enameled metal sections with markings
in feet and hundredths are available where particularly accurate stage
data are desired.   If a stream carries a large amount of fine sediment or
industrial waste, scale markings may be quickly obliterated.   In this
case, a serrated edge on the staff or raised marking symbols may be
helpful.

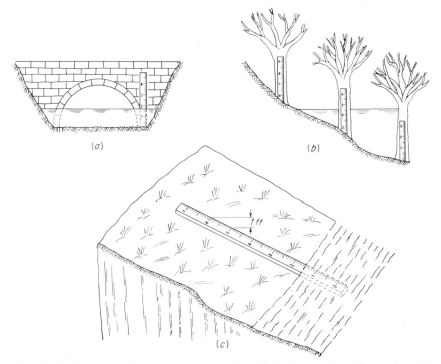

FIG. 4-1. Staff gages.   (a) Simple vertical staff.   (b) Sectional staff.   (c) Inclined staff.

4-2. Suspended-weight gages.   Another type of manual gage is
the *suspended-weight gage* in which a weight is lowered from a bridge or
other overhead structure until it reaches the water surface.   By subtracting the length of line paid out from the elevation of a fixed reference
point on the bridge, the water-surface elevation can be determined.
The *wire-weight gage* (Fig. 4-2) has a drum with a circumference such
that each revolution unwinds 1 ft of wire.   A counter records the number
of revolutions of the drum while a fixed reference point indicates hundredths of feet on a scale around the circumference.

4-3. Recording gages.   Manual gages are simple and inexpensive
but must be read frequently to define the hydrograph adequately when

stage is changing rapidly. Water-stage recorders, in which the motion of a float is recorded on a chart, overcome this difficulty. In a *continuous recorder*, the motion of the float moves a pen across a long strip chart. The chart is usually 10 in. wide and, at a scale of 2 in. = 1 ft, represents a 5-ft change in stage. When the pen reaches the edge of the chart it reverses direction and records the next 5 ft in the other direction across the chart (Fig. 4-3*a*). The chart roll contains enough paper to operate for a year at a scale of 2.4 in./day. Clocks are usually weight-driven

FIG. 4-2. Wire-weight gage. (*Leupold and Stevens Instrument* Co.)

and will run as long as there is room for the clock weight to drop. Small electric clocks that can operate for 30 days on a flashlight battery have been used.

A short-term recorder usually has a chart wrapped around a drum which is rotated by the float while the pen is driven at constant speed parallel to its axis. The circumference of the drum represents any selected change in stage. Larger changes are recorded beginning again at the bottom of the chart (Fig. 4-3*b*).

A float-type water-stage recorder requires a shelter house and stilling well (Fig. 4-4). The stilling well serves to protect the float and counterweight cables from floating debris and, if the intakes are properly designed, suppresses fluctuations resulting from surface waves in the stream. Inexpensive stilling wells have been made from timber and corrugated-steel pipe, while more elaborate structures are usually reinforced concrete.

Generally two or more intake pipes are placed from the well into the
stream so that at least one will admit water at all times. Sometimes
the water enters through the open bottom of the well. In this case an
inverted cone may be placed over the bottom of the well to reduce the
size of the opening and suppress the effect of surface waves. The open-
bottom type of stilling well has the advantage that it is less likely to

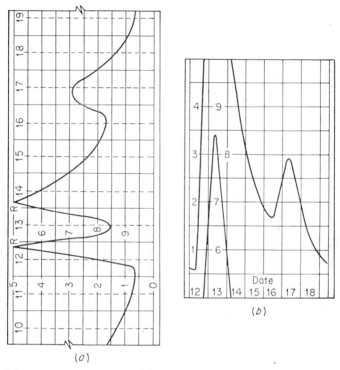

FIG. 4-3. Recording-gage charts: (a) continuous-strip chart and (b) weekly chart.

fill with sediment. If a stilling well with a closed bottom is installed
on a stream with a high sediment load, it is necessary to provide for
removal of the sediment which accumulates in the well. This can be
done by digging the sediment out and removing it in buckets or by providing valves on the intake pipes which may be closed while the well
is pumped full of water and then opened to flush out the sediment. It
is customary to install staff gages inside and outside the well. These
staff gages serve to check the performance of the recorder and are read
each time the station is visited.

Recent developments in recording gages include a float recorder which
uses a tubular float and requires only a small-diameter pipe as a stilling
well. Efforts are also being made to develop pressure-sensitive gages

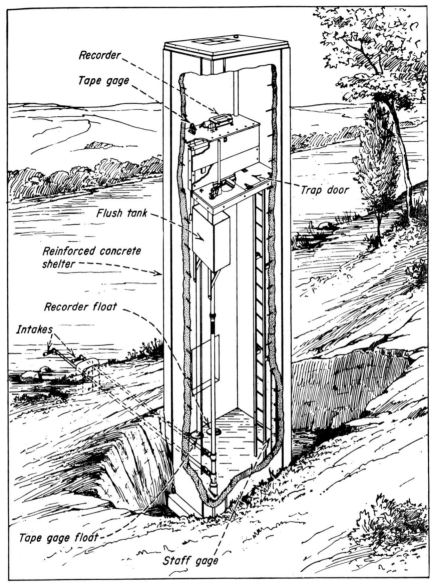

FIG. 4-4. A typical water-stage recorder installation. (U.S. Geological Survey.)

and gages activated by radioisotopes as well as other devices. The aim of all of these is to eliminate the costly stilling well required with conventional float-operated gages. It has proved difficult to develop gages accurate to 0.01 ft at low stages yet having the ruggedness and range required to record flood stages.

4-4. Crest-stage gages. A third type of stage-measuring device is the *crest gage*, used to obtain a record of flood crests at sites where recording gages are not installed. A variety of such gages have been devised, including small floats which rise with the stage but are restrained at the maximum level[1] and water-soluble paints[2] on bridge piers where

they are protected from rain and can indicate a definite high-water mark. The gage used by the U.S. Geological Survey consists of a length of pipe (Fig. 4-5) containing a graduated stick and a small amount of ground cork.[3] The cork floats as the water rises and some adheres to the stick at the highest level reached by the water. The stick can be removed, the crest reading recorded, the cork wiped off, and the stick replaced ready for the next rise. Crest gages provide low-cost, supplementary records of crest stages at locations where recorders are not justified and where manually read staff gages are inadequate.

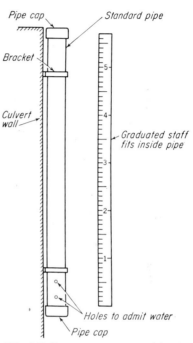

FIG. 4-5. Crest-stage gage used by the U.S. Geological Survey.

4-5. Miscellaneous stage gages. Water- or mercury-filled manometers are often used to indicate reservoir water levels or to actuate recording devices. If flow rate is dependent on the difference in water level, a single recorder with two floats and two stilling wells may be used to record water-level differences. Remote recorders in which a system of selsyn motors is used to transmit water-level information from stream side to a recorder at a distance are available, as are numerous remote transmitting telephonic or radio gages. These latter gages use a coding device which converts stage to a signal which can be transmitted in the form of a series of impulses which can be counted, a change in frequency of oscillation which can be measured, or the time interval required for

---

[1] M. H. Collet, Crest-stage Meter for Measuring Static Heads, *Civil Eng.*, Vol. 12, p. 396, 1942.

J. C. Stevens, Device for Measuring Static Heads, *Civil Eng.*, Vol. 12, p. 461, 1942.

[2] F. J. Doran, High Water Gaging, *Civil Eng.*, Vol. 12, pp. 103–104, 1942.

[3] G. E. Ferguson, Gage to Measure Crest Stages of Streams, *Civil Eng.*, Vol. 12, pp. 570–571, 1942.

a sensing element to move from a zero point to the water surface at constant speed. Such remote recording devices are used primarily for flood forecasting or reservoir operation. Cost usually precludes their use for routine data collection.

4-6. Selection of a station site. If a stream gage is solely to record water level for flood warning or as an aid to navigation, the prime factor in its location is accessibility. If the gage is to be used to obtain a record of discharge, the location should be carefully selected. The relation between stage and discharge is controlled by the physical features of the channel downstream from the gage. When the controlling features are situated in a short length of channel a *section control* exists. If the stage-discharge relation is governed by the slope, size, and roughness of the channel over a considerable distance the station is under *channel control*. In many cases no single control is effective at all stages but a complex of controlling elements function as stage varies.

The ideal low-water control is a section control consisting of a rapids or riffle. If this control is in rock it will be reasonably permanent and once calibrated, need be checked only infrequently. Where no such natural low-water control exists, an artificial control consisting of a low concrete weir, sometimes with a shallow V notch, may be constructed to maintain a stable low-water rating. A channel control is more likely to change with time as a result of scour or deposition of sediment, and more frequent flow measurements are required to maintain an accurate stage-discharge relation.

Rapids may also be effective controls at high flows if the slope of the stream is steep, but where slopes are flat, the section control is likely to be submerged and ineffective at high flows. High-water controls are more likely to be channel controls although in some cases the contraction at a bridge or the effect of a dam may control at high stages. It is advisable to avoid locations where varying backwater from a dam, an intersecting stream, or tidal action occurs. These situations require special ratings which tend to be less accurate.

DISCHARGE

4-7. Current meters. The stage record is transformed to a discharge record by calibration. Since the control rarely has a regular shape for which the discharge can be computed, calibration is accomplished by relating field measurements of discharge with the simultaneous river stage (Secs. 4-8 to 4-11).

The most common current meter in the United States is the Price meter (Fig. 4-6), the type used by the U.S. Geological Survey. It consists of six conical cups rotating about a vertical axis. Electric contacts driven by the cups close a circuit through a battery and the wire of the supporting cable to cause a click for each revolution (or each fifth revolution) in headphones worn by the operator. For measurements in deep water, the meter is suspended from a cable. Tail vanes to keep the meter facing into the current and a heavy weight to keep the meter cable as nearly vertical as possible are provided. Special cranes are available to support the meter over a bridge rail, to simplify handling of the heavy weights, and to permit measuring the length of cable paid

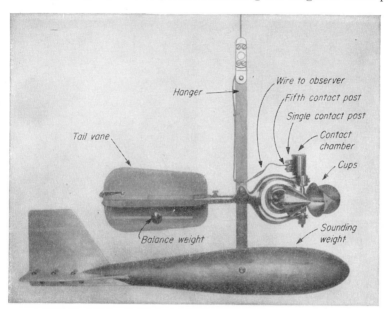

FIG. 4-6. Price current meter and 30-lb C-type sounding weight. (U.S. Geological Survey.)

out. In shallow water the meter is mounted on a rod, and the observer wades the stream. A *pygmy* Price meter has been used for measuring flow at very shallow depths.

The other type of current meter is the *propeller* type, in which the rotating element is a propeller turning about a horizontal axis (Fig. 4-7). The contacting mechanism of a propeller meter is similar to that of a Price meter, and similar suspensions are used. The vertical-axis meter has an important advantage in that the bearing supporting the shaft can be enclosed in inverted cups which trap air around the bearings and prevent entrance of sediment-laden water. The bearings of propeller meters cannot be so protected and are therefore exposed to damage by abrasion. On the other hand, the vertical-axis meter has a disadvantage in that vertical currents or upstream velocity components rotate the cups in the same direction as the downstream currents. A Price meter moved vertically in still water will indicate a positive velocity. Hence,

the Price meter tends to overestimate the velocity in a stream.   If the
measuring section is well chosen with the current flow nearly parallel
to the channel axis and with a minimum of turbulence, the error is
probably not more than 2 per cent.[1]

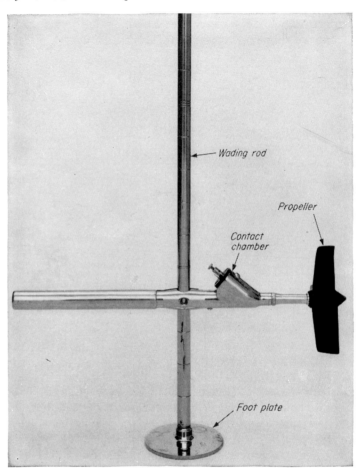

FIG. 4-7. Propeller-type current meter.

The relation between revolutions per second N of the meter cups and
water velocity v in feet per second is given by an equation of the form

$$v = a + bN \tag{4-1}$$

where a is the starting velocity or velocity required to overcome mechanical friction.   For the Price meter, a is about 0.1 and b about 2.2.   Some

[1] M. P. O'Brien and R. G. Folsom, Notes on the Design of Current Meters, *Trans.
Am. Geophys. Union*, Vol. 29, pp. 243–250, April, 1948.

variation in these constants must be expected as a result of manufacturing limitations and the effects of wear. Consequently each meter should be individually calibrated. This is usually done by mounting the meter

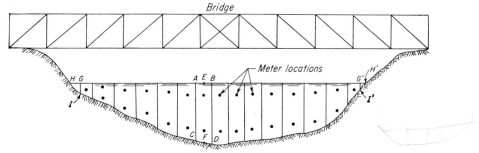

FIG. 4-8. The procedure for current-meter measurement.

on a carriage which moves it through still water. The carriage may run on rails along a straight channel or may rotate about a central pivot in a circular basin. The speed of the carriage is determined by the time required to travel a known distance. With several runs at various speeds it is possible to plot a curve showing the relation between meter contacts per unit time and water speed.

4-8. Current-meter measurements. A discharge measurement requires the determination of sufficient point velocities to permit computation of an average velocity in the stream. The cross-sectional area multiplied by the average velocity gives the total discharge. The number of velocity determinations must be limited to those which can be made within a reasonable time interval. This is especially true if the stage is changing rapidly, since it is desirable to complete the measurement with a minimum change in stage.

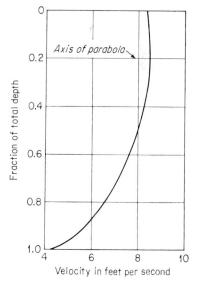

FIG. 4-9. A typical vertical velocity profile in a stream.

The practical procedure involves dividing the stream into a number of vertical sections (Fig. 4-8). No section should include more than about 10 per cent of the total flow; thus 15 to 20 vertical sections are typical. Velocity varies approximately as a parabola (Fig. 4-9) from zero at the channel bottom to a

9-275-F
Jan. 1952

UNITED STATES
DEPARTMENT OF THE INTERIOR
GEOLOGICAL SURVEY
WATER RESOURCES DIVISION

DISCHARGE MEASUREMENT NOTES

Meas. No. 147
Comp. by EMW
Checked by JBC

Antietam Cr. nr Sharpsburg, Md.
Date May 4, 1945 Party P.W. Brewer
Width 75 Area 257 Vel. 1.78 G. H. 3.40 Disch. 459
Method .2+.8 No. secs. 32 G. H. change +0.04 in 1⅓ hrs. Susp. 30#C
Method coef. 1.00 Hor. angle coef. 1.00 Susp. coef. 1.005 Meter No. 1378

GAGE READINGS

Time		Recorder	Inside	Outside
8:45a		3.37	3.37	3.35
9:00a		3.38		
10:20		3.42		
10:25		3.42	3.42	3.40
Weighted M. G. H.		3.40	3.40	
G. H. correction				
Correct M. G. H.		3.40	3.40	

Date rated 10-21-42 Used rating for rod susp. Meter 0.5 ft. above bottom of wt. Tags checked
Spin before meas. ok after ok
Meas. plots ___ % diff. from ___ rating
Wading, cable, ice, boat, upstr., downstr., side bridge 6.0 feet, ~~mile~~ above, ~~below~~ gage, and
Check-bar, chain found
changed to ___ at ___
Correct
Levels obtained

Measurement rated excellent (2%), good (5%), fair (8%), poor (over 8%), based on following conditions: Cross section Fairly smooth
Flow Smooth Weather Cloudy, cool
Other Air °F@
Gage Ok Water °F@
Record removed Yes Intake flushed Yes
Observer
Control Clean. Removed small log @ 8:40 a.m. No change in gage height
Remarks
G. H. of zero flow — ft.

16—58354-3

River at—

Angle coefficient	Dist. from initial point	Width	Depth	Observation depth	Revolutions	Time in seconds	Velocity At point	Velocity Mean in vertical	Adjusted for hor. angle or	Area	Discharge
	30		0								
	33	3	2.3	.6	15	51		.66		6.9	4.55
	36	3	2.8	.2	30	42	1.58	1.36		8.4	11.42
				.8	20	39	1.14				
	39	3	3.1	.2	40	48	1.84	1.56		9.3	14.51
				.8	25	43	1.29				
	42	3	3.2	.2	40	43	2.05	1.74		9.6	16.71
				.8	30	46	1.44				
	45	3	3.2	.2	50	46	2.39	2.06		9.6	19.76
				.8	40	51	1.73				
	48	2.5	3.3	.2	50	43	2.55	2.26		8.25	18.65
				.8	40	45	1.96				
	50	2	3.4	.2	50	45	2.44	2.14		6.8	14.53
				.8	40	48	1.84				
	52	2	3.4	.2	50	44	2.50	2.28		6.8	15.51
				.8	40	43	2.05				
	54	2	3.6	.2	50	43	2.55	2.30		7.2	16.55
				.8	40	43	2.05				
	57	2.5	3.5	.2	50	45	2.44	2.20		8.75	19.28
				.8	40	45	1.96				

FIG. 4-10. Sample current-meter field notes used by the U.S. Geological Survey.

maximum at (or near) the surface. On the basis of many field tests, the variation for most channels is such that the average of the velocities at 0.2 and 0.8 depth below the surface equals the mean velocity in the vertical. The velocity at 0.6 depth below the surface is also nearly equal to the mean in the vertical. The adequacy of these assumptions for a particular stream may be tested by making a large number of velocity determinations in the vertical.

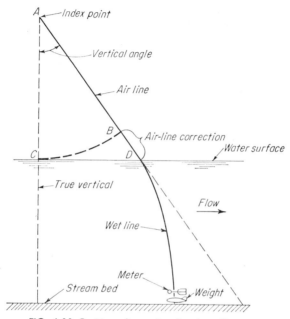

FIG. 4-11. Position of sounding line in swift water.

Sample current-meter field notes are shown in Fig. 4-10. The determination of the mean velocity in a vertical is as follows:

(a) Measure the total depth of the water by sounding with the meter cable.

(b) Raise the meter to the 0.8 depth and measure the velocity by starting a stopwatch on an impulse from the meter and stopping it on another impulse about 60 sec later. The number of impulses counted (taking the first as zero) and the elapsed time permit calculation of velocity from the meter calibration.

(c) Raise the meter to the 0.2 depth and repeat step (b).

In the shallow water near the shore a single velocity determination at 0.6 depth may be used.

If water velocities are very high, the meter and weight will not hang vertically below the point of suspension but will be carried downstream by the current (Fig. 4-11). Under these conditions the length of line paid out is greater than the true vertical depth, and the meter is higher than the true 0.2 and 0.8 depths. Very heavy weights are used to minimize this effect, but if the angle between the line and a vertical becomes large it is necessary to apply a correction to the measured depths.[1] The actual correction depends on the relative lengths of line above and below the water surface, but at a vertical angle of 12° the error will be about 2 per cent. A slight additional error is introduced if the current is not normal to the measuring section.

Computation of total discharge is made as follows[2] (Fig. 4-10):

(*a*) Compute the average velocity in each vertical by averaging the velocities at 0.2 and 0.8 depths.

(*b*) Multiply the average velocity in a vertical by the area of a vertical section extending halfway to adjacent verticals (*ABCD*, Fig. 4-8). This area is taken as the measured depth at the vertical (*EF*) times the width of the section (*AB*).

(*c*) Add the increments of discharge in the several verticals. Incremental discharge in the shore section (*GHI*, Fig. 4-8) is taken as zero.

Access to the individual verticals of a section may be obtained by wading if the water is shallow. Usually, wading is impractical at high stages, and the meter must be lowered from an overhead support. Where possible, bridges are used as the measuring section, if the bridge is normal to the stream axis and the current essentially parallel to the stream axis. The measuring section need not be at the same location as the control section. However, the distance between the sections should be short enough so that the intervening inflow is not large. Where no existing bridge is suitable, a special cableway may be used. The hydrographer rides in a small car suspended beneath the cable and lowers the meter through an opening in the floor of the car. Where neither bridge nor cableway is practical, measurements may be made from a boat. This is far less satisfactory because of the difficulty of maintaining position during a measurement and because either vertical or horizontal motion of the boat results in a positive velocity indication by the Price current meter.

4-9. Stage-discharge relations. Periodic meter measurements of flow and simultaneous stage observations provide the data for a calibration curve called a *rating curve* or *stage-discharge relation*. For most stations a simple plot of stage vs. discharge (Fig. 4-12) is satisfactory. Such a curve is approximately parabolic but may show some irregularities

---

[1] D. M. Corbett and others, Stream-gaging Procedure, *U.S. Geol. Survey Water-supply Paper* 888, pp. 43–51, 1945.

[2] This describes the procedure adopted by the U.S. Geological Survey about 1950. See K. B. Young, "A Comparative Study of Methods for Computation of Discharge," U.S. Geological Survey, February, 1950.

if the control changes between low and high flows or if the cross section is irregular.

The adequacy of a rating curve is measured by the scatter of the measured flows about the mean line. If the control is reasonably permanent and the slope of the energy line at the station reasonably constant for all occurrences of a given stage, a simple rating will suffice.

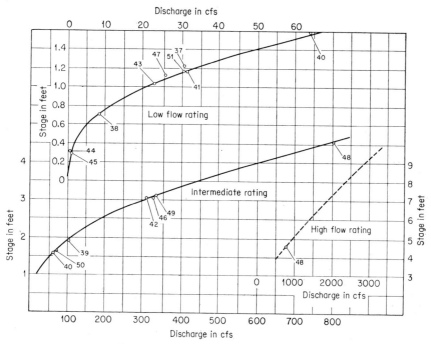

FIG. 4-12. A simple stage-discharge relation.

If the control is altered by scour or deposition, frequent meter measurements are necessary. Under conditions of *shifting control*, discharge is usually estimated by noting the difference between the stage at the time of a discharge measurement and the stage on the mean rating curve which shows the same discharge. This difference is applied as a correction to all stages before entering the rating. If the correction changes between measurements, a linear change with time is usually assumed.

Individual measurements may deviate from the mean stage-discharge relation as a result of differences in water-surface slope at the control. Since velocity head is usually small, the slopes of the water surface and of the energy line are nearly equal. Differences in slope may be caused by varying backwater as a result of an obstruction downstream or high stages in an intersecting stream. If either of these factors is present,

the rating curve must include slope as a parameter.[1]   The basic approach
is represented by

$$\frac{q}{q_0} = \left(\frac{s}{s_0}\right)^m = \left(\frac{F}{F_0}\right)^k \tag{4-2}$$

The equation states that discharge q is proportional to a power of water-
surface slope s.   From fluid mechanics the exponent m would be expected
to be $\frac{1}{2}$.   The fall F is the difference in water-surface elevation between

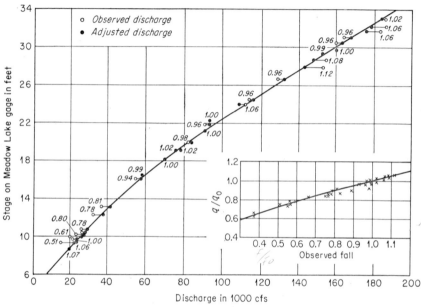

FIG. 4-13. A slope-stage-discharge rating curve for the Tennessee River at Chattanooga,
Tennessee.   (*U.S. Geological Survey.*)

two fixed sections and is usually measured by two conventional river
gages.   There is no assurance that the water surface between these
gages is a straight line, i.e., that $F/L = s$.   Consequently the exponent k
need not be $\frac{1}{2}$ and must be determined empirically.

A *slope-stage-discharge relation* requires two gages, a base gage and an
auxiliary gage.   The gages should be far enough apart so that F is at
least 1 ft to minimize the effect of observational errors.   The fall F
applicable to each discharge measurement is determined, and, if the
observed falls do not vary greatly, an average value F_0 is selected. F_0
need not be a mathematical average of the falls and for convenience

[1] M. C. Boyer, Determining Discharge at Gaging Stations Affected by Variable
Slope, *Civil Eng.*, Vol. 9, p. 556, 1939.

W. D. Mitchell, Stage-Fall-Discharge Relations for Steady Flow in Prismatic Channels, *U.S. Geol. Survey Water-supply Paper* 1164, 1954.

should be an even foot. All measurements with values of $F = F_0$ are plotted as a simple stage-discharge relation and a curve is fitted (Fig. 4-13). This is the q_0 curve representing the discharge when $F = F_0$. If $F \neq F_0$, the ratio F/F_0 is plotted against q/q_0 on an auxiliary chart. The discharge at any time can be computed by calculating the ratio F/F_0 and selecting a value of q/q_0 from the auxiliary curve. A value of q_0 corresponding to the existing stage is taken from the q_0 curve and

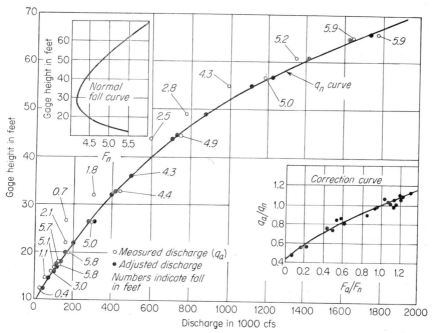

FIG. 4-14. Normal-fall rating curve for the Ohio River at Metropolis, Illinois. (U.S. Geological Survey.)

multiplied by q/q_0 to give q. If the auxiliary curve plots as a straight line on logarithmic paper, the slope of the line is k in Eq. (4-2). The rating just described is known as a *constant-fall rating*, since the adopted mean fall F_0 is constant.

In some cases the range of F is large and its variation is related to stage. In this case a *normal-fall rating* may be used. This rating is similar to the constant-fall rating except that the normal fall F_n which is used in place of F_0 is taken as a function of stage and defined by a second auxiliary curve (Fig. 4-14). To compute discharge with a normal-fall rating, the actual fall F is computed, a value of F_n is read from the curve, and the ratio F/F_n is calculated. The ratio q/q_n can then be determined and multiplied by q_n from the rating curve to give q.

Figure 4-15 shows the profile of a flood wave as it moves past a station. The slope is equal to $s_b + s_r$, where s_b is the slope of the channel bottom (or the slope of the water surface in uniform flow) and $s_r = dg/u\,dt$. Here dg/dt is the slope of the flood wave expressed as a rate of change of stage with time and u is the celerity of movement of the flood wave. Since s_r is the variable factor in the slope, a rating can be constructed by plotting stage against discharge for those measurements for which dg/dt is near zero. If u is assumed to be constant, a correction curve can then be established by plotting q/q_c vs. dg/dt, where q_c is the discharge corresponding to the existing stage when $dg/dt = 0$. Theoretically, dg/dt is the

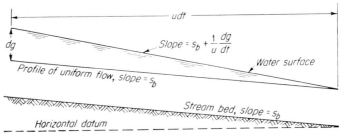

FIG. 4-15. The profile of a flood wave.

tangent to the water-stage recorder trace, but in practice it is convenient to use Δg, the change in stage during a finite time period, usually 1 hr but sometimes much longer.

4-10. Extension of rating curves. There is no completely satisfactory method for extrapolating a rating curve beyond the highest measured discharge. It is often assumed that the equation of the rating curve is

$$q = k(g - a)^b \tag{4-3}$$

where a, b, and k are constants for the station. This is the equation of a parabola in which a is approximately the distance between the zero elevation of the gage and the elevation of zero flow. If the correct value of a is determined by trial the equation will plot as a straight line on logarithmic paper and is easily extended. However, the procedure includes the assumption of a parabolic rating and cannot account for any marked change in the hydraulic geometry of the stream at high flows.

Another method[1] of extending rating curves is based on the Chézy formula

$$q = AC \sqrt{Rs} \tag{4-4}$$

where C is a roughness coefficient, s is the slope of the energy line, A is the cross-sectional area, and R is the hydraulic radius. If $C \sqrt{s}$ is

[1] J. C. Stevens, A Method of Estimating Stream Discharge from a Limited Number of Gagings, *Eng. News*, pp. 52–53, July 18, 1907.

assumed to be constant for the station and D, the mean depth, is substituted for R,

$$q = kA \sqrt{D} \tag{4-5}$$

Known values of q and $A \sqrt{D}$ are plotted on a graph and usually define something close to a straight line which may be readily extended. Values of $A \sqrt{D}$ for stages above the existing rating can be obtained by field measurement and used with the extended curve for estimates of q.

A third method of estimating high flows is by application of hydraulic principles. The procedure is often referred to as a *slope-area computation*. Sufficient high-water marks must be located along a reach of channel to permit determination of the water-surface slope at the time of peak. Cross sections of the channel may be determined by leveling or sounding, and the area and hydraulic radius calculated. The Chézy-Manning formula is ordinarily used to compute discharge:

$$q = \frac{1.49}{n} A R^{2/3} s^{1/2} \tag{4-6}$$

The main source of error in applying Eq. (4-6) is in estimating the roughness coefficient n (Appendix B). Since q is inversely proportional to n and the average value of n for natural streams is about 0.035, an error of 0.001 in n represents about 3 per cent in discharge. Considerable doubt may exist as to whether the cross section measured after the flood is the section which existed at the time of peak. A stream often scours during rising stages and redeposits material during falling stages (Fig. 4-16). Under the most favorable conditions, an error of 10 per cent may be expected in a slope-area estimate of flow.

4-11. The effect of ice on streamflow. When ice covers a stream, a new friction surface is formed and the stream becomes a closed conduit with lower discharge because of the increased hydraulic radius. The underside of the ice sheet may be extremely rough if ice cakes are tilted helter-skelter and then frozen together. Movement of the water under the ice gradually develops a smooth surface. If the stage falls, leaving the ice as a bridge across the stream, the stage-discharge characteristics return to those of a free stream.

In turbulent streams the first ice to form is *frazil ice*, small crystals suspended in the turbulent flow. Frazil ice collecting on rocks on the stream bed is called *anchor ice* and may cause a small increase in stage. If the turbulence is not sufficient to keep the frazil ice mixed in the stream, it rises to the surface to form sheet ice. Until a complete ice sheet is formed, small variations in the stage-discharge relation must be expected from time to time.

When ice conditions exist it is necessary to make periodic measurements[1] through holes in the ice and to interpolate the discharge between these measurements in any manner which seems reasonable. The meter must be moved rapidly from hole to hole and should be kept in the water at all times (except when being moved) to prevent freezing. Fortunately, if the stream is solidly frozen over, the flow is usually small since there will be little snowmelt or other source of runoff within the tributary area.

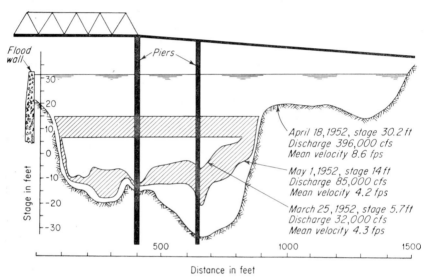

FIG. 4-16. Cross sections of the Missouri River at Omaha, Nebraska, showing the progressive scour and filling during the passage of a flood wave.

4-12. Other methods of obtaining streamflow data. On large streams the discharge at dams may be determined from calibration of the spillway, sluiceway, and turbine gates. If a careful record of gate and turbine operation is maintained, the discharge can be computed. This often requires that the spillway be rated by model tests and the turbines by salt-velocity[2] measurements. Some progress has been made in generalized rating curves based on the geometry of the gate structure.[3]

On small streams, flow measurements may be made with weirs or

[1] W. G. Hoyt, The Effect of Ice on Stream Flow, *U.S. Geol. Survey Water-supply Paper* 337, pp. 24–30, 1913.

[2] C. M. Allen and E. A. Taylor, The Salt Velocity Method of Water Measurement, *Trans. ASME*, Vol. 45, p. 285, 1923.

[3] J. N. Bradley, Rating Curves for Flow Over Drum Gates, *Trans. ASCE*, Vol.119, pp. 403–431, 1954.

flumes.[1] These devices are commonly rated on the basis of laboratory calibration although the rating may be checked in place with current meters. For small streams, a combination of a V-notch weir for low flows and a venturi flume for high flows may be necessary to assure accuracy. Large weirs are usually unsatisfactory because deposition of sediment in the upstream pool changes the discharge characteristics.

Highway culverts have frequently been suggested as flow-measuring devices, and in many instances this is feasible. However, the hydraulics of culverts is quite complex.[2] In flat terrain, care must be taken to avoid culverts affected by backwater unless both headwater and tail-water stages are measured. On steep slopes it is necessary to establish whether the culvert flows full with control in the barrel or partially full with control at the entrance. Temporary changes in discharge capacity may occur as the result of sediment or debris deposits.

Rough measurements of discharge can be made by timing the speed of floats. A surface float travels with a velocity which is about 1.2 times the mean velocity. Objects floating with a greater submerged depth will travel at speeds closer to the mean velocity in the section.[3]

INTERPRETATION OF STREAMFLOW DATA

4-13. Units. The basic flow unit in the United States is the *cubic foot per second* (also called *second-foot* and abbreviated *cusec*, or *cfs*). Countries using the metric system usually express flow in *cubic meters per second*. Volume of flow may be expressed in cubic feet or cubic meters but this leads to very large numbers, and larger volume units are commonly used. In the United States the *second-foot-day*, or the volume of water discharged in 24 hours, with a flow of one cubic foot per second is widely used. One second-foot-day (sfd) is $24 \times 60 \times 60 = 86,400$ cu ft. The average flow in cubic feet per second for any 24-hr period is the volume of flow in second-foot-days. The other common unit of volume is the *acre-foot*, the volume of water required to cover an acre to a depth of one foot. Hence, an acre-foot contains 43,560 cu ft and equals 0.504 sfd. Within an error of 1 per cent, one acre-foot equals one-half second-foot-day. In some cases it is convenient to use second-foot-hours ($\frac{1}{24}$ sfd) as a volume unit. In countries using the metric system, volume

---

[1] R. L. Parshall, The Parshall Measuring Flume, *Colo. Agr. Expt. Sta. Bull.* 423, 1936.

[2] Culvert Hydraulics, *Highway Research Board Rept.* 15-B, 1953.

F. T. Mavis, The Hydraulics of Culverts, *Penn. State Coll. Eng. Expt. Sta. Bull.* 56, 1943.

C. L. Larson and H. M. Morris, "Hydraulics of Flow in Culverts," University of Minnesota, October, 1948.

[3] A float extending from the surface to mid-depth travels with a velocity about 1.1 times the mean velocity.

is usually expressed in some multiple of cubic meters, commonly 10,000 cu m which equals 4.09 sfd (Appendix B).

Less common units of flow are the cubic foot per second per sq mi (csm), the inch, and the miner's inch. *Cubic feet per second per square mile* is a convenient unit for comparing rates of flow on streams with differing tributary area and is the flow in cubic feet per second divided by the drainage area in square miles. The *inch*, the amount of water required to cover the drainage area to a depth of one inch, is a useful unit for comparing streamflow with the precipitation which caused it. The inch is a unit of volume only when associated with a specific drainage area.

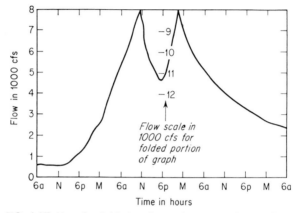

FIG. 4-17. Use of a folded scale to plot extremely high flows.

One inch on one square mile = 640/12 acre-ft = 53.3 acre-ft = 26.9 sfd. The *miner's inch* is an old unit used in the western United States and defined as the rate of discharge through an orifice one inch square under a specified head. By statute the miner's inch has been defined between 0.020 and 0.028 cfs, depending on the state (Appendix B). The unit is no longer used except where old water rights are specified in terms of miner's inches.

It is desirable to treat annual streamflow data in such a way that the flood season is not divided between successive years. Various *water years* have been used for special purposes but the U.S. Geological Survey uses the period October 1 to September 30 for data publication, and this is the usual water year in the United States.

4-14. Hydrographs. A *hydrograph* is a graph of stage or discharge against time. Many different methods of plotting may be used, depending on the purpose of the chart. Monthly and annual mean or total flow is used to display the record of past runoff at a station. The characteristics of a particular flood, however, usually cannot be shown successfully by plotting average flow for periods longer than one day. Prefer-

Cumberland River at Williamsburg, Ky.

Location.--Lat 36°45', long 84°10', on left bank 10 ft downstream from bridge on U. S.
Highway 25W and State Highway 92 at Williamsburg, Whitley County, and 2.1 miles downstream from Clear Fork.

Drainage area.--1,673 sq mi.

Records available.--October 1950 to September 1954. Gage-height records collected in this
vicinity since 1908 are contained in reports of U. S. Weather Bureau.

Gage.--Water-stage recorder. Datum of gage is 891.52 ft above mean sea level, unadjusted.
Prior to July 2, 1951, wire-weight gage at same site and datum.

Extremes.--Maximum discharge during year, 20,500 cfs Jan. 23 (gage height, 20.38 ft);
minimum, 6.1 cfs Oct. 23, 25, 26, 27 (gage height, 1.64 ft).
1950-54: Maximum discharge, 37,200 cfs Feb. 2, 1951 (gage height, 29.85 ft); minimum, that of Oct. 23, 25, 26, 27, 1953.
Maximum stage since at least 1918, 34.2 ft Jan. 10, 1946, from graph based on U. S.
Weather Bureau gage readings. Flood of Mar. 26, 1929, reached a stage of 32.7 ft
from graph based on U. S. Weather Bureau gage readings.

Remarks.--Records good. Records of chemical analyses, suspended sediment loads, and water
temperature for the water year 1954 are given in WSP 1350.

Rating tables, water year 1953-54 (gage height, in feet, and discharge,
in cubic feet per second)

Oct. 1 to June 18				June 19 to Sept. 30			
1.64	6.1	2.6	205	1.65	10	1.9	30
1.7	9.0	3.0	360	1.7	13	2.0	45
1.75	12	4.0	920	1.8	20		
1.8	17	6.0	2,420				
1.9	29	10.0	6,500	Note.--Same as preced-			
2.0	45	21.0	21,500	ing table above 2.0 ft.			
2.3	115						

Discharge, in cubic feet per second, water year October 1953 to September 1954

Day	Oct.	Nov.	Dec.	Jan.	Feb.	Mar.	Apr.	May	June	July	Aug.	Sept.
1	13	19	110	181	2,130	9,700	2,390	2,360	460	151	118	65
2	11	22	98	169	1,740	12,600	2,080	1,910	608	136	95	72
3	9.6	21	85	157	1,500	12,100	1,820	1,830	1,030	127	90	65
4	9.6	25	75	145	1,450	13,600	1,640	3,030	902	130	108	53
5	10	28	63	136	*1,360	11,600	1,530	3,940	824	226	98	44
6	11	25	61	133	1,210	7,440	1,470	3,180	674	184	105	33
7	11	24	57	124	1,070	4,870	1,490	2,620	542	208	145	28
8	11	26	55	121	*927	*3,800	1,720	3,230	440	222	178	26
9	11	28	70	118	842	3,620	2,410	3,940	380	320	187	24
10	11	29	171	163	788	4,100	2,760	3,630	332	292	178	21
11	11	29	380	316	746	4,390	2,460	2,870	304	296	148	17
12	14	28	794	878	698	4,000	2,320	2,310	276	340	121	14
13	17	26	608	1,400	626	3,460	2,110	1,900	288	244	105	14
14	15	25	512	934	548	4,760	1,880	1,750	292	193	90	13
15	*13	26	764	1,950	506	5,590	1,800	2,000	348	160	78	*13
16	12	26	934	12,700	524	4,540	*1,770	2,030	710	142	70	13
17	11	26	806	18,900	976	3,380	4,770	*21,40	1,170	118	63	11
18	9.6	25	566	16,500	1,470	2,650	9,280	2,030	2,200	90	59	*10
19	9.6	25	372	*10,300	1,490	2,260	7,100	2,130	2,000	70	80	10
20	9.6	25	280	3,330	1,370	2,110	4,590	2,590	1,260	75	68	17
21	9.0	28	222	10,100	1,300	2,030	3,170	2,450	824	88	61	26
22	7.5	37	212	18,900	1,240	1,840	2,500	1,970	596	115	108	40
23	*8.0	*34	216	*20,000	1,130	1,720	2,120	1,560	*460	166	133	105
24	7.0	32	208	15,700	1,200	1,780	2,220	1,300	372	566	136	132
25	6.5	115	202	9,640	1,610	2,490	2,310	1,100	312	674	160	190
26	6.1	175	190	4,600	1,720	4,800	1,950	934	288	420	133	151
27	6.5	157	169	2,980	1,530	7,030	1,920	818	264	296	115	118
28	7.0	151	160	3,200	2,450	5,580	2,410	722	222	219	115	92
29	8.5	151	166	3,980	–	3,700	3,470	638	193	178	100	75
30	9.6	130	*178	3,580	-------	3,150	2,900	560	172	*154	*80	64
31	10	-------	178	2,750	-------	2,690	-------	500	-------	142	68	..... -
Total	315.7	1,518	8,962	164,085	34,151	157,380	82,360	63,972	18,743	6,742	3,393	1,556
Mean	10.2	50.6	289	5,293	1,220	5,077	2,745	2,064	625	217	109	51.9
Cfsm	0.0061	0.030	0.173	3.16	0.729	3.03	1.64	1.23	0.374	0.130	0.065	0.031
In.	0.007	0.03	0.20	3.65	0.76	3.50	1.83	1.42	0.42	0.15	0.08	0.03

Calendar year 1953: Max 18,300   Min 6.1   Mean 2,150   Cfsm 1.29   In. 17.43
Water year 1953-54: Max 20,000   Min 6.1   Mean 1,488   Cfsm 0.889   In. 12.08

Peak discharge (base, 20,000 cfs).--Jan. 23 (7 a.m.) 20,500 cfs (20.38 ft).
* Discharge measurement made on this day.

FIG. 4-18. Sample page from U.S. Geological Survey _Water-supply Paper._

ably, flood hydrographs are plotted by computing instantaneous flow values from the water-stage recorder chart. A sufficient number of values should be plotted to indicate adequately all significant changes in the slope of the hydrograph. The plotting scales will vary with the problem—cubic feet per second and minutes on the smallest basins to

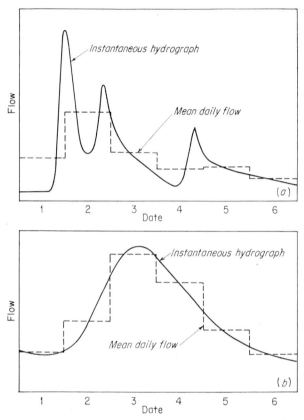

FIG. 4-19. The relationship between instantaneous and mean daily flows (upper and lower charts typical of small and large streams, respectively).

thousands of cubic feet per second and hours or days on very large basins. The shape of the hydrograph is determined by the scales used, and (in any particular study) it is good practice to use the same scales for all floods on a given basin. In order to obtain scales adequate for low flows it is sometimes necessary to use a folded scale for very high flows (Fig. 4-17).

4-15. Mean daily flows. Streamflow data are usually published in the form of mean daily flows (Fig. 4-18). This is the average discharge rate in cubic feet per second for the period from midnight to midnight.

Since 1945 the U.S. Geological Survey has included the magnitude and time of occurrence of all significant flood peaks. On large streams this form of publication is quite satisfactory, but on small streams it leaves something to be desired. The picture presented by mean daily flows depends on the chance relation between time of storm occurrence and fixed clock hours (Fig. 4-19). On large streams the maximum instantaneous flow may be only slightly higher than the maximum mean

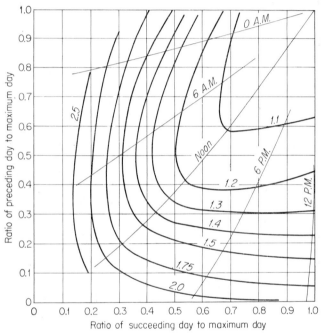

FIG. 4-20. Peak discharge and time of crest in relation to daily mean discharge. Labels on curves indicate clock time of crest on maximum day and ratio of instantaneous peak flow to maximum daily discharge. (U.S. Geological Survey.)

daily flow. On small streams the maximum instantaneous flow is usually much greater than the highest mean daily flow. Wherever possible, the hydrologist should secure copies of the recorder charts and work with a hydrograph of instantaneous flow when dealing with small basins. If this is not feasible, Fig. 4-20 may be used as a guide to estimate the peak flow and time of peak. The figure is an average relationship[1] developed from data for stations all over the United States and cannot be expected to give exact results. On very small basins where a complete

[1] W. B. Langbein, Peak Discharge from Daily Records, *U.S. Geol. Survey Water Resources Bull.*, p. 145, Aug. 10, 1944.

rise and fall of a storm hydrograph may take only a fraction of a day, use of the recorder charts is essential if one wishes to study rates of flow.

4-16. Adjustment of streamflow data. The streamflow data published by the U.S. Geological Survey are carefully reviewed and adjusted for errors resulting from instrumental and observational deficiencies until they are as accurate a presentation of the flow as it is possible to make. For a number of reasons, the published flow may not represent the data actually required by the analyst. The location of the station may have changed during the period of record with a resultant change in drainage area and, hence, volume and rate of flow. In this case an adjustment of the record is possible by use of the double-mass curve (Sec. 3-7). The base for the double-mass curve may be either flow at one or more gaging stations that have not been moved or average precipitation at a number of stations in the area. It should be emphasized that the double-mass-curve method implies a relationship of the form $q = kP$, which may not be correct if precipitation is used as a base. A more effective procedure is to develop a relationship between precipitation and runoff and make a double-mass curve of observed streamflow vs. runoff as estimated from this relation (Sec. 8-13).

Man-made works—storage reservoirs, diversions, levees, etc.—cause changes in either total flow volume or rate of flow or both. An analysis of the effects on the record at a given station requires a careful search to determine the number and size of reservoirs and the number and quantity of diversions and the date of their construction. Many small diversions may be unmeasured, and estimates of the flow diverted must be based on electric-power consumption of pumps, capacity of pump equipment, duration of pumping, or conduit capacities for gravity diversions. Diversions for irrigation may be estimated from known irrigable or irrigated acreage and estimated unit water requirements (Sec. 5-13). The adjustment of the streamflow record for the effect of reservoirs or diversions on flow volume requires the addition of the net change in storage and/or the total diversion to the reported total flow. It may be necessary to consider also channel losses and losses by evaporation from the reservoirs.

Adjustment of short-period or instantaneous flow rates for the effect of storage or diversion is a much more complex problem. Levees, channel improvement, and similar works may also affect flow rate. In some instances pumping of groundwater has markedly reduced low flows, as has also the construction of stock ponds.[1] Correction for the effect of storage or diversion on flow rates is made by adding the rate of change of storage or the diversion rate to the observed flows. In addition,

---

[1] R. C. Culler and H. V. Peterson, Effect of Stock Reservoirs on Runoff in the Cheyenne River Basin above Angostura Dam, *U.S. Geol. Survey Circ.* 223, 1953.

FIG. 4-21. Normal annual runoff in the United States.   (U.S. Geological Survey.)

it may be necessary to use storage-routing techniques (Chap. 10) to correct for the effect of channel storage between the reservoir or diversion point and the gaging station. Channel improvement and levee work affect flow through their effects on the channel storage of the stream. Unless it is possible to establish "before" and "after" correlations with some station outside the influence of the channel works, corrections must be made entirely by storage-routing methods.

4-17. Mean annual runoff. Figure 4-21 is a map of mean annual runoff in the United States. In addition to the problems of representing any highly variable element by isopleths drawn on the basis of limited data, there are other problems peculiar to streamflow. The record of flow at a gaging station represents the integrated runoff for the entire basin above the station. In many areas the production of runoff is not uniform over the basin. The average annual runoff of the Missouri River at Omaha is 10,800,000 acre-ft or 1.26 in. over the 322,800-sq mi area tributary to this station. The headwater areas produce much heavier runoff (Yellowstone River at Corwin Springs = 15.6 in.) whereas other large areas must average below the mean for Omaha. In addition, storage and diversion further complicate the picture. Figure 4-21 was prepared by the Geological Survey,[1] using all available information, and represents the most reliable map available for the United States. Such a map is intended to present a general picture of geographical variations in runoff. It cannot possibly show fine detail and should be used only for general information and preliminary studies. It should not be used as a source of information for a specific design problem. Such information can be developed more reliably through use of actual streamflow data and the analytical techniques discussed in the chapters which follow.

4-18. Streamflow variations. The normal or average values of runoff serve an important purpose but they do not disclose all the pertinent information concerning the hydrology of an area. Especially significant are the variations of streamflow about this normal. These variations include the following:

1. Variations in total runoff from year to year.
2. Variations of daily rates of runoff throughout the year.
3. Seasonal variations in runoff.

To some extent these variations are regional characteristics, but the size of the drainage area is invariably a factor. Figure 4-22 shows the ratio of the maximum annual runoff to the mean annual runoff as a function of drainage area for a number of stations in the Upper Ohio River Basin having at least 20 yr of record. On the same chart is a curve showing the ratio of the maximum flood of record to the average

[1] W. B. Langbein and others, Annual Runoff in the United States, *U.S. Geol. Survey Circ.* 52, June, 1949.

flow.   In the first instance, little effect of area is evident, but in the second case substantially higher ratios are associated with the smaller basins.   The relationships are not perfect, for basin shape, geology, and climatic exposure are also significant factors.   The map of Fig. 4-23 indicates the variation of these two ratios over the United States.   To minimize the effect of area, ratios are given for stations having drainage areas between 1000 and 2000 sq mi.   High ratios are generally located in arid regions with low normal annual runoff.

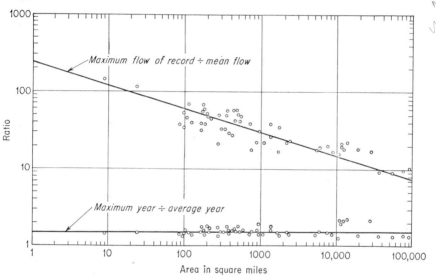

FIG. 4-22. Ratio of maximum annual runoff to average annual runoff and maximum flow of record to mean flow for stations in the Upper Ohio River Basin.

Median monthly runoff for selected stations is shown in Fig. 4-24. Here again there are significant regional differences.   A marked summer dry season is characteristic of the Pacific Southwest and is an important factor in the need for irrigation in that area.   In contrast, the low-flow season in the northern tier of states is during the winter months when precipitation is largely in the form of snow.   In the eastern and southeastern states runoff is more uniformly distributed throughout the year as a result of a more uniform precipitation distribution (Fig. 3-14).

4-19. Record peak flows.   Table 4-1 summarizes outstanding flood peaks in the various parts of the United States.   The flow in cubic feet per second and cubic feet per second per square mile, date of the peak, area of the basin, and Myers rating[1] are given.   Stations are selected

---

[1] Myers rating is the ratio of the peak flow in cubic feet per second to $100 \sqrt{A}$, where A is the drainage area in square miles.   The Myers rating is sometimes considered to be a regional constant (Sec. 9-10).

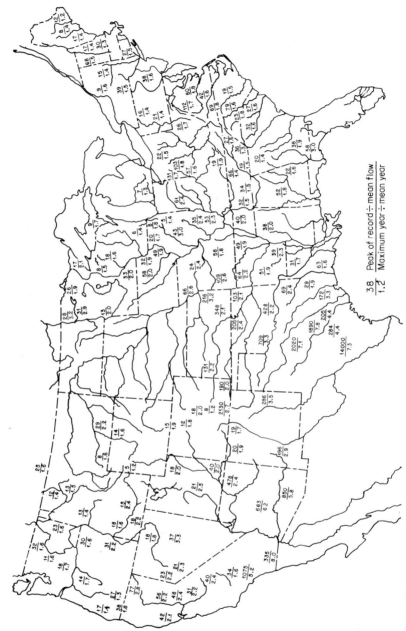

FIG. 4-23. Ratios of maximum annual flow and maximum peak flow to mean flow in the United States for stations with drainage areas from 1000 to 2000 sq mi.

$$\frac{3.8}{1.2} \quad \begin{array}{l} \text{Peak of record} \div \text{mean flow} \\ \text{Maximum year} \div \text{mean year} \end{array}$$

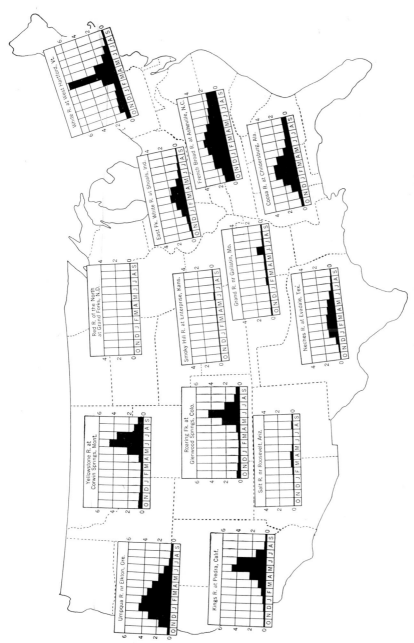

FIG. 4-24. Median monthly runoff at selected stations in the United States.

81

TABLE 4-1. Record Peak Flows at Selected Stations

Stream	Station	Peak flow		Area, sq mi	Myers rating	Date
		Cfs	Csm			
North Atlantic Slope						
Salem R.	at Woodstown, N.J.	22,000	1509	14.6	58	9/40
South Fk., South Br., Potomac R.	at Brandywine, Va.	41,200	404	102	41	6/49
Esopus Cr.	at Coldbrook, N.Y.	59,600	310	192	43	3/51
White R.	at West Hartford, Vt.	120,000	174	690	46	11/27
West Br., Susquehanna R. . . .	at Renovo, Pa.	236,000	79	2,975	43	3/36
Potomac R.	at Paw Paw, W.Va.	240,000	77	3,109	42	3/36
Potomac R.	at Hancock, Md.	340,000	83	4,073	53	3/36
Potomac R.	at Point of Rocks, Md.	480,000	50	9,651	49	3/36
Susquehanna R.	at Harrisburg, Pa.	740,000	31	24,100	48	3/36
South Atlantic and Eastern Gulf of Mexico						
Morgan Cr.	near Chapel Hill, N.C.	30,000	1110	27	58	8/24
Linville R.	at Branch, N.C.	39,500	609	65	49	8/40
Catawba R.	near Marion, N.C.	71,400	416	171	54	8/40
Yadkin R.	at Wilkesboro, N.C.	160,000	324	493	72	8/40
Catawba R.	at Catawba, N.C.	177,000	115	1,535	45	8/40
Escambia R.	at Century, Fla.	315,000	83	3,810	51	3/29
Ohio River Basin						
Elk R.	near Elk Park, N.C.	27,500	654	42	42	8/40
Wautauga R.	at Sugar Grove, N.C.	50,800	559	91	54	8/40
North Fk., New R.	near Crumpler, N.C.	79,400	286	277	48	8/40

Buffalo R.	near Flat Woods, Tenn.	90,000	202	447	42	2/48
New R.	near Galax, Va.	141,000	125	1,131	42	8/40
South Fk., Cumberland R. . .	at Nevelsville, Ky.	160,000	127	1,264	45	3/29
New R.	at Ivanhoe, Va.	155,000	116	1,340	42	8/40
Caney Fk.	near Rock Island, Tenn.	210,000	128	1,640	52	3/29
Kiskiminetas R.	at Vandergrift, Pa.	185,000	101	1,825	43	3/36
New R.	at Allisonia, Va.	185,000	84	1,825	39	8/40
Miami R.	at Dayton, Ohio	250,000	100	2,202	50	3/13
Miami R.	at Miamisburg, Ohio	257,000	94	2,513	49	3/13
New R.	at Radford, Va.	218,000	79	2,718	42	8/40
New R.	at Eggleston, Va.	219,000	74	2,748	40	8/40
Miami R.	at Hamilton, Ohio	352,000	97	2,941	58	3/13
Scioto R.	at Chillicothe, Ohio	260,000	68	3,639	42	3/13
Ohio R.	at Sewickly, Ohio	574,000	29	3,847	41	3/36
Ohio R.	at Owensboro, Ohio	1,210,000	12	19,500	39	1/37
Ohio R.	at Metropolis, Ill.	1,850,000	9	97,200	41	2/37

St. Lawrence Basin

Trumansburg Cr.	at Trumansburg, N.Y.	17,800	1550	11.5	52	7/35
Glen Cr.	at Watkins Glen, N.Y.	27,900	1310	21.3	61	7/35
East Cr.	at Rutland, Vt.	36,500	719	51	51	6/47
Lamoille R.	at Fairfax Falls, Vt.	66,900	120	559	28	11/27
Winooski R.	near Essex Junction, Vt.	113,000	108	1,044	35	11/27
Auglaize R.	near Defiance, Ohio	120,000	52	2,329	25	3/13

Hudson Bay and Upper Mississippi River Basin

East Fk., Galena R.	at Council Hill, Ill.	16,600	830	20	37	4/47
Dry Run	at Decorah, Iowa	16,000	720	22.3	34	3/19
Farm Cr.	at East Peoria, Ill.	22,000	361	61	28	4/47
Platte R.	near Rockville, Wis.	43,500	313	139	37	7/50

TABLE 4-1. Record Peak Flows at Selected Stations (Continued)

Stream	Station	Peak flow Cfs	Peak flow Csm	Area, sq mi	Myers rating	Date
Hudson Bay and Upper Mississippi River Basin (Continued)						
Salt Cr.	near Elberon, Iowa	34,000	170	200	24	6/44
Big Eau Pleine R.	near Stratford, Wis.	41,000	183	224	27	9/38
Jump R.	at Sheldon, Wis.	46,000	80	574	19	8/41
Shoal Cr.	near Breese, Ill.	52,000	69	760	19	5/43
Black R.	at Neillsville, Wis.	48,800	65	756	18	9/38
Cuivre R.	near Troy, Mo.	120,000	133	903	40	10/41
Sangamon R.	at Oakford, Ill.	123,000	24	5,120	17	5/43
Chippewa R.	at Chippewa Falls, Wis.	102,000	18	5,600	14	9/41
Des Moines R.	near Tracy, Iowa	155,000	12	12,400	15	6/47
Des Moines R.	at Ottumwa, Iowa	135,000	10	13,200	12	6/47
Mississippi R.	at Clinton, Iowa	243,000	3	85,600	8	6/1880
Mississippi R.	at Keokuk, Iowa	360,000	3	119,000	10	6/1851
Missouri River Basin						
East Fk., Fishing Cr.	near Excelsior Springs, Mo.	23,100	1165	20	52	7/51
Salt Cr.	near Lyndon, Kans.	36,400	328	111	35	7/51
Big Bull Cr.	near Hillsdale, Kans.	45,200	308	147	37	7/51
Little Nemaha R.	near Syracuse, Nebr.	225,000	1030	218	152	5/50
Weeping Water Cr.	at Union, Nebr.	60,300	253	238	39	5/50
Marais des Cygnes R.	at Melvern, Kans.	68,500	189	363	36	7/51
Little Nemaha R.	near Auburn, Nebr.	164,000	205	801	58	5/50
Medicine Cr.	at Cambridge, Nebr.	120,000	112	1,070	37	6/47
Sac R.	near Stockton, Mo.	120,000	103	1,160	35	5/43
Marias des Cygnes R.	at Ottawa, Kans.	142,000	113	1,260	40	7/51

Lower Mississippi River Basin

Green Acre Br.	near Rolla, Mo.	1,900	3062	0.6	24	6/50
Sallisaw Cr.	near Sallisaw, Okla.	110,000	604	182	82	4/45
Neosho R.	at Council Grove, Kans.	121,000	484	250	77	7/51
Middle Fk., Little Red R.	at Shirley, Ark.	101,000	344	294	59	1/49
Little Missouri R.	near Murfreesboro, Ark.	120,000	316	380	62	3/45
Neosho R.	at Strawn, Kans.	400,000	136	2,933	74	7/51
Neosho R.	at Iola, Kans.	436,000	116	3,818	70	7/51
Neosho R.	at Parsons, Kans.	410,000	85	4,817	59	7/51

Western Gulf of Mexico

East Fk., James R.	at Old Noxville, Texas	105,000	1730	61	135	7/32
Johnson Cr.	near Ingram, Texas	138,000	1240	111	131	7/32
Salado Cr.	near Salado, Texas	143,000	966	148	117	9/21
West Nueces R.	near Bracketville, Texas	580,000	1440	402	290	6/35
Pedernales R.	near Johnson City, Texas	441,000	466	947	143	9/52
Nueces R.	below Uvalde, Texas	616,000	317	1,947	140	6/35

Colorado River Basin

Skyrocket Cr.	at Ouray, Colo.	2,000	2000	1	20	7/23
Clear Cr.	near Winslow, Colo.	50,000	82	607	20	4/29
San Pedro R.	at Charleston, Ariz.	98,000	80	1,219	28	9/26
Aqua Fria	at Lake Pleasant Dam, Ariz.	105,000	72	1,460	28	1/46
Bill Williams R.	at Planet, Ariz.	200,000	39	5,140	28	2/1891

The Great Basin

Whitewater R.	at Whitewater, Calif.	42,000	730	57	56	3/38
Deep Cr.	near Hesperia, Calif.	46,600	340	137	40	3/38
Mojave R.	near Victorville, Calif.	70,600	134	530	31	3/38
Humboldt R.	near Imlay, Nev.	6,080	0.4	13,500	0.5	5/52

TABLE 4-1. Record Peak Flows at Selected Stations (Continued)

Stream	Station	Peak flow Cfs	Peak flow Csm	Area, sq mi	Myers rating	Date
	Pacific Slope in California					
San Antonio Cr................	near Claremont, Calif.	21,400	1267	17	52	3/38
Cucamonga Cr................	near Upland, Calif.	10,300	1020	10	32	3/38
East Fk., San Gabriel R......	near Camp Bonita, Calif.	46,000	522	88	48	3/38
Tujunga R....................	near Sunland, Calif.	50,000	471	106	49	3/38
South Fk., Eel R.............	near Miranda, Calif.	173,000	316	547	74	12/55
Smith R.....................	near Crescent City, Calif.	165,000	269	613	66	12/55
Eel R.......................	at Scotia, Calif.	541,000	176	3,070	98	12/55
	Pacific Slope Basins in Washington and Upper Columbia Basin					
Elwha R.....................	near Port Angeles, Wash.	41,600	155	269	25	11/1897
North Fk., Skokomish R.......	near Hoodsport, Wash.	27,000	464	58	36	11/34
South Fk., Skokomish R.......	near Index, Wash.	70,000	197	355	37	11/1897
Skokomish R.................	near Gold Bar, Wash.	88,700	166	535	39	12/33
	Snake River Basin					
East Fk., Wallowa R..........	near Joseph, Ore.	450	45	10	1.4	7/37
Lake Fk., Payette R..........	near McCall, Idaho	2,600	53	49	3.7	6/48
Lostine R....................	near Lostine, Ore.	2,540	36	70	3.0	5/13
North Fk., Clearwater R......	near Ahsahka, Idaho	100,000	41	2,440	20	12/33
	Pacific Slope Basins in Oregon and Lower Columbia River Basin					
Willow Cr...................	near Heppner, Ore.	36,000	401	87	38	7/03
Lewis R.....................	at Ariel, Wash.	129,000	177	731	48	12/33
Santiam R...................	at Jefferson, Ore.	202,000	113	1,790	48	11/21
Willamette R................	at Harrisburg, Ore.	210,000	62	3,420	36	12/45
Umpqua R...................	near Elkton, Ore.	208,000	56	3,680	34	10/50
Willamette R................	near Albany, Ore.	266,000	55	4,840	38	1/1881
Willamette R................	at Salem, Ore.	315,000	43	7,280	37	1/23
Columbia R..................	near The Dalles, Ore.	1,240,000	5	237,000	25	6/1894

in such a way that the tabulated data represent those cases in which the peak flow exceeds 75 per cent of the maximum recorded flow rate for corresponding drainage areas in each region.

BIBLIOGRAPHY

Corbett, D. M., and others: Stream-gaging Procedure, *U.S. Geol. Survey Water-supply Paper* 888, 1945.
Grover, N. C., and A. W. Harrington: "Stream Flow," Wiley, New York, 1943.
King, H. W., and E. F. Brater: "Handbook of Hydraulics," 4th ed., McGraw-Hill, New York, 1954.
Linsley, R. K., M. A. Kohler, and J. L. H. Paulhus: "Applied Hydrology," Chap. 9, pp. 182–242, McGraw-Hill, New York, 1949.

DATA SOURCES

The main sources of streamflow data are the *Water-supply Papers* published annually by the U.S. Geological Survey and the *Daily River Stages* published by the U.S. Weather Bureau. More detailed information may be obtained by writing to either of these agencies or by contacting their field offices located in principal cities throughout the country.

The U.S. Corps of Engineers, U.S. Bureau of Reclamation, and U.S. Soil Conservation Service make occasional observations of flow. Information from these sources can usually be obtained from the nearest field office. Many states have agencies which make or cooperate in streamflow measurement.

PROBLEMS

4-1. Compute the streamflow for the measurement data below. Take the meter rating from Eq. (4-1) with $a = 0.1$ and $b = 2.2$.

Distance from bank, ft	Depth, ft	Meter depth, ft	Revo-lutions	Time, sec
2	1	0.6	10	50
4	3.5	2.8	22	55
		0.7	35	52
6	5.2	4.2	28	53
		1.0	40	58
9	6.3	5.0	32	58
		1.3	45	60
11	4.4	3.5	28	45
		0.9	33	46
13	2.2	1.3	22	50
15	0.8	0.5	12	49
17	0			

4-2. The table that follows measures discharge, base stage, and stage at an auxiliary gage 2000 ft downstream. Develop a slope-stage-discharge relationship from these data. Compute the average error of the rating, using the tabulated data. What is the estimated discharge for base and auxiliary stages of 25.00 and 24.20 ft, respectively?

Base stage, ft	Discharge, cfs	Auxiliary stage, ft
14.02	2,400	13.00
23.80	29,600	23.25
17.70	21,200	16.60
24.60	85,500	23.55
20.40	28,200	19.55
17.00	7,400	16.40
18.65	34,000	17.50
26.40	55,000	25.70
22.20	74,200	21.00
16.20	9,550	15.30
21.10	43,500	20.13
25.60	84,000	24.60
23.20	93,500	21.95

4-3. Given below are data for a station rating curve. Extend the relation and estimate the flow at a stage of 14.5 ft by both the logarithmic and $A \sqrt{D}$ methods.

Stage, ft	Area, sq ft	Depth, ft	Discharge, cfs	Stage, ft	Area, sq ft	Depth, ft	Discharge, cfs
1.72	263	1.5	1,020	2.50	674	1.8	2,700
3.47	1200	2.1	4,900	4.02	1570	2.8	6,600
4.26	1790	3.2	7,700	5.08	2150	3.9	9,450
5.61	2380	4.6	10,700	5.98	2910	4.9	13,100
6.70	3280	5.2	15,100	6.83	3420	5.4	16,100
7.80	3960	5.7	19,000	8.75	4820	6.0	24,100
9.21	5000	6.1	25,000	9.90	5250	6.5	27,300
14.50	8200	9.0					

4-4. What volume is represented by 1.43 in. of runoff from a basin of 254 sq mi? Give answer in cubic feet, second-foot-days, and acre-feet.

4-5. Given below are the daily mean flows in cubic feet per second at a gaging station for a period of 5 days. What is the mean flow rate for the period in cubic feet per second? What is the total discharge during the period in second-foot-days? Acre-feet? If the drainage area is 756 sq mi, what is the runoff volume in inches?

Day.............	1	2	3	4	5
Flow, cfs.........	700	4800	3100	2020	1310

4-6. Using the data of Prob. 4-5 and the relationship of Fig. 4-20, estimate the peak rate of flow and the time of peak.

4-7. Obtain a copy of a *U.S. Geological Survey Water-supply Paper*, and for some stream in your area determine the maximum flow of record in cubic feet per second and in cubic feet per second per square mile. The paper will give the mean annual flow in cubic feet per second.   Find the average annual runoff in acre-feet, second-foot-days, and inches.

4-8. For some stream selected by your instructor determine the mean flow for each month on the basis of 10 yr of record.   What per cent of the total annual flow occurs each month?   Compare these percentages with the normal monthly distribution of precipitation.   Can you explain the differences?

4-9. For three basins in your area find the ratio of the maximum peak flow of record to the average daily flow rate.   Is there an apparent relationship with drainage area?   Can you explain the differences?

4-10. Compare the data in Table 4-1 for the several regions of the country.   What regional differences do you see?   Look for such things as date of floods, relative magnitude of flood peaks, apparent areal extent of floods, etc.   Can you explain the differences?

5

EVAPORATION AND TRANSPIRATION

This chapter discusses that phase of the hydrologic cycle in which precipitation reaching the earth's surface is returned to the atmosphere as vapor. Of the precipitation falling earthward, a portion evaporates before reaching the ground. Since the hydrologist measures precipitation just a few feet above the ground, evaporation from raindrops is of no practical concern. Likewise, evaporation from the oceans lies beyond his scope of direct interest. Precipitation caught on vegetation (interception) eventually evaporates, and the quantity of water actually reaching the soil surface is correspondingly reduced below that observed in a precipitation gage. Other evaporative mechanisms to be considered are transpiration by plants and evaporation from soil, snow, and free water surfaces (lakes, reservoirs, streams, and depressions).

Anticipated evaporation is a decisive element in the design of reservoirs to be constructed in arid regions. Ten reservoirs the size of Lake Mead would evaporate virtually the entire flow of the Colorado River in a normal year, and normal evaporation from Lake Mead alone is equivalent to almost one-third of the minimum annual inflow to the reservoir. Evaporation and transpiration are indicative of changes in the moisture deficiency of a basin and, in this capacity, are sometimes used to estimate storm runoff in the preparation of river forecasts. Estimates of these factors are also used in the determination of water-supply requirements of proposed irrigation projects.

EVAPORATION

Although there is always continuous exchange of water molecules to and from the atmosphere, the hydrologic definition of *evaporation* is restricted to the net rate of vapor transport to the atmosphere. This change in state requires an exchange of approximately 600 cal for each gram of water evaporated (Sec. 2-9). If the temperature of the surface is to be maintained, these large quantities of heat must be supplied by radiation and conduction from the overlying air or at the expense of energy stored below the surface.

5-1. Factors controlling the evaporation process. Rates of evaporation vary, depending on certain meteorological factors and the nature of the evaporating surface. Much of the ensuing discussion of meteorological factors is couched in terms of evaporation from a free water surface. The extent to which the material is applicable to other surfaces of interest in hydrology is believed to be self-evident.

Meteorological factors. If natural evaporation is viewed as an energy-exchange process, it can be demonstrated that radiation is by far the most important single factor and that the term "solar evaporation" is basically applicable. On the other hand, theory and wind-tunnel experiments have shown that the rate of evaporation from water of specified temperature is proportional to wind speed and is highly dependent on the vapor pressure of the overlying air. How are these two conclusions to be reconciled? In essence, it can be said that water temperature is not independent of wind speed and vapor pressure. If radiation exchange and all other meteorological elements were to remain constant over a shallow lake for an appreciable time, the water temperature and the evaporation rate would become constant. If the wind speed were then suddenly doubled, the evaporation rate would also double momentarily. This increased rate of evaporation would immediately begin to extract heat from the water at a more rapid rate than it could be replaced by radiation and conduction. The water temperature would approach a new, lower equilibrium value, and evaporation would diminish accordingly. On a long-term basis, a change of 10 per cent in wind speed will change evaporation only 1 to 3 per cent, depending on other meteorological factors. In deep lakes with capacity for considerable heat storage, sudden changes in wind and humidity are more effective for longer periods of time; heat into or from storage assists in balancing the energy demands. Thus excessive evaporation during a dry, windy week can, by utilization of stored energy, reduce evaporation which would otherwise have occurred in subsequent weeks.

The relative effect of controlling meteorological factors is difficult to evaluate at best, and any conclusions must be qualified in terms of the time period considered. Evaluation of the relative importance of meteorological factors without an understanding of the subsequent discussion on energy-budget and mass-transfer equations would be placing the "cart before the horse." It can be stated, however, that the rate of evaporation is influenced by solar radiation, air temperature, vapor pressure, wind, and possibly atmospheric pressure. Since solar radiation is an important factor, evaporation varies with latitude, season, time of day, and sky condition.

Nature of the evaporating surface. All surfaces exposed to precipitation, such as vegetation, buildings, and paved streets, are potentially evaporation surfaces. Since the rate of evaporation during rainy periods is small, the quantity of storm rainfall disposed of in this manner is essentially limited to that required to saturate the surface. Although this evaporation is appreciable on an annual basis, it is seldom evaluated separately but is considered part of over-all evaporation and transpiration.

The rate of evaporation from a saturated soil surface is approximately the same as that from an adjacent water surface of the same temperature. As the soil begins to dry, evaporation decreases and its temperature rises to maintain the energy balance. Eventually, evaporation virtually ceases since there is no effective mechanism for transporting water from appreciable depths except when the surface layers are frozen. Thus the rate of evaporation from soil surfaces is limited by the availability of water, or the *evaporation opportunity*.

Evaporation from snow and ice constitutes a special problem since the melting point (32°F) lies within the range of temperatures normally experienced. Evaporation can occur only when the vapor pressure of the air is less than that of the snow surface [Eq. (5-9)], i.e., only when the dewpoint is lower than the temperature of the snow. Evaporation from snow is small relative to that from liquid water (with the same spread between surface and dewpoint temperatures) because of the curvature in the saturation-vapor-pressure vs. temperature relation. With a snow temperature of 30°F and a dewpoint of 20°F the evaporation rate is only one-fifth that from a water surface at 80°F when the dewpoint is 70°F, with the same wind speed assumed in both cases. Moreover, it requires more heat to evaporate snow than water; at 0°C the latent heat of sublimation (fusion plus vaporization) is 677 cal/g and the heat of vaporization is 597. These and other considerations lead to the conclusion that, with temperatures much above freezing, the rate of snowmelt must exceed evaporation. The impression that a chinook,[1] or foehn, is conducive to excessive evaporation from the snow cover is fallacious. The dewpoint increases downslope, and evaporation from the snow must cease when the dewpoint rises to 32°F. Reasonable assumptions yield an upper limit of about 0.2 in. (water equivalent) per day for evaporation from a snow surface.

Akin to the above discussion concerning the nature of the surface is the effect of water quality on evaporation rates. The effect of salinity, or dissolved solids, is brought about by the reduced vapor pressure of the solution. The vapor pressure of sea water (35,000 ppm dissolved salts) is about 2 per cent less than that of pure water at the same temperature. The reduction in evaporation is less than that indicated by the change in

---

[1] A *chinook* is a downslope wind in which the air is warmed by adiabatic heating.

vapor pressure [Eq. (5-9)] because with reduced evaporation there is an increase in water temperature which partially offsets the vapor-pressure reduction.[1] Even in the case of sea water, the reduction in evaporation is never in excess of a few per cent (over an extended period of time), so that salinity effects can be neglected in the estimation of reservoir evaporation.

5-2. Water-budget determinations of reservoir evaporation. The direct measurement of evaporation under field conditions is not feasible, at least not in the sense that one is able to measure river stage, discharge, etc. As a consequence, a variety of techniques have been derived for determining, or estimating, vapor transport from water surfaces. The most obvious approach involves the maintenance of a water budget. Assuming that storage S, surface inflow I, surface outflow O, subsurface seepage O_g, and precipitation P can be measured, evaporation E can be computed from

$$E = (S_1 - S_2) + I + P - O - O_g \qquad (5\text{-}1)$$

This approach is simple in theory, but application rarely produces reliable results since all errors in measuring outflow, inflow, and change in storage are reflected directly in the computed evaporation.

Of those factors required, seepage is usually the most difficult to evaluate since it must be estimated indirectly from measurements of groundwater levels, permeability, etc. If seepage approaches or exceeds evaporation, reliable evaporation determinations by this method are quite unlikely. Recent studies indicate that both seepage and evaporation can be estimated by simultaneous solution of the water-budget and mass-transfer equations.[2] If a stage-seepage relation can be derived, the water budget can be applied on a continuing basis.

The determination of rainfall generally does not represent a major obstacle except possibly where a lake is surrounded by very rugged terrain or where precipitation is relatively much greater than evaporation. Snowfall, on the other hand, often renders the water budget totally unreliable for short periods of time. A lake tends to trap blowing snow, and the quantity added to a small lake may be several times as great as that observed in the gage.

Water-stage recorders are sufficiently precise for determining the storage changes provided that the stage-area relationship is accurately established. Variations in bank storage are sometimes an important source of error in monthly computations but can usually be neglected in

---

[1] G. E. Harbeck, Jr., The Effect of Salinity on Evaporation, *U.S. Geol. Survey Profess. Paper* 272-A, 1955.

[2] W. B. Langbein, C. H. Hains, and R. C. Culler, Hydrology of Stock-water Reservoirs in Arizona, *U.S. Geol. Survey Circ.* 110, 1951.

estimates of annual evaporation. Similarly, expansion or contraction of stored water with large temperature changes can introduce appreciable errors. At Lake Hefner, Oklahoma,[1] corrections as large as 0.4 in./month were required as a result of this effect.

The relative effect of errors in the surface-inflow and outflow terms varies considerably from lake to lake, depending upon the extent of ungaged areas, the reliability of the rating curves, and the relative magnitude of flows with respect to evaporation. Determinations of streamflow to within 5 per cent are normally considered "excellent," and corresponding evaporation errors may be expected in an off-channel reservoir without appreciable outflow. If the quantity of water passing through a reservoir is large in comparison with evaporation losses, water-budget results are of questionable accuracy.

Under somewhat idealized conditions, it was found that daily evaporation from Lake Hefner, Oklahoma, could be reliably computed from a water budget; results were considered to be within 5 per cent one-third of the time and within 10 per cent two-thirds of the time. It should be emphasized that Lake Hefner was selected, after a survey of more than 100 lakes and reservoirs[2] in the West, as one of the three or four best meeting water-budget requirements. The requirements are not nearly so stringent for estimates of annual or mean annual reservoir evaporation, and reasonable estimates can be made for a number of reservoirs in the United States.

5-3. Energy-budget determinations of reservoir evaporation. The energy-budget approach, like the water budget, employs a continuity equation and solves for evaporation as the residual required to maintain a balance. Although the continuity equation in this case is one of energy, an approximate water budget is required as well, since inflow, outflow, and storage of water represent energy values which must be considered in conjunction with the respective temperatures.[3] Application of the energy budget has been attempted by numerous investigators,[4] with cases selected so as to minimize the effect of terms that could not be evaluated. However, the Lake Hefner experiment is believed to constitute the first test of the method with adequate control.

[1] See Bibliography at the end of this chapter.

[2] G. E. Harbeck and others, Utility of Selected Western Lakes and Reservoirs for Water-loss Studies, *U.S. Geol. Survey Circ.* 103, March, 1951.

[3] E. R. Anderson, L. J. Anderson, and J. J. Marciano, A Review of Evaporation Theory and Development of Instrumentation, *U.S. Navy Electronics Lab. Rept.* 159, pp. 41–42, February, 1950.

[4] G. F. McEwen, Results of Evaporation Studies, *Scripps Inst. Oceanog. Tech. Ser.*, Vol. 2, pp. 401–415, 1930.

B. Richardson, Evaporation as a Function of Insolation, *Trans. ASCE*, Vol. 95, pp. 996–1019, 1931.

The energy budget for a lake or reservoir may be expressed as

$$Q_s - Q_r - Q_b - Q_h - Q_e = Q_\theta - Q_v \tag{5-2}$$

where Q_s is sun and sky short-wave radiation incident at the water surface; Q_r, reflected short-wave radiation; Q_b, net energy lost by the water body through exchange of long-wave radiation with the atmosphere; Q_h, sensible-heat transfer (conduction) to the atmosphere; Q_e, energy used for evaporation; Q_θ, the increase in energy stored in the water body; Q_v, net energy advected[1] into the water body; and all are in calories per square centimeter. Letting H_v represent the latent heat of vaporization and R the ratio of heat loss by conduction to heat loss by evaporation (*Bowen ratio*), Eq. (5-2) becomes

$$E = \frac{Q_s - Q_r - Q_b + Q_v - Q_\theta}{\rho H_v (1 + R)} \tag{5-3}$$

where E is the evaporation in centimeters and ρ is the density of water. The Bowen ratio[2] can be computed from the equation

$$R = 0.61 \frac{T_s - T_a}{e_s - e_a} \frac{p}{1000} \tag{5-4}$$

where p is the atmospheric pressure; T_a and e_a, the temperature and vapor pressure of the air, respectively; T_s, the water-surface temperature; e_s, the saturation vapor pressure corresponding to T_s; and all temperatures and pressures are in degrees centigrade and millibars.

Sensible-heat transfer cannot be readily observed or computed, and the Bowen ratio was conceived as a means of eliminating this term from the energy-budget equation. The validity of the constant in Eq. (5-4) has been the subject of much discussion.[3] Bowen found limiting values of 0.58 and 0.66, depending on the stability of the atmosphere, and concluded that 0.61 was applicable under normal atmospheric conditions. Using an independent approach, Pritchard (unpublished notes) derived values of 0.57 and 0.66 for smooth and rough surfaces, respectively. At Lake Hefner, Oklahoma, monthly values of the ratio [computed from Eq. (5-4)] were found to vary from $-\frac{1}{3}$ in February to $\frac{1}{4}$ in November, while the annual value was -0.03. It is obvious that one need not be concerned over variations in the constant of Eq. (5-4) for annual computations. If the correct value is assumed to have been one of the limits

[1] Net energy content of inflowing and outflowing water is termed *advected energy.*

[2] I. S. Bowen, The Ratio of Heat Losses by Conduction and by Evaporation from Any Water Surface, *Phys. Rev.*, Vol. 27, pp. 779–787, 1926.

[3] E. R. Anderson, L. J. Anderson, and J. J. Marciano, A Review of Evaporation Theory and Development of Instrumentation, *U.S. Navy Electronics Lab. Rept.* 159, pp. 43–48, February, 1950.

determined by Bowen, the extreme error in monthly evaporation at Lake Hefner would be only about 4 per cent.

In the application of Eq. (5-3), it is important that the radiation exchange be accurately evaluated. Most routine observations from established networks provide measurements of incident short-wave radiation only, and prior to the development of radiometers,[1] radiation exchange was necessarily estimated from empirical relations.[2] Radiometers can be designed to measure either the total incoming or *net radiation*—the algebraic sum of incident and reflected sun and sky short-wave radiation, incident and reflected atmospheric long-wave radiation, and long-wave radiation emitted by the water body. Another promising approach to the determination of net radiation involves the maintenance of an energy budget for an insulated pan, known as a *Cummings radiation integrator*.[3] The assumption is made that incident and reflected solar and long-wave radiation are the same for the pan as for an adjacent lake. Having the sum of these items for the pan and computing the long-wave radiation from the lake on the basis of its surface temperature, net radiation for the lake can be determined. Whereas net radiation is an independent factor in computing lake evaporation, it is the dependent factor in the case of the integrator, pan evaporation being one of the observed elements.

The energy advection and storage terms $(Q_v - Q_\theta)$ of Eq. (5-3) are computed from an approximate water budget and temperatures of the respective water volumes. Equation (5-1) can be written as

$$S_2 - S_1 = I + P - O - O_g - E \tag{5-5}$$

Variations in density are neglected and all terms are expressed in cubic centimeters. The energy content per gram of water is the product of its specific heat and temperature. Assuming unity for the values of density and specific heat,

$$Q_v - Q_\theta = \frac{1}{A} \left(IT_I + PT_P - OT_O - O_gT_g - ET_E + S_1T_1 - S_2T_2 \right) \tag{5-6}$$

where T_I, T_P, etc., are the temperatures (°C) of the respective volumes

[1] R. V. Dunkle et al., Non Selective Radiometers for Hemispherical Irradiation and Net Radiation Interchange Measurements, *Univ. Calif. Eng. Dept. Thermal Radiation Project Rept.* 9, October, 1949.

V. E. Suomi, M. Franssila, and N. F. Islitzer, An Improved Net-radiation Instrument, *Am. Meteorol. Soc. J.*, Vol. 11, pp. 276–282, 1954.

[2] H. L. Penman, Natural Evaporation from Open Water, Bare Soil, and Grass, *Proc. Royal Soc. (London): A*, Vol. 193, pp. 120–145, April, 1948.

[3] G. E. Harbeck, Cummings Radiation Integrator, in Water-loss Investigations, Vol. 1, Lake Hefner Studies, *U.S. Geol. Survey Profess. Paper* 269, pp. 120–126, 1954 (reprint of *U.S. Geol. Survey Circ.* 229, 1952).

of water, and the surface area of the lake A is introduced to convert energies to units of calories per square centimeter. Equation (5-5) should be balanced before solving Eq. (5-6), although approximate values of the individual terms will suffice. The temperature of precipitation can be taken as the wet-bulb temperature, seepage temperature as that of the water in the lowest levels of the lake, and T_E as the lake-surface temperature. Advected energy and change in energy storage tend to balance for most lakes, particularly over long periods of time, and are frequently assumed to cancel when considering annual or mean annual evaporation.

5-4. Mass-transfer determinations of reservoir evaporation. The theoretical development of turbulent-transport equations has followed two basic approaches: the discontinuous, or mixing length, concept introduced by Prandtl and Schmidt and the continuous mixing concept of Taylor. An extensive physical and mathematical review[1] of the two approaches was prepared in advance of the Lake Hefner experiment, and a number of the equations were tested at Lake Hefner and Lake Mead.[2] Equations derived by Sverdrup and Sutton gave good results at Lake Hefner but were considered inadequate when applied to Lake Mead. There is reason to believe, however, that the Thornthwaite-Holzman equation would give satisfactory results with instrumentation meeting the exacting requirements. A complete discussion of mass-transfer theory is beyond the scope of this text, and, in view of the present status of the approach, only the Thornthwaite-Holzman equation is presented.

Assuming an adiabatic atmosphere and logarithmic distribution of wind speed and moisture in the vertical, the derived equation is

$$E = \frac{833k^2(e_1 - e_2)(v_1 - v_2)}{(T + 459.4) \log_e (z_2/z_1)^2} \tag{5-7}$$

where E is the evaporation in inches per hour, k is von Kármán's constant (0.4), e is the vapor pressure in inches of mercury, v is the wind speed in miles per hour, and T is the mean temperature in degrees Fahrenheit of the layer between the lower level z_1 and upper level z_2. Since computed evaporation is proportional to the small differences in wind and vapor pressure at two levels near the surface, instrument requirements are not easily satisfied under field conditions.

Numerous empirical formulas[3] have been derived which express evapo-

[1] E. R. Anderson, L. J. Anderson, and J. J. Marciano, A Review of Evaporation Theory and Development of Instrumentation, *U.S. Navy Electronics Lab. Rept.* 159, pp. 3–37, February, 1950.

[2] Water-loss Investigations, Lake Mead Studies, *U.S. Geol. Survey Profess. Paper* 298, pp. 29–37, 1958.

[3] R. K. Linsley, M. A. Kohler, and J. L. H. Paulhus, "Applied Hydrology," pp. 165–169, McGraw-Hill, New York, 1949.

ration as a function of atmospheric elements and which parallel the mass-transfer approach in some respects. The Meyer formula[1] for evaporation in inches per day is

$$E = c(e_s - e_a) \left(1 + \frac{v}{10}\right)$$ (5-8)

where e_s and e_a are the vapor pressure of the water surface and over-running air (in. of Hg) and v is the wind speed (mph). Meyer states that the coefficient c has a value of about 0.36 when the formula is applied to daily data for an ordinary lake, provided that the wind and humidity observations are about 25 ft above the surface.

Several empirical equations have been derived from the data collected at Lake Hefner:

$$E = 0.00304(e_s - e_2)v_4 \qquad (e_2 \text{ and } v_4 \text{ over lake}) \qquad (5\text{-}9)$$
$$E = 0.00241(e_s - e_8)v_8 \qquad (e_8 \text{ and } v_8 \text{ over lake}) \qquad (5\text{-}10)$$
$$E = 0.00270(e_s - e_2)v_4 \qquad (e_2 \text{ and } v_4 \text{ upwind of lake}) \qquad (5\text{-}11)$$

where E is lake evaporation in inches per day, vapor pressure is in inches of mercury, wind is in miles per day, and numerical subscripts designate heights above the surface in meters. Equation (5-9) was found to yield excellent results for Lake Mead, and there is good reason to believe that it is of general applicability. Equation (5-10) yielded a satisfactory value of annual evaporation for Lake Mead, but there was a seasonal bias which appeared to be correlated with stability.

Vapor pressure of the air increases downwind across an open-water surface; hence mass-transfer concepts have led to the belief that point evaporation decreases downwind. Sutton[2] concluded that average depth of evaporation from a circular water surface is proportional to the -0.11 power of its diameter under adiabatic conditions, and this functional relation has been verified in wind-tunnel experiments.[3] The theory assumes that water temperature and wind are unchanging downwind, and this condition tends to prevail in a wind tunnel where solar radiation is not a factor. Observations show that wind speed increases downwind from the leading edge of a lake, however, and a consideration of energy conservation requires that any immediate reduction in evaporation rate

[1] A. F. Meyer, "Evaporation from Lakes and Reservoirs," Minnesota Resources Commission, St. Paul, Minn., 1942.

[2] E. R. Anderson, L. J. Anderson, and J. J. Marciano, A Review of Evaporation Theory and Development of Instrumentation, *U.S. Navy Electronics Lab. Rept.* 159, p. 10, February, 1950.

[3] H. Lettau and F. Dorffel, Der Wasserdampfübergang von einer Nassen Platte an Strömende Luft, *Ann. Hydrographie u. Maritimen Meteorol.*, Vol. 64, pp. 342, 504, 1936.

brought about by decreased vapor-pressure gradient be followed by an increase in water temperature. Although experimental data are presently insufficient to determine the magnitude of the "size effect," Eqs. (5-9) and (5-10) can be applied to lakes ranging up to several hundred square miles in area without appreciable error in this respect.

5-5. Estimation of reservoir evaporation from pan evaporation and related meteorological data. The pan is undoubtedly the most widely used evaporation instrument today, and its application in hydrologic design and operation is of long standing. Although criticism of the pan approach may be justified on theoretical grounds, the ratio of annual lake-to-pan evaporation is quite consistent, year by year, and does not vary excessively from region to region.

Pan observations. There are three types of exposures employed for pan installations—sunken, floating, and surface—and divergent views persist as to the best exposure. Burying the pan tends to eliminate objectionable boundary effects, such as radiation on the side walls and heat exchange between the atmosphere and the pan itself, but creates observational problems. Sunken pans collect more trash; they are difficult to install, clean, and repair; leaks are not easily detected; and height of vegetation adjacent to the pan is quite critical. Moreover, appreciable heat exchange does take place between the pan and the soil, depending on such factors as soil type, moisture content, and vegetative cover. Rather than attempt the necessary observations required to adjust for heat exchange with the soil, it would appear advisable to use a large pan to minimize the relative effect.

The evaporation from a pan floating in a lake more nearly approximates evaporation from the lake than that from an on-shore installation. Observational difficulties are prevalent with floating pans—splashing frequently renders the data unreliable—and installation and operational expense is excessive. Relatively few such installations are now in existence, and, consequently, floating pans are not considered in the subsequent discussion.

Pans exposed above ground experience greater evaporation than sunken pans, primarily because of the radiant energy intercepted by the side walls. Moreover, sensible-heat transfer through the walls results in geographical (climatological) variations in lake-to-pan ratios. While both these deficiencies can be eliminated by insulating the pan, this approach is unduly expensive. It would appear more economical to adjust data collected from an uninsulated pan. The principal advantages of surface exposure are economy and ease of installation, operation, and maintenance.

Of the various sunken pans used, only three gained prominence in the United States: the Young screened pan, the Colorado pan, and the

Bureau of Plant Industry (BPI) pan. The Young pan[1] is 2 ft in diameter, 3 ft deep, and is covered with ¼-in.-mesh hardware cloth. The screen modifies the *pan coefficient* (lake evaporation divided by pan evaporation) to near unity, on an average, but the small size of the pan leads to an unstable coefficient, and the over-all effect of screening may be adverse. The Colorado pan is 3 ft square and 18 in. deep. The BPI

FIG. 5-1. Class A evaporation station. Numbered items are as follows: (1) thermometer shelter, (2) evaporation pan and anemometer, (3) standard 8-inch nonrecording precipitation gage, and (4) weighing-type recording precipitation gage. (*U.S. Weather Bureau.*)

pan, 6 ft in diameter by 2 ft deep, provides by far the best index to lake evaporation because of its size.

The standard Weather Bureau Class A pan is the most widely used evaporation pan in the United States; in 1956 records were published for about 350 stations. It is of unpainted galvanized iron 4 ft in diameter by 10 in. deep and is exposed on a wood frame in order that air may circulate beneath the pan (Fig. 5-1). It is filled to a depth of 8 in., and instructions[2] require that it be refilled when the depth has fallen to 7 in. Water-surface level is measured daily with a hook gage in a stilling well, and evaporation is computed as the difference between observed levels, adjusted for any precipitation measured in a standard rain gage. At many new installations, water is added each day to bring the level up to

[1] A. A. Young, Some Recent Evaporation Investigations, *Trans. Am. Geophys. Union*, Vol. 28, pp. 279–284, April, 1947.

[2] Instructions for Climatological Observers, *U.S. Weather Bur. Circ.* B, 10th ed., November, 1952.

a fixed point in the stilling well.   This method assures proper water level at all times.

Pan evaporation and meteorological factors.   Many attempts have been made to derive reliable relations between pan evaporation and meteorological factors.[1]   Obvious purposes to be served by such relations are as follows:

1. To increase our knowledge of the phenomenon.

2. To estimate missing pan records (pans are not operated during winter in areas where ice cover would occur much of the time, and records for days with snow or heavy rain are frequently fallacious).

3. To derive estimated data for stations at which pan observations are not made.

4. To test the reliability and representativeness of observed data.

5. To aid the study of lake-pan relations.

Some of the relations which have been developed involve the substitution of air temperature for water temperature with a resultant seasonal and geographic bias.   Pan evaporation can be reliably estimated from empirical functions involving wind, dewpoint, and water temperature, but such relations are of little practical value; when water temperature is observed, pan evaporation is also measured.   Penman[2] has shown that the need for water-temperature observations can be eliminated, however, through simultaneous solution of an empirical mass-transfer equation and one expressing an energy balance.   Assuming the change in heat storage of the water body and the heat conducted through the containing walls to be negligible, Penman derived the equation

$$E = \frac{1}{\Delta + \gamma} (Q_n \Delta + \gamma E_a) \tag{5-12}$$

where Δ is the slope of the saturation-vapor-pressure vs. temperature curve at the air temperature T_a; E_a is the evaporation given by an empirical mass-transfer equation, assuming water temperature $T_s = T_a$; Q_n is the net radiant-energy exchange expressed in the same units as evaporation E; and γ is defined by the Bowen ratio equation [Eq. (5-4)]

$$R = \gamma \frac{T_s - T_a}{e_s - e_a} \tag{5-13}$$

The Penman approach was applied to the composite record from a number of stations over the United States to derive (Appendix A) the coaxial

[1] R. K. Linsley, M. A. Kohler, and J. L. H. Paulhus, "Applied Hydrology," pp. 168–169, McGraw-Hill, New York, 1949.

[2] H. L. Penman, Natural Evaporation from Open Water, Bare Soil, and Grass, *Proc. Royal Soc.* (*London*): A, Vol. 193, pp. 120–145, 1948.

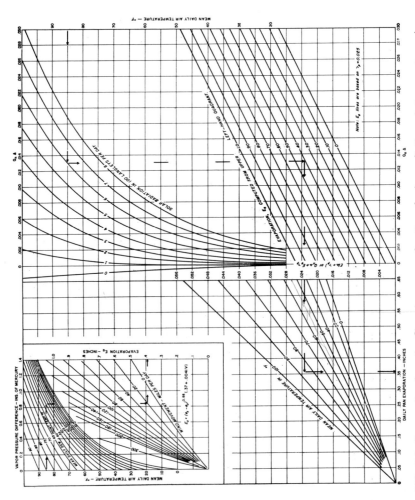

FIG. 5-2. Evaporation from the Class A pan as a function of solar radiation, air temperature, dew-point, and wind movement.   (U.S. Weather Bureau.)

relation[1] shown in Fig. 5-2. It was found that the value of γ for the Class A pan is about two and one-half times the theoretical value, because of the fact that evaporation is restricted to the water surface while sensible-heat transfer also occurs through the pan walls. To compute pan evaporation, E_a is first determined from the upper left-hand chart of Fig. 5-2 by entering with values of air temperature, dew-point, and wind. Equation (5-12) is solved by entering the other three curve families of Fig. 5-2 with air temperature, solar radiation, E_a, and air temperature. Although the correlation was based on daily data,

TABLE 5-1. Variation of Class A Pan Evaporation with Related Factors

Case No.	T_a (°F)	% error/ F° change in T_a	T_d (°F)	% error/ F° change in T_d	Q_s (ly/day)	% error/ % change in Q_s	v (mi/day)	% error/ % change in v	E (in./day)
1	91	1.8	41	0.4	700	0.7	50	0.2	0.51
2	91	2.3	63	0.8	700	0.8	50	0.1	0.46
3	84	3.8	75	2.7	600	0.9	50	0.1	0.28
4	66	6.0	55	4.0	300	0.6	50	0.2	0.12
5	45	6.3	28	2.9	250	0.3	50	0.3	0.09
6	91	1.8	41	0.3	700	0.6	100	0.3	0.60
7	91	2.3	63	1.0	700	0.7	100	0.2	0.52
8	84	4.4	75	3.1	600	0.8	100	0.2	0.31
9	66	6.2	55	4.6	300	0.5	100	0.4	0.15
10	45	6.2	28	3.1	250	0.3	100	0.5	0.11

experience has shown that only minor errors result when monthly evaporation (i.e., mean daily value for the month) is computed from monthly averages of the daily values of the parameters.

There are only a limited number of locations where all the data required for application of Fig. 5-2 are available; solar radiation is observed at only about 60 stations in the United States. There are reasonably reliable means of estimating this factor,[2] however, and the other required elements can usually be estimated accurately enough to provide adequate values of monthly or normal monthly evaporation. Table 5-1 shows the magnitude of evaporation error resulting from error in each of the various factors, for selected meteorological situations. In view of the high degree of correlation found to exist between computed and observed

[1] M. A. Kohler, T. J. Nordenson, and W. E. Fox, Evaporation from Pans and Lakes, *U.S. Weather Bur. Research Paper* 38, May, 1955.

[2] R. W. Hamon, L. L. Weiss, and W. T. Wilson, Insolation as an Empirical Function of Daily Sunshine Duration, *Monthly Weather Rev.*, Vol. 82, pp. 141–146, June, 1954.

Sigmund Fritz and T. H. MacDonald, Average Solar Radiation in the United States, *Heating and Ventilating*, Vol. 46, pp. 61–64, July, 1949.

evaporation, Table 5-1 is also indicative of the relative influence of the various elements under typical meteorological situations.

It will be noted from Eqs. (5-4) and (5-13) that γ is directly proportional to pressure and thus might be expected to cause a bias in computed evaporation when Fig. 5-2 is applied through a wide range of elevation. Although high-elevation data are notably sparse, analysis of limited data

TABLE 5-2. Summary of Pan Coefficients (Lake-to-pan Ratios) as Determined by Various Investigators*

Location	Years of record	Basis of coefficient	Class A	BPI† (sunken)	Colorado (sunken)	Screened‡ (sunken)
Lake Hodges, Calif..........	1919–21	June–Oct.	....	....	0.96	
Newell Reservoir, Canada....	1919–25	May–Sept.	....	0.95		
Ft. Collins, Colo. (85-ft diam.)..	1926–28	April–Nov.	0.70	....	0.79	
Denver, Colo.§..............	1915–16	Mean annual	0.67			
Denver, Colo.§..............	1916	June–Oct.	....	0.94		
Milford Expt. Sta., Utah§.....	1926–27	May–Oct.	0.67			
Fullerton, Calif.§............	1936–39	Mean annual	0.77	0.94	0.89	0.98
Lake Elsinore, Calif..........	1939–41	Mean annual	0.77	....	....	0.98
Ft. McIntosh, Texas§........	1950	Feb.–Dec.	0.72	....	....	0.89
Red Bluff Reservoir, Texas....	1939–47	Mean annual	0.68			
Lake Okeechobee, Fla.......	1940–46	Mean annual	0.81	....	0.98	
Lake Hefner, Okla..........	1950–51	Mean annual	0.69	0.91	0.83	0.91
Lake Mead, Ariz.-Nev........	1952–53	Mean annual	0.60¶			

* For detailed information on the derivation of these data, consult the Lake Hefner and Lake Mead reports (see Bibliography).

† Bureau of Plant Industry pan, 6 ft in diameter and 2 ft deep.

‡ Pan 2 ft in diameter and 3 ft deep.

§ Computations based on assumption that evaporation from a sunken pan 12 ft in diameter and 3 ft deep is equivalent to that from a lake for periods during which advected energy and stored energy in the lake may be neglected.

¶ For a pan at representative site.

for Salt Lake City, Utah, and Grand Junction, Colorado, indicates that the relation can be used for elevations up to 5000 ft, mean sea level, without appreciable error.

Pan coefficients. Water-budget, energy-budget, and mass-transfer techniques can be used to estimate evaporation from existing reservoirs and lakes. However, these methods are not directly applicable to design problems, since water-temperature data are required for their use. Virtually all estimates of reservoir evaporation, both for design and operation, have been made by applying a coefficient (Table 5-2) to observed or derived pan evaporation. Although too few determinations have been made to appraise the approach accurately, assuming an annual Class A pan coefficient of 0.70 for the lakes included in the table would result in a maximum difference of 12 per cent. Part-year coefficients are more variable because energy storage in the lake can be appreciably different at the beginning and end of the period. Changes in heat storage cause pronounced variation in monthly coefficients.

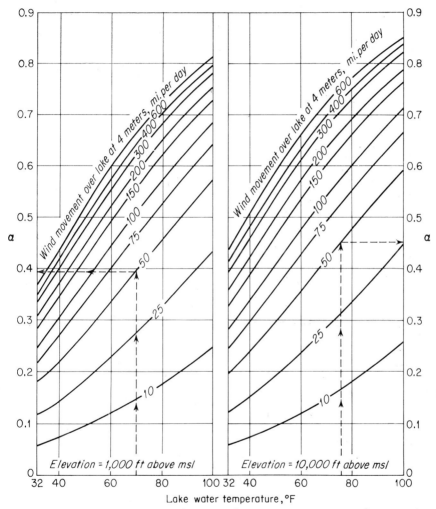

FIG. 5-3. Portion of advected energy (into a lake) utilized for evaporation. (*U.S. Weather Bureau.*)

Effects of advected energy on lake and pan. Observations demonstrate that the sensible-heat transfer across the pan walls can be appreciable for the Class A pan and that it may flow in either direction, depending upon the pan and air temperatures. Since heat transfer through the bottom of the reservoir is essentially zero, the pan data require adjustment. Similarly, the pan does not account for advection to and energy storage in the reservoir.

Not all energy advected into a lake is dissipated through increased evaporation. Since the increased energy results in higher water-surface temperatures, radiation loss and sensible-heat exchange are also affected. It has been shown that the portion a of advected energy utilized in the

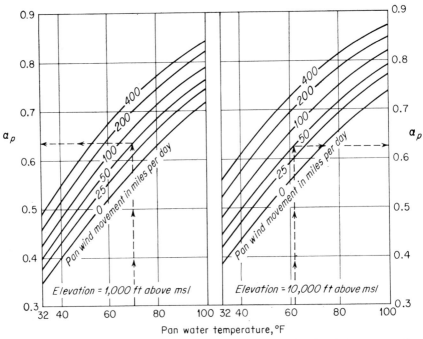

FIG. 5-4. Portion of advected energy (into a Class A pan) utilized for evaporation. (U.S. Weather Bureau.)

evaporation process is approximately that given by Fig. 5-3. Since a varies with atmospheric pressure, two relations are shown, one for an elevation of 1000 ft and the other for 10,000 ft, mean sea level. Since advection can be either into or out of the lake and heat storage may either increase or decrease during the period under consideration, an adjustment should be made for the difference between these two terms (*net advection*). Thus, for comparison with pan evaporation, observed lake evaporation should be adjusted by adding the quantity $a(Q_\theta - Q_v)$, where Q_θ is the change in energy storage during the period and Q_v is the advection into the lake, both in equivalent inches of evaporation (Sec. 5-3).

Annual net advection is usually small and may generally be neglected in the design of reservoirs. If outflow is to be primarily from a low

level in a deep reservoir, however, this may not be the case. Average
net advection at Lake Mead is equivalent to about one foot of evaporation
per year.

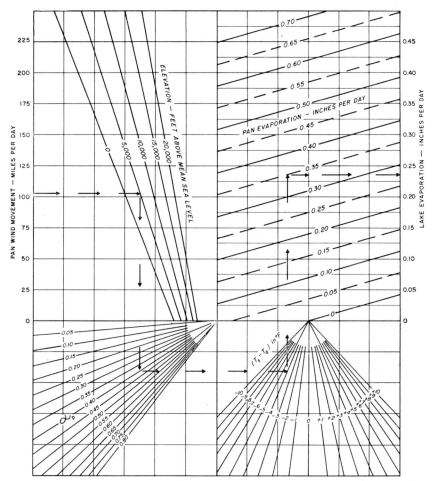

FIG. 5-5. Lake evaporation as a function of Class A pan evaporation and heat transfer
through the pan. (U.S. Weather Bureau.)

Figure 5-4, derived in much the same manner as Fig. 5-3, shows the
relative effect a_p of net advection on pan evaporation. Advection by
means of water added to the pan is normally unimportant, but advection
of sensible heat through the pan walls is sufficient to produce moderate
variation in the pan coefficient under varying climatic regimes. From the
Bowen-ratio concept and the empirical relation of Fig. 5-2, a function
can be derived for estimating heat transfer through the pan from observations of air and water temperature, wind movement, and atmospheric

pressure.   This is the underlying relation of the chart in Fig. 5-5 which further assumes a 0.7 pan coefficient when air and water temperatures are equal.   Lake evaporation computed from the chart should be adjusted for any appreciable net advection to the lake.

"Theoretical" pan concept.   Reliable data are notably limited, but such data as are available indicate that the ratio of lake to Class A pan evaporation is, for practical purposes, 0.70, provided that

1. Net advection to the lake is negligible.
2. Net transfer of sensible heat through the pan is negligible.
3. Pan exposure is representative.

Figure 5-2 yields estimates of evaporation from a Class A pan with its boundary losses; that is, γ is two and one-half times the theoretical value.   If the theoretical value of γ is substituted into the relation, computed values of evaporation should correspond to those which would be observed in a "theoretical" pan which has the radiation characteristics of the Class A pan but which permits no sensible-heat transfer through the pan.   On the basis of the data now available, it is evident that the annual coefficient for this "theoretical" pan is near 0.70 and is essentially independent of climatic variation.   Figure 5-6 was derived from Fig. 5-2 by substituting the theoretical value of γ and assuming a pan coefficient of 0.70, to provide a convenient means of estimating reservoir evaporation. Although the relation is strictly applicable only for daily data, use of monthly averages will, in general, cause no appreciable bias.   Adjustment should be made, however, for advection to the reservoir.

5-6. Summary and appraisal of techniques for estimating reservoir evaporation.   When conditions are such that satisfactory results cannot be obtained by applying a water budget, evaporation from an existing reservoir can be determined by either the empirical mass-transfer or the energy-budget approach.   Both instrumentation and maintenance of observations are expensive for these two approaches, and their widespread use may not be economically feasible for some time. The operation of a pan station (near the reservoir, but not so close as to be materially affected by it) is relatively inexpensive and should provide satisfactory estimates of annual reservoir evaporation (Fig. 5-5).   Some reliability would be gained if supplementary data were obtained for estimating net reservoir advection, but this item is frequently not of great importance.   If monthly or seasonal distribution of annual evaporation is considered necessary, net advection to the reservoir must be evaluated.   Figure 5-6 can also be applied where the required data (or reliable estimates thereof) are available.

For reservoir design studies, Fig. 5-5 may be applied if data are available from a representative pan.   If such data are not available, Fig. 5-6 is believed to constitute the best approach.   Results should be checked by applying what appears to be an appropriate coefficient to data from the most nearly representative pans (or generalized map such as Fig. 5-7). There is seldom justifiable reason, however, for constructing a major reservoir prior to the collection of at least 1 or 2 yr of pan data at the site for checking purposes.

In reservoir design, the engineer is really concerned with the increased loss at the reservoir site resulting from the construction of the dam, i.e., reservoir evaporation less evapotranspiration under natural conditions. Thus in humid areas construction of a dam causes only a nominal increase in water loss. If reliable streamflow data are available at the dam site and immediately above the reservoir both before and after construction, the resulting average increased loss can be determined by direct computation, provided that climatic conditions are comparable for the two periods.[1]

5-7. Increased water supplies through reduced evaporation. Any steps which can be taken to reduce reservoir evaporation per unit of storage provide a corresponding increase in usable water supply. Selecting the site and design yielding a minimum of reservoir area per unit of storage is advantageous. Small municipal reservoirs are sometimes covered to minimize the losses from evaporation.[2] Natural or constructed windbreaks around the reservoir have been advocated, but this approach is obviously ineffective. A 25 per cent reduction in wind speed will seldom reduce evaporation by more than 5 per cent, and wind reductions of this magnitude are not feasible over reservoirs of appreciable size.

In deep reservoirs, summer water-surface temperature may be 30 F° or more above that near the bottom. If the dam is designed to permit discharge of warm surface water, evaporation will be less than if colder water is discharged. The use of monomolecular films on the water surface offers another possibility for evaporation reduction. It has been demonstrated that extremely small amounts of cetyl alcohol will reduce pan evaporation by as much as 40 per cent under some meteorological conditions.[3] The feasibility of its use on major reservoirs is still to be determined.

[1] W. B. Langbein, Research on Evaporation from Lakes and Reservoirs, *Trans. Intern. Assoc. Hydrology*, Brussels Assembly, pp. 9–11, 1951.

[2] Putting a Sun Shade on Five Acres of Water, *Eng. News-Record*, Vol. 156, p. 47, May 31, 1956.

[3] W. W. Mansfield, Influence of Monolayers on the Natural Rate of Evaporation of Water, *Nature*, Vol. 175, p. 247, 1955.

"Experiments of the Use of Cetyl Alcohol to Reduce Evaporation Losses from Free Water Surfaces," Interim Report January–October, 1955, East African Meteorological Department, November, 1955.

Pilot Studies for Reservoir Evaporation Control—Interim Results with Cetyl Alcohol (Sept. 9, to Nov. 4, 1955), *U.S. Bur. Reclamation Spec. Invest. Memo. 55-15*, Nov. 18, 1955.

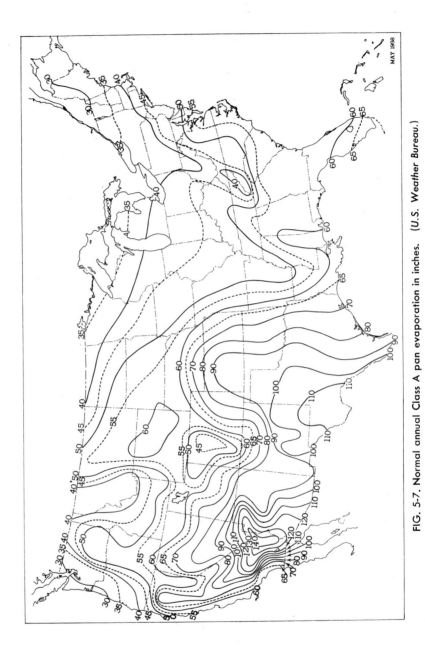

MAY 1958

FIG. 5-7. Normal annual Class A pan evaporation in inches.   (U.S. Weather Bureau.)

TRANSPIRATION

Only minute portions of the water absorbed by the root systems of plants remain in the plant tissues; virtually all is discharged to the atmosphere as vapor through the process known as *transpiration*. This process constitutes an important phase of the hydrologic cycle since it is the principal mechanism by which the precipitation falling on land areas is returned to the atmosphere. In studying the water balance of a drainage basin, it is usually found impracticable to separate evaporation and transpiration, and the practicing engineer therefore treats the two factors as a single item. Nevertheless, a knowledge of each process is required to assure that the techniques employed are consistent with physical reality.

5-8. Factors affecting transpiration. The meteorological factors which influence evaporation are also active in the transpiration process. The importance of solar radiation is amplified since the rate of movement of water within the plant depends upon sunlight; transpiration and plant growth are both closely related to radiation received. Thus while 75 to 90 per cent of daily soil evaporation occurs between sunrise and sunset,[1] about 95 per cent of the daily transpiration occurs during the daylight hours.[2] Optimum temperature and radiation for maximum growth vary with plant species, but all activity virtually ceases when the temperature drops to near 40°F.

Transpiration is limited by the rate at which moisture becomes available to the plants. Although there is little doubt that the rate of soil evaporation, under fixed meteorological conditions, decreases quasi-exponentially with time, divergent views persist with respect to transpiration.[3] It is believed that the controversy and apparent discrepancies can be attributed to the varied methods of deriving supporting data and the nondescript terminology used to describe the results. Some investigators believe that transpiration is independent of available moisture until it has receded to the *wilting point* (moisture content at which permanent wilting of plants occurs) while others assume that transpiration is roughly proportional to the moisture remaining in the soil and available to the plants. The *field capacity* is defined as the amount of water held in the soil after excess gravitational water has drained, and the range in soil moisture from field capacity to wilting point (*available water*) is a measure of the maximum quantity of water available for

[1] H. Landsberg, "Physical Climatology," p. 136, Pennsylvania State University, University Park, Pa., 1941.

[2] C. H. Lee, Transpiration and Total Evaporation, Chap. VIII, p. 280, in O. E. Meinzer (ed.), "Hydrology," McGraw-Hill, New York, 1942.

[3] F. J. Veihmeyer and A. H. Hendrickson, Does Transpiration Decrease as the Soil Moisture Decreases, *Trans. Am. Geophys. Union*, Vol. 36, pp. 425–448, June, 1955.

plant use without replenishment (Sec. 6-3). Available water varies with soil type, ranging from about 0.5 in. per foot of depth for sand to 2 in. or more per foot of depth for clay loams.

Penman[1] states that soil type, crop type, and root range are of minor importance in the determination of transpiration rates immediately following wetting. On the other hand, Blaney[2] reports that annual transpiration (including evaporation and with adequate irrigation) in the San Fernando Valley, California, is 47 in. for alfalfa and only 24 in. for orange groves. This difference may result in large part from (1) excess watering of the alfalfa, (2) insufficient watering of the groves, and (3) less than 100 per cent vegetal cover in the orange groves. Whether or not soil type, crop type, and root range appreciably affect transpiration rates during periods of fully adequate water supply, all three factors become important as drying proceeds, since they all affect the water available for plant growth.

That transpiration is closely related to the rate of plant growth is well established. Thus there is pronounced seasonal and annual variation in addition to the diurnal cycle. Transpiration is restricted to the growing season, and the stage of development is an important factor.

5-9. Measurement of transpiration. It is not possible to measure transpiration loss from an appreciable area under natural conditions, and, hence, determinations are restricted to studies of small samples under laboratory conditions. One method involves placing one or more potted plants in a closed container and computing transpiration as the increase in moisture content of the confined space. Most measurements are made with a *phytometer*, a large vessel filled with soil in which one or more plants are rooted. The only escape of moisture is by transpiration (the soil surface is sealed to prevent evaporation), which can be determined by weighing the plant and container at desired intervals of time. By providing aeration and additional water, a phytometer study may be carried through the entire life cycle of a plant. It is virtually impossible to simulate natural conditions and therefore the results of phytometer observations are mostly of academic interest to the hydrologist. They can be considered to constitute little more than an index to water use by a crop under field conditions.

EVAPOTRANSPIRATION

In studying the hydrologic balance for an area, one is usually concerned only with the *total evaporation* (*evapotranspiration* or *consumptive use*),

---

[1] H. L. Penman, Natural Evaporation from Open Water, Bare Soil, and Grass, *Proc. Roy. Soc. (London): A*, Vol. 193, pp. 120–145, April, 1948.

H. L. Penman, Estimating Evaporation, *Trans. Am. Geophys. Union*, Vol. 37, pp. 43–46, February, 1956.

[2] H. F. Blaney, Discussion of paper by H. L. Penman, *Trans. Am. Geophys. Union*, Vol. 37, pp. 46–48, February, 1956.

the evaporation from all water, soil, snow, ice, vegetative, and other surfaces plus transpiration. Although attempt has been made in the past to draw fine distinctions between the terms evapotranspiration and consumptive use, they are now generally considered synonymous.[1] *Potential evapotranspiration* is defined[2] as the evapotranspiration that would occur were there an adequate moisture supply at all times.

There are numerous approaches to estimation of evapotranspiration and potential evapotranspiration, none of which is generally applicable for all purposes. The type of data required depends on the intended use. In some hydrologic studies, mean basin evapotranspiration is required, while in other cases we are interested in water use of a particular crop cover or the change in water use resulting from changed vegetal cover.

5-10. Water-budget determination of mean basin evapotranspiration. Assuming that storage and all items of inflow and outflow except evapotranspiration can be measured, the volume of water (usually expressed in inches depth) required to balance the continuity equation for a basin represents evapotranspiration. Among other things, the reliability of a water-budget computation hinges largely on the time increments considered. As a rule, normal annual evapotranspiration can be reliably computed as the difference between long-time averages of precipitation and streamflow, since the change in storage over a long period of years is inconsequential.[3] Any deficiencies in such computations are usually attributable either to inadequate precipitation or runoff data or to subterranean flow into or out of the basin. Estimates of annual evapotranspiration are subject to appreciable errors if changes in storage are neglected, except where moisture storage in a basin is nearly the same on a given date each year. Generally it is necessary to evaluate soil-moisture, groundwater, and surface storage at the beginning of each year.

The water-budget method can also be applied to short time periods[4] (Fig. 5-8). Over 6 in. of rain fell in a 3-day period, resulting in the rise of June 21, and 4.60 in. more fell by June 29. The runoff (June 26–30) produced by the second storm was 2.37 in. If it is assumed that the soil was equally near saturation at the end of rain on June 21 and 29, the evapotranspiration during the period was 2.23 in. $(4.60 - 2.37)$, or 0.28 in./day. The error in computations for periods as short as a week

[1] H. F. Blaney, Consumptive Use of Water, *Trans. ASCE*, Vol. 117, pp. 949–973, 1952.

[2] C. W. Thornthwaite, An Approach toward a Rational Classification of Climate, *Geograph. Rev.*, Vol. 38, pp. 55–94, 1948.

[3] C. E. Knox and T. J. Nordenson, Average Annual Runoff and Precipitation in the New England–New York Area, *U.S. Geol. Survey Hydrologic Invest. Atlas* HA-7, undated.

[4] W. E. Fox, "Computation of Potential and Actual Evapotranspiration," U.S. Weather Bureau (processed), 1956.

can be appreciable, and it is advisable to use longer periods when feasible. If the computations are carried through July 16, the estimated evapotranspiration averages about 0.23 in./day, undoubtedly a more realistic value. The computations must be based on total runoff (Sec. 7-5). This procedure is best adapted to regions where depth to groundwater is relatively small and precipitation is evenly distributed throughout the year. Although evapotranspiration estimates derived in the manner

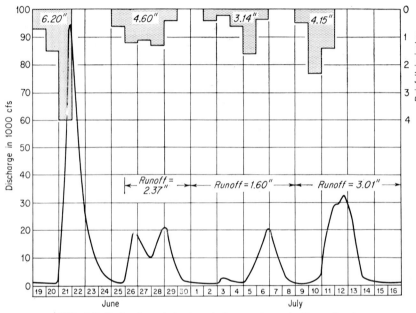

FIG. 5-8. Derivation of short-period evapotranspiration estimates.

described must be geared to the fortuitous occurrence of large storms or relatively wet periods, sufficient determinations can be made from many years of record to define the seasonal distribution (Fig. 5-9). If the resulting curve is to represent normal annual evapotranspiration, the computations must be carried on a continuous basis, since omitting dry periods will bias the results. If the curve is to represent potential evapotranspiration, computations should be made only for those periods during which potential conditions existed.

5-11. Field-plot determinations of evapotranspiration. Application of a water budget to field plots produces satisfactory results only under ideal conditions which are rarely attained. Precise measurement of percolation is not possible, and consequent errors tend to be accumulative. If the groundwater table lies at great depth, accretions may be inconsequential. Under these circumstances, soil-moisture measurements become the principal source of error—random in nature but of such magnitude as to preclude computation of short-period evapotranspiration.

The energy budget can be applied to the determination of evapotranspiration from a field plot much as for a lake (Sec. 5-3). Instead of being concerned with heat storage in a mass of water, however, that stored in the soil profile must be computed. Specific heat of soil varies from about 0.2 to 0.8 cal/cc, depending upon moisture content and soil type, and so one must know the specific heat as well as temperature throughout

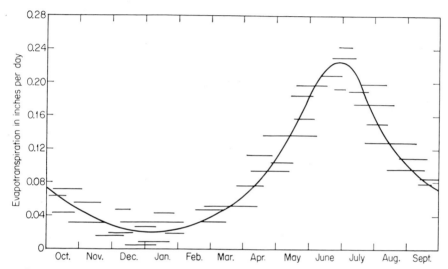

FIG. 5-9. Mean evapotranspiration curve derived through analysis of rainfall and streamflow data.

the profile. In applying Bowen's ratio [Eq. (5-4)] to a lake, temperature and vapor pressure of the surface are used. Measuring the vapor pressure of a vegetated surface presents quite another problem, and it becomes necessary to measure the temperature and vapor-pressure gradients between two levels above the surface. Advected energy, in terms of water-budget items, is usually small and customarily neglected.

The Thornthwaite-Holzman-type mass-transfer equation [Eq. (5-7)] is particularly suited for evapotranspiration measurements. It has frequently been used for the purpose,[1] although there is some question as to whether it has been adequately tested. Instrumental requirements are not easily satisfied under field conditions, since computed evapotran-

[1] C. W. Thornthwaite and B. Holzman, Measurement of Evaporation from Land and Water Surfaces, *U.S. Dept. Agr. Tech. Bull* 817, 1942.

N. E. Rider, Evaporation from an Oat Field, *Quart. J. Roy. Meteorol. Soc.*, Vol. LXXX, pp. 198–211, April, 1954.

spiration is proportional to the differences in measured wind and vapor pressure at two levels near the surface under investigation.

5-12. Determination of potential evapotranspiration. All the techniques discussed in Secs. 5-10 and 5-11 are also suited to determination of potential evapotranspiration, the only added requirement being that the area under observation have sufficient water at all times. Many observations of potential evapotranspiration are now being made[1] in grass-covered soil containers, variously known as *tanks, evapotranspirometers,* and *lysimeters.* The first two terms customarily refer to containers with sealed bottoms, while there has been an attempt to restrict the word lysimeter to containers with pervious bottoms. Evapotranspiration is computed by maintaining a water budget for the container.

Like evaporation pans, evapotranspirometers provide only an index to potential evapotranspiration. Accordingly, instrumental and operational standardization is of extreme importance. In summarizing the results of world-wide observations, Mather states:

> The evapotranspirometer, when properly operated, i.e., when watered sufficiently so that there is no moisture deficiency and no appreciable moisture surplus in the soil of the tank, and when exposed homogeneously within a protective buffer area of the proper size to eliminate the effect of moisture advection, is an instrument which should give reasonably reliable values of potential evapotranspiration. Great care must be taken in the operation of the instrument, and standardized soil, vegetation, cultivation, and watering practices must be maintained on the tanks in order to insure comparable results from one installation to another.

Reliable tank observations of natural evapotranspiration (when appreciably less than potential) are seldom attained, since it is virtually impossible to maintain comparable soil moisture and vegetal cover in and adjacent to the tank under such conditions. There is serious doubt that lysimeters (with pervious bottoms) can be expected to provide satisfactory results, unless provision is made to apply a suction force at the bottom comparable to that in the natural soil profile.[2]

5-13. Estimating potential evapotranspiration from meteorological data. Several empirical techniques have been developed for estimating potential evapotranspiration from readily available climatological data and latitude (duration of possible sunshine). Thornthwaite[3] has derived a somewhat involved procedure using only temper-

[1] J. R. Mather (ed.), The Measurement of Potential Evapotranspiration, *Publ. in Climatology*, Vol. VII, No. 1, Johns Hopkins University Laboratory of Climatology, Seabrook, N.J., 1954.

L. L. Harrold and F. R. Dreibelbis, Agricultural Hydrology as Evaluated by Monolith Lysimeters, *U.S. Dept. Agr. Tech. Bull.* 1050, 1951.

[2] C. W. Thornthwaite, Discussion of paper by L. L. Harrold and F. R. Dreibelbis, *Trans. Am. Geophys. Union*, Vol. 26, pp. 292–297, October, 1945.

[3] C. W. Thornthwaite, An Approach toward a Rational Classification of Climate,

ature and duration of possible sunshine. Blaney's approach[1] involves the same two factors but was designed primarily to transpose observed consumptive-use data for irrigated areas to other localities on the basis of derived coefficients. Using average yearly data, Lowry and Johnson[2] found high correlations between consumptive use and accumulated degree days during the growing season. Procedures which rely on temperature as the sole index to heat supply at a particular latitude and which neglect cloudiness, humidity, wind, and other factors are subject to rather large errors under adverse circumstances. Variations in solar radiation at a given latitude and temperature constitute the greatest source of error.

Potential evapotranspiration and evaporation from a thin free-water surface are affected by the same meteorological factors: radiation, humidity, wind, and temperature. Even though the relative importance of these factors may be appreciably different with respect to the two phenomena, free-water evaporation should be a better index to potential evaporation than is air temperature. Fritz[3] has observed that the albedo of the eastern United States is within a few per cent of that of a fresh-water surface. Blaney[4] finds that the consumptive use of alfalfa is 0.66 that from a Class A pan or nearly equal to lake evaporation, assuming a pan coefficient of 0.7. Penman[5] found annual potential evapotranspiration in southeastern England to be 0.75 of the evaporation computed from Eq. (5-12) with E_a estimated from an empirical equation like Eq. (5-8) and Q_n estimated from Brunt's equations.[6] Thus, his finding is that potential evapotranspiration is about 0.75 of lake evaporation. This conclusion is dependent on his assumption that evapotranspiration proceeds at the potential rate until the available moisture is depleted to the wilting point throughout the root zone. If he had assumed that evapotranspiration rates decreased as soil moisture decreases, his estimates of potential evapotranspiration would have been

Geograph. Rev., Vol. 38, pp. 55–94, 1948.

J. R. Mather (ed.), The Measurement of Potential Evapotranspiration, *Publ. in Climatology*, Vol. VII, No. 1, Johns Hopkins University Laboratory of Climatology, Seabrook, N.J., 1954.

[1] H. F. Blaney, Consumptive Use of Water, *Trans. ASCE*, Vol. 117, pp. 949–973, 1952.

[2] R. L. Lowry and A. F. Johnson, Consumptive Use of Water for Agriculture, *Trans. ASCE*, Vol. 107, p. 1252, 1942.

[3] S. Fritz, The Albedo of the Ground and Atmosphere, *Bull. Am. Meteorol. Soc.*, Vol. 29, pp. 303–312, June, 1948.

[4] H. F. Blaney, Discussion of paper by H. L. Penman, Estimating Evaporation, *Trans. Am. Geophys. Union*, Vol. 37, pp. 46–48, February, 1956.

[5] H. L. Penman, Natural Evaporation from Open Water, Bare Soil, and Grass, *Proc. Royal Soc. (London): A*, Vol. 193, pp. 120–145, 1948.

[6] D. Brunt, "Physical and Dynamical Meteorology," Cambridge, London, pp. 136, 144, 1939.

higher.   There is also indication that Penman overcomputes free-water evaporation[1] as compared with Figs. 5-5 and 5-6.   Much work needs to be done, but the evidence suggests that annual lake evaporation and potential evapotranspiration are approximately equal.

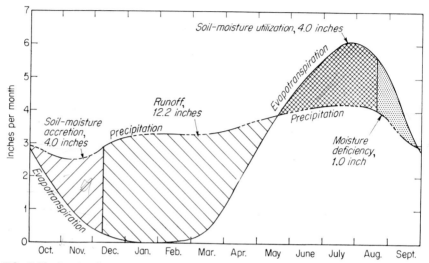

FIG. 5-10. March of normal precipitation and potential evapotranspiration at College Park, Maryland.   (*After Thornthwaite.*)

5-14. Moisture-deficiency accounting.   The normal monthly potential evapotranspiration and precipitation for College Park, Maryland, are plotted in Fig. 5-10.   Potential evapotranspiration exceeds precipitation beginning in late May, and by late September the accumulated difference is 5.0 in.   Since the estimated maximum possible soil-moisture deficiency is 4.0 in., actual evapotranspiration during the summer is limited to precipitation plus 4.0 in. of moisture depletion.   By early December the 4.0 in. of soil moisture has been replaced by excess precipitation, and a continued excess until late May produces 12.2 in. of runoff. Although this illustration is schematic in some respects, the annual magnitudes of the various factors are realistic.   Thus while there is an excess of precipitation in an average year (40.75 in. compared with 29.45 in. of potential evapotranspiration), its distribution is such that a deficiency develops in August and September.

Numerous attempts have been made to apply the bookkeeping approach to maintain a continuing accounting of evapotranspiration and soil-moisture deficiency.[2]   In most cases it has been assumed that evapo-

---

[1] Penman actually treated a small sunken pan as a "free-water surface."

[2] C. W. Thornthwaite, The Moisture Factor in Climate, *Trans. Am. Geophys. Union*, Vol. 27, pp. 41–48, February, 1946.

C. W. Thornthwaite, Contribution to Report of the Committee on Transpiration

transpiration is at the potential rate at all times when the soil-moisture deficiency is less than some predetermined value (*root-zone constant*) representing the available moisture (3 to 5 in.) within the root zone. With deficiencies in excess of this limiting value, it is assumed that evapotranspiration either ceases or drops to some small fixed proportion of the potential rate.

As indicated in Sec. 5-8, considerable difference of opinion exists over the effect of a moisture deficiency on the rate of transpiration; some investigators claim to have demonstrated that transpiration continues at an undiminished rate until moisture content throughout the root zone drops to the wilting point, while others insist that the rate is approximately proportional to the moisture content throughout this range. Be this as it may, the actual evapotranspiration from a field plot and that from a natural basin differ in many respects. In a natural basin of appreciable size it can be said that:

1. There are numerous types of vegetation at varying stages of development and having roots extending to various depths.

2. Differences in slope and aspect are reflected in evapotranspiration rates so that, all other things being equal, the wilting point should be reached sooner in some areas than others.

3. There are areas of bare soil where evaporation decreases with decreasing moisture content. Also, evaporation from other surfaces (buildings, streets, etc.) decreases with time subsequent to rainfall.

4. Depression storage is a source of free-water evaporation. The area of such water surfaces decreases as evaporation and infiltration proceed subsequent to rainfall.

When these and other facts are considered, it seems obvious that the rate at which moisture is lost from a natural basin tends to be proportional to the quantity of moisture available, that evapotranspiration is in this sense a decay function, possibly similar in form to Eq. (8-2).

BIBLIOGRAPHY

Anderson, E. R., L. J. Anderson, and J. J. Marciano: A Review of Evaporation Theory and Development of Instrumentation, *U.S. Navy Electronics Lab. Rept.* 159, February, 1950.

Blaney, H. F., and others: Consumptive Use of Water—A Symposium, *Trans. ASCE*, Vol. 117, pp. 949–1023, 1952.

---

and Evaporation, 1943–1944, *Trans. Am. Geophys. Union*, Vol. 25, Part 5, pp. 886–893, 1944.

H. L. Penman, The Dependence of Transpiration on Weather and Soil Conditions, *J. Soil Sci.*, Vol. 1, pp. 74–89, 1949.

W. B. Langbein, Monthly Evapotranspiration Losses from Natural Drainage Basins, *Trans. Am. Geophys. Union*, Vol. 23, Part 2, pp. 604–614, 1942.

M. A. Kohler, Computation of Evaporation and Evapotranspiration from Meteorological Observations, *U.S. Weather Bur. Rept.*, 1957 (mimeographed).

Hydrology Handbook, *ASCE Manual* 28, 1949.

Kohler, M. A., T. J. Nordenson, and W. E. Fox: Evaporation from Pans and Lakes, *U.S. Weather Bur. Research, Paper* 38, May, 1955.

Mather, J. R. (ed.): The Measurement of Potential Evapotranspiration, *Publ. in Climatology*, Vol. VII, No. 1, Johns Hopkins University Laboratory of Climatology, Seabrook, N.J., 1954.

Thornthwaite, C. W., and J. R. Mather: The Water Balance, *Publ. in Climatology*, Vol. VIII, No. 1, Drexel Institute Laboratory of Climatology, Centerton, N.J., 1955.

Water-loss Investigations, Vol. 1, Lake Hefner Studies, *U.S. Geol. Survey Profess. Paper* 269, 1954 (reprint of *U.S. Geol. Survey Circ.* 229, 1952).

Water-loss Investigations, Lake Mead Studies, *U.S. Geol. Survey Profess. Paper* 298, 1958.

SOURCES OF DATA

Regular observations of pan evaporation are summarized in the Weather Bureau's monthly publication *Climatological Data*. Summarized data on water loss by evaporation and transpiration may be found in the following publications:

Lowry, R. L., and A. F. Johnson: Consumptive Use of Water for Agriculture, *Trans. ASCE*, Vol. 107, pp. 1243–1302, 1942.

Williams, G. R., and others: Natural Water Loss in Selected Drainage Basins, *U.S. Geol. Survey Water-supply Paper* 846, 1940.

Young, A. A., and H. F. Blaney: Use of Water by Native Vegetation, *Calif. Div. of Water Resources Bull.* 50, 1942.

PROBLEMS

5-1. A variety of units appear in the literature on evaporation, and familiarity with the relevant conversion factors is therefore desirable. As an exercise, rewrite Eq. (5-4) for application with temperatures in degrees Fahrenheit and pressures in millimeters of mercury. Rewrite Eq. (5-7) converting E to centimeters per hour, e to millibars, v to centimeters per second, and T to degrees centigrade.

5-2. Entering the upper left-hand relation of Fig. 5-2 or Fig. 5-6 with evaporation, wind movement, and dewpoint in reverse of the order indicated provides an estimate of surface-water temperature in the pan (on the axis labeled "air temperature"). In this manner, compute water temperature for each of the 10 meteorological conditions enumerated in Table 5-1. Describe those conditions which result in a water temperature higher than that of the overlying air, and vice versa.

5-3. Using Fig. 5-6, compute lake evaporation (thus neglecting advection and changes in heat storage) for each set of data presented in Table 5-1. Also compute the pan coefficient for each case. Is the range of coefficient displayed here indicative of the range in annual coefficients to be expected over the United States? Why?

5-4. An indication of the gross variation of lake evaporation with elevation can be obtained from Fig. 5-6 for specified conditions if values of the respective parameters are known for two elevations. Considering the data in Table 5-1 to constitute a series of sea-level observations, compute the evaporation at 3000 ft, mean sea level, using the following elevation gradients (per 1000 ft): air temperature, -3 F°; dewpoint, -1 F°; wind, 10 per cent; and radiation, 2 per cent. If these results are compared with those of Prob. 5-3, is the "elevation effect" reasonably constant for these selected circumstances? Discuss.

5-5. Given the data tabulated below, compute monthly and annual lake evaporation from Fig. 5-6. Assuming that a proposed reservoir will experience this computed amount of evaporation per year (and noting that precipitation less runoff is natural evapotranspiration), what would be the net anticipated loss from the reservoir per acre of surface area? On the basis of the computed lake evaporation and that provided for a Class A pan, compute monthly, mean monthly, and annual pan coefficients. Discuss qualitatively the effects of heat storage in a deep reservoir on the derived monthly pan coefficients.

Period	Air temperature, °F	Dew-point, °F	Wind, mi/day	Radiation, ly/day	Pan evaporation, in.	Precipitation, in.	Runoff, in.
Oct......	57	46	52	290	3.2	2.7	0.8
Nov......	46	35	59	200	1.7	2.4	1.1
Dec......	37	28	68	150	1.0	3.1	1.3
Jan......	34	25	81	150	0.8	3.4	1.6
Feb......	36	24	90	230	1.0	2.9	1.7
Mar.....	44	30	92	310	2.8	3.5	1.8
Apr......	54	39	83	400	4.8	3.6	1.7
May.....	65	51	66	480	6.0	3.7	1.4
June.....	72	60	50	510	6.4	3.9	1.2
July......	77	65	44	500	7.1	4.0	0.8
Aug......	75	64	41	440	5.8	4.6	1.0
Sept.....	69	58	44	370	4.2	3.6	0.7
Sum.....	...	...	...	...	44.8	41.4	15.1
Mean....	56	44	70	336			

5-6. Using the precipitation and potential evapotranspiration data tabulated below, develop a chart similar to Fig. 5-10 (assume moisture capacity of 4.0 in.). What are the annual moisture excess and annual moisture deficiency? During what period of the year is a need for supplemental irrigation most apt to develop? What geographical section of the United States is typified by the derived chart?

Month..............	Oct.	Nov.	Dec.	Jan.	Feb.	Mar.	Apr.	May	June	July	Aug.	Sept.
Precipitation..........	1.2	2.4	4.2	5.2	4.5	3.7	1.5	0.8	0.3	0.1	0.1	0.6
Potential evapotranspiration..............	2.5	1.8	1.0	0.9	1.2	1.8	2.3	2.8	3.2	3.5	3.2	2.9

5-7. Using data published in *Water-supply Papers* and *Climatological Data*, plot hydrographs of mean daily flow and bar charts of daily precipitation (several years) for a selected small basin. The basin and period should be selected to include reasonably saturated conditions on a number of occasions. Compute mean daily evapotranspiration for several periods delineated by times of assumed basin saturation (Fig. 5-8). Which of the periods analyzed do you believe to be indicative of "potential" conditions?

6

GROUNDWATER

In 1950 about 25 billion gallons of water[1] was pumped each day from groundwater in the United States. This quantity was about one-sixth of the total water use in the country exclusive of hydroelectric-power generation. Because groundwater is relatively free of pollution it is especially useful for domestic purposes, particularly for isolated farms and small towns. In the arid regions of the West, groundwater is often the only source of water for irrigation. Groundwater temperatures remain relatively low during the summer, and large quantities are used for air conditioning in the East and South.

Aside from its great economic importance, groundwater is also an important phase of the hydrologic cycle. Most perennial streams derive the greater part of their flow from groundwater, while in arid regions much of the surface streamflow percolates to the groundwater. The occurrence and movement of subsurface water are necessarily intimately related to geological structure, and a knowledge of geology is prerequisite to a thorough comprehension of groundwater hydrology. This chapter stresses the hydrologic aspects of groundwater and presumes only elementary knowledge of geology.

6-1. The occurrence of subsurface water. Figure 6-1 is a schematic cross section of the upper portion of the earth's crust. Near the surface in the *zone of aeration* pore spaces contain both air and water. Water in the zone of aeration is known as *suspended* or *vadose water*, or *soil moisture*. The thickness of the zone of aeration varies from practically zero in swamplands to several hundred feet in arid regions with substantial relief.

Below the zone of aeration the pores are filled with water. This is the *zone of saturation*, or the *groundwater*. At the surface separating these zones, called the *water table* or *phreatic surface*, the hydrostatic pressure in the groundwater is atmospheric. The zone of saturation may extend

---

[1] C. L. McGuinness, The Water Situation in the United States with Special Reference to Ground Water, *U.S. Geol. Survey Circ.* 114, p. 95, 1951.

to considerable depth but, as depth increases, the weight of the overlying material tends to close the pore spaces, and relatively little water is found at depths greater than 2000 ft.

Occasionally local zones of saturation exist as *perched groundwater* above a locally impervious stratum. Sometimes a body of groundwater

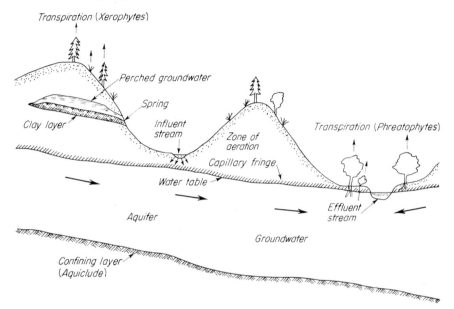

FIG. 6-1. Schematic cross section showing the occurrence of groundwater.

is overlain by an impervious stratum to form *confined* or *artesian water.* Confined groundwater is usually under pressure because of the weight of the overlying soil and the hydrostatic head. If a well penetrates the confining layer, water will rise to the *piezometric level,* the artesian equivalent of the water table. If the piezometric surface is above ground level, the well discharges as a *flowing well.*

MOISTURE IN THE ZONE OF AERATION

6-2. Soil-water relationships. Moisture in the zone of aeration may be present as *gravity water* in transit in the larger pore spaces, as *capillary water* in the smaller pores (Fig. 6-2), as *hygroscopic moisture* adhering in a thin film to the soil grains, and as water vapor. Gravity water is a transient state. After a rain, water may move downward in the larger pores, but this water must either be dispersed into capillary pores or pass through the zone of aeration to the groundwater or to a stream channel. Hygroscopic water, on the other hand, is held by molecular attraction and is not normally removed from the soil under usual climatic conditions. The important variable element of soil moisture is, therefore, the capillary water.

If a soil-filled tube is placed with its lower end in a container of water, some water will move up into the soil. The rate of upward movement

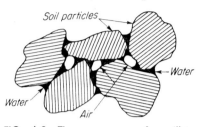

becomes progressively smaller with time, until it eventually approaches zero. Measurement of the moisture content of the soil at various levels will show that moisture in the soil column decreases with height above the water surface (Fig. 6-3). If a sample of soil is saturated with water and then subjected to successively greater negative pressures and the

FIG. 6-2. The occurrence of capillary moisture in soil.

moisture content is noted after each change in pressure, a similar curve (Fig. 6-4) results.

Buckingham[1] first proposed characterizing soil-moisture phenomena on the basis of energy relationships. He introduced the concept of

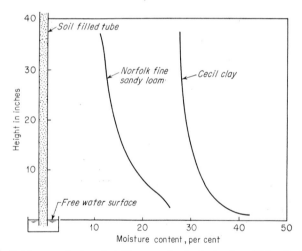

FIG. 6-3. Moisture-content vs. height curves for typical soils. (After Buckingham.)

capillary potential to describe the attraction of soil for water. With a free water surface taken as reference, *capillary potential* is defined as the work required to move a unit mass of water from the reference plane to any point in the soil column. Thus, capillary potential is the potential energy per unit mass of water. By definition, capillary potential is

[1] E. Buckingham, Studies on the Movement of Soil Moisture, *U.S. Dept. Agr. Bur. Soils Bull.* 38, 1907.

negative since water will move upward by capillarity without external work. It can be shown that capillary potential ψ is related to the acceleration of gravity g and height above datum y (negative) by the equation

$$\psi = gy \qquad (6\text{-}1)$$

Curves such as Fig. 6-3 provide a basis for relating capillary potential and moisture content for a particular soil. Schofield[1] suggested the term pF to represent the common logarithm of the capillary potential in centimeters of water. This is analogous to the use of pH in chemistry.

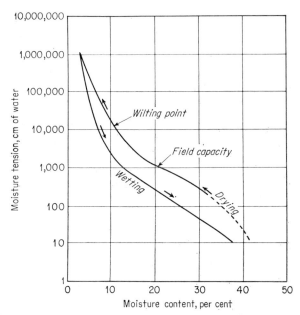

FIG. 6-4. Moisture-tension curves for a typical soil. (*After Schofield.*)

6-3. Equilibrium points. Visualizing the several states of water in soil, early soil scientists tried to define the limits of these states by "equilibrium points." Figures 6-3 and 6-4 indicate that no clear-cut boundaries exist, but the equilibrium points are convenient for discussing soil moisture. The two of greatest interest to the hydrologist are field capacity and wilting point. *Field capacity* is defined as the moisture content of soil after gravity drainage is complete. Colman[2] has shown

[1] R. K. Schofield, The pF of the Water in Soil, *Trans. Third Intern. Congr. Soil Sci.*, Vol. 2, pp. 37–48, 1935.

[2] E. A. Colman, A Laboratory Procedure for Determining the Field Capacity of Soils, *Soil Sci.*, Vol. 63, p. 277, 1947.

that field capacity is essentially the water retained in soil subjected to a tension of $\frac{1}{3}$ atm. Veihmeyer and Hendrickson[1] found that the *moisture equivalent*, the water retained in a soil sample $\frac{3}{8}$ in. deep after being centrifuged for 30 min at a speed equivalent to a force of $1000g$, was also nearly the field capacity of fine-grained soils.

The *wilting point* represents the soil moisture at the time that plants cannot extract water from the soil. It is the moisture held at a tension equivalent to the osmotic pressure exerted by the plant roots. For many years the standard method of finding the wilting point was to grow sunflower seedlings in soil samples. Recent tests indicate that it is represented by the moisture content at a tension of about 15 atm. The difference between the moisture content at field capacity and at wilting point is called *available moisture*. It represents the useful storage capacity of the soil (Secs. 5-8 and 5-14) and the maximum water available to plants. Typical values of moisture content at field capacity and wilting point and available moisture are given in Table 6-1.

TABLE 6-1. Typical Moisture Values for Various Soil Types

Soil type	Field capacity	Wilting point	Available water	Specific weight, lb/cu ft
	Per cent dry weight of soil			
Sand................	5	2	3	95
Sandy loam...........	12	5	7	90
Loam................	19	10	9	85
Silt loam..............	22	13	9	80
Clay loam............	24	15	9	80
Clay.................	36	20	16	75
Peat.................	140	75	65	20

6-4. Measurement of soil moisture. The conventional method of measuring soil moisture is the laboratory determination of weight of water lost when a sample is oven-dried. This is slow and is not adapted to continuous measurement. A *tensiometer* (Fig. 6-5) consists of a porous ceramic cup buried in the soil. The cup is filled with water and connected to a manometer. If the soil is dry, water leaves the cup, creating negative pressure which is indicated by the manometer. When the tension exceeds 1 atm the system is no longer workable. Thus a

[1] F. J. Veihmeyer and A. H. Hendrickson, The Moisture-Equivalent as a Measure of the Field Capacity of Soils, *Soil Sci.*, Vol. 32, pp. 181–193, 1931.

tensiometer[1] is satisfactory for moisture contents from slightly below field capacity to saturation.

Numerous indirect measurements of moisture content have been devised, including measurement of gamma-radiation penetration,[2] heat transmission,[3] and electrical resistivity. Resistivity[4] methods are most widely used. A pair of electrodes embedded in a porous dielectric are buried in the soil with wires running to a surface terminal. Plaster of paris, nylon, and Fiberglas have been used as dielectrics. The resistance between the electrodes varies with the moisture content of the dielectric which is assumed to be in moisture equilibrium with the soil. Resistance is usually measured with an alternating-current bridge so as to avoid polarization of the element. The resistance element must be carefully installed in close contact with the soil and with minimum soil disturbance.

Soil moisture is related to resistance by calibration. This may be done by embedding the block in a pan of soil and noting the change in resistance as the soil dries. Nonuniform drying of the soil sample, difficulty of simulating the in-place condition of the soil, and lack of representativity of the sample make this method of calibration unsatisfactory. A more realistic, although seemingly less accurate, calibration can be obtained by taking numerous soil samples around the site where the block is placed. The moisture content of these samples is related to the resistance readings at the time the sample was taken. This calibration makes the resistance element an index to the moisture content

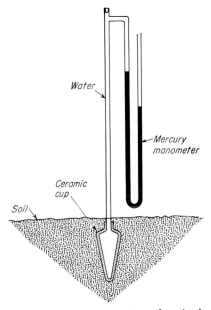

FIG. 6-5. Schematic drawing of a simple tensiometer.

[1] L. A. Richards, M. B. Russell, and O. R. Neal, Further Developments on Apparatus for Field Moisture Studies, *Proc. Soil Sci. Soc. Am.*, Vol. 2, pp. 55–64, 1937.

[2] D. J. Belcher, T. R. Cuykendall, and H. S. Sack, The Measurement of Soil Moisture and Density by Neutron and Gamma-ray Scattering, *U.S. Civil Aeronaut. Admin. Tech. Develop. and Evaluation Center Rept.* 127, 1950.

[3] C. F. Shaw and L. D. Baver, Heat Conductivity as an Index of Soil Moisture, *J. Am. Soc. Agron.*, Vol. 31, pp. 886–891, 1939.

[4] W. M. Broadfoot and others, Some Field, Laboratory and Office Procedures for Soil-moisture Measurement, *Southern Forest Expt. Sta. Occasional Paper* 135, 1954.

of the soil zone encompassing the sample sites. Since the elements actually measure soil-moisture tension they have about the same resistance at field capacity in any type of soil. The same is true at the wilting point.

6-5. Movement of soil moisture. *Infiltration* is the movement of water through the soil surface into the soil and is distinguished from *percolation* which is movement of water through the soil. When water is first applied to the soil surface, gravity water begins to move down through the larger soil openings while the smaller surface pores take in water by capillarity. The downward-moving gravity water is also taken in by capillary pores. As the capillary pores at the surface are filled and the intake capacity is reduced, the infiltration rate decreases. In homogeneous soil, as pores at lower levels are filled, infiltration decreases gradually until the zone of aeration is saturated. Normally, the soil is stratified and frequently the subsoil layers are less permeable than the surface soil. In this case, the infiltration rate is eventually limited to the rate of percolation through the least pervious subsoil stratum.

Two cases of infiltration must be recognized. Infiltration from rainfall is distinguished by very shallow depths of water on the soil surface but is extensive over large areas. Quantities of water infiltrated are usually very small (a few inches per day maximum) and rarely sufficient to saturate a great depth of soil. At the termination of rain, gravity water remaining in the soil continues to move downward and, at the same time, is taken up in capillary pore spaces. Usually the infiltrated water is distributed within the upper few feet of soil, with little or no contribution to groundwater unless the soil is highly permeable or the zone of aeration very thin. Infiltration from rainfall is discussed in greater detail in Sec. 8-2.

For irrigation and artificial recharge of the groundwater (Sec. 6-16), water is ponded to a considerable depth over limited areas for long periods of time. The aim of recharge operations is to saturate the soil down to the water table. Under these conditions the time variation of infiltration is complex, with temporary increases in rate superimposed on a gradually declining trend. Escape of soil air around the infiltration basin, bacterial action, changes in water temperature, changes in soil structure, and many other factors appear to influence these variations.

Movement of moisture within the soil is governed by the moisture potential following the equation

$$q = -K_w \frac{\partial \Lambda}{\partial x} \tag{6-2}$$

where q is the flow per unit time through unit area normal to the direction of flow, x is distance along the line of flow, K_w is conductivity, and Λ is potential. After gravity water has left the soil, the principal component of total potential is the capillary potential. Equation (6-2) states that flow is from a region of high potential to a region of lower potential. Quantitative determination of the conductivity is difficult although it has been shown to increase with moisture content and decrease with pore size. Thus capillary movement decreases as soil dries and is least in fine-grained soils. Fortunately, a qualitative understanding of these phenomena is normally sufficient for engineering hydrology.

Transport of water vapor in the soil is controlled by temperature differences. Vapor movement is from high temperature (high vapor pressure) to low temperature. Vapor transport is an important factor in moisture movement when the moisture content is lowered to the point where capillary moisture is discontinuous. Under this condition, however, moisture-content and temperature gradients are usually so small that the quantity of moisture moved is negligible. When the surface soil is frozen, the vapor-pressure gradient is upward and is accentuated by the lower vapor pressure of ice relative to water at the same temperature. Thus when frozen soil thaws, its moisture content may be greater than at the time of freezing. Conversely, during summer, vapor-pressure gradients would be downward were it not for evaporation and transpiration.

MOISTURE IN THE ZONE OF SATURATION

Within the zone of saturation all pore spaces are filled with water, and the different states of moisture, moisture tension, etc., are of little concern. Interest is centered on the amount of water present, the amount which can be removed, and the movement of this water.

6-6. Aquifers. A geologic formation which contains water and transmits it from one point to another in quantities sufficient to permit economic development is called an *aquifer*. In contrast, an *aquiclude* is a formation which contains water but cannot transmit it rapidly enough to furnish a significant supply to a well or spring. An *aquifuge* has no interconnected openings and cannot hold or transmit water. The ratio of the pore volume to the total volume of the formation is called *porosity*. The *original porosity* of a material is that which existed at the time the material was formed. *Secondary porosity* results from fractures and solution channels.

Secondary porosity cannot be measured without an impossibly large sample. Original porosity is usually measured by oven-drying an undisturbed sample and weighing it. It is then saturated with some liquid and weighed again. Finally, the saturated sample is immersed in the same liquid and the weight of displaced liquid is noted. The weight of liquid required to saturate the sample divided by the weight of liquid displaced is the porosity as a decimal. If the material is fine-grained, the liquid may have to be forced into the sample under pressure to assure complete saturation.

High porosity does not necessarily indicate a productive aquifer, since much of the water may be retained in small pore spaces under capillary tension as the material is dewatered. The *specific yield* of an aquifer is the ratio of the water which will drain freely from the material to the total volume of the formation and must always be less than the porosity. The relation between specific yield and porosity is dependent on the size of the particles in the formation. Specific yield of a fine-grained aquifer will be small whereas coarse-grained material will yield a greater amount of its contained water. Table 6-2 lists approximate average

TABLE 6-2. Approximate Average Porosity, Specific Yield, and Permeability of Various Materials

Material	Porosity, %	Specific yield, %	Permeability $[K_p$, Eq. (6-4)], gpd/sq ft
Clay..........................	45	3	1
Sand..........................	35	25	800
Gravel........................	25	22	5000
Gravel and sand..............	20	16	2000
Sandstone.....................	15	8	700
Dense limestone and shale..........	5	2	1
Quartzite, granite...............	1	0.5	0.1

values of porosity and specific yield for some typical materials. Large variations from these average values must be expected. Note that clay, although having a high porosity, has a very low specific yield. Sand and gravel which make up most of the more productive aquifers in the United States will yield about 80 per cent of their total water content.

6-7. Movement of groundwater. In 1856 Darcy confirmed the applicability of principles of fluid flow in capillary tubes, developed several years earlier by Hagen and Poisseule, to the flow of water in permeable media. *Darcy's law* is

$$v = ks \qquad (6\text{-}3)$$

where v is the velocity of flow, s is the slope of the hydraulic gradient, and k is a coefficient having the units of v (usually ft/day). The discharge q is the product of area A and velocity. The effective area is the gross area times the porosity p of the media. Hence

$$q = 7.48kpAs = K_pAs \qquad (6\text{-}4)$$

where 7.48 converts to gallons when the other terms are in feet. The *coefficient of permeability* K_p is usually expressed in *Meinzer units*, the discharge in gallons per day through an area of one square foot under a gradient of one foot per foot at 60°F (Table 6-2). Values at other temperatures can be found by multiplying by the ratio of the kinematic viscosities, i.e.,

$$K_{pT} = K_p \frac{\nu_{60}}{\nu_T} \tag{6-5}$$

It is convenient to use the *transmissibility* T to represent the flow in gallons per day through a section 1 ft wide and the thickness of the aquifer under a unit head (slope of 1 ft/ft).

$$T = K_p Y \tag{6-6}$$

where Y is the thickness of the aquifer. With this coefficient Eq. (6-4) becomes

$$q = TBs \tag{6-7}$$

where B is the width of the aquifer.

Note that the equations of groundwater flow are analogous to the electrical equation

$$i = \frac{1}{R} E \tag{6-8}$$

where the current i is equivalent to q, the voltage E is comparable to s, and the reciprocal of resistance R is equivalent to permeability. This similarity is sometimes used to advantage in electrical models of groundwater-flow problems.

6-8. Determination of permeability. Laboratory measurements of permeability are made with instruments called *permeameters* (Fig. 6-6). A sample of the material is subjected to water under a known head, and the flow through the sample in a known time is measured. Such tests have limited practical value because of the difficulty of placing samples of unconsolidated materials into the permeameter in their natural state and the uncertainty as to whether a sample is truly representative of the aquifer. Flow in solution cavities or rock fractures and the effect of large boulders in gravel aquifers cannot be duplicated in a permeameter.

The earliest field techniques for determining permeability involved introducing salt into the aquifer at one well and timing its movement to a downstream well.[1] Fluorescein dye,[2] detectable at a concentration of 0.03 ppm by the unaided eye and in concentrations as low as 0.0001 ppm

[1] C. S. Slichter, Field Measurements of Rate of Movement of Underground Water, *U.S. Geol. Survey Water-supply Paper* 140, 1905.

[2] R. B. Dole, Use of Fluorescein in Study of Underground Waters, *U.S. Geol. Survey Water-supply Paper* 160, pp. 73–85, 1906.

under ultraviolet light, has also been used as a tracer.   More recently, radioactive materials have been tested.   Tracer techniques have encountered numerous difficulties.[1]   Chemical reactions between the tracer elements and the formation sometimes occur.   Because of diffusion, tests must be conducted over short distances in order to have detectable concentrations at the downstream well, and even then it is difficult to

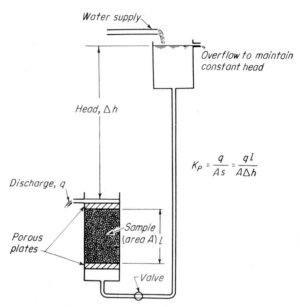

FIG. 6-6. A simple upward-flow permeameter.

determine a representative time of arrival.   Tracers are most useful for determining path of flow as, for example, when it is necessary to locate a source of pollution.

Today permeability is most commonly determined by pumping tests. By using the principles of well hydraulics (Sec. 6-12) it is possible to estimate average permeability of an aquifer for a large distance around the test well.

6-9. Sources of groundwater.   Almost all groundwater is *meteoric water* derived from precipitation.   *Connate water*, present in the rock at its formation and frequently highly saline, is found in some areas. *Juvenile water*, formed chemically within the earth and brought to the surface in intrusive rocks, occurs in small quantities.   Connate and juvenile waters are sometimes important sources of undesirable minerals

[1] W. J. Kaufman and G. T. Orlob, An Evaluation of Ground-water Tracers, *Trans. Am. Geophys. Union*, Vol. 37, pp. 297–306, June, 1956.

in the groundwater.   Groundwater in the San Joaquin Valley, California, contains considerable boron brought to the surface from great depths.

Water from precipitation reaches the groundwater by the process of infiltration and by percolation from streams and lakes.   Direct percolation cannot yield large quantities of groundwater except where the soil is highly permeable or the water table is close to the surface.   Large quantities of direct percolation occur through the permeable basaltic lavas of northern California, eastern Oregon, southern Idaho, and Hawaii, and in the southern Appalachian region where thin soil overlies cavernous limestone.

In the southern part of the Central Valley of California groundwater is hundreds of feet below the surface, and little or no recharge from rain can occur.   In such cases most of the recharge is from stream channels. Streams contributing to the groundwater are called *influent streams.* Such streams frequently go dry during prolonged dry spells when percolation absorbs all the available flow.   Streams are rarely influent throughout their entire length.   Often the channel crosses strata of varying permeability, with most of the percolation loss in short reaches of high permeability.   Considerable percolation often occurs from stream channels crossing coarse gravels in an alluvial fan.   In areas of artesian groundwater, the overlying aquiclude prevents appreciable direct recharge; the recharge area may be far removed from the artesian area.

6-10. Discharge of groundwater.   Without interference by man, a groundwater basin fills with water and discharges its excess by several routes.   Streams intersecting the water table and receiving flow from the groundwater are known as *effluent streams.*   Perennial streams are generally effluent through at least a portion of their length and may flow in impermeable formations elsewhere so that there is little or no loss by seepage.

Where an aquifer intersects the earth's surface, a spring may form. There may be a concentrated flow constituting the headwater source of a small stream or merely effluent seepage which evaporates from the ground surface.   Figure 6-7 illustrates several types of springs.   The flow of most springs is small and usually of little hydrologic significance, although even a small spring may provide water for a single farmstead. Meinzer[1] classified springs from first to eighth magnitude with respect to flow.   First-magnitude springs discharge 100 cfs or more while eighth-magnitude springs have a flow less than 1 pt/min.   According to Meinzer[2]

[1] O. E. Meinzer, Outline of Ground-water Hydrology, *U.S. Geol. Survey Water-supply Paper* 494, 1923.

[2] O. E. Meinzer, Large Springs in the United States, *U.S. Geol. Survey Water-supply Paper* 557, 1927.

there are 65 first-magnitude springs in the United States—38 in volcanic rocks of California, Oregon, and Idaho; 24 in limestone in the Ozarks, the Balcones Fault area of Texas, and in Florida; and 3 sandstone springs in Montana. The Fontaine de Vaucluse in France has a discharge often exceeding 4000 cfs. It is the world's largest spring and is in a limestone formation.

Where the water table is close to the surface, groundwater may be discharged by direct evaporation or by transpiration from the capillary

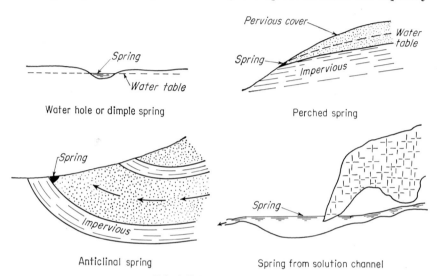

FIG. 6-7. Types of springs.

fringe. Plants deriving their water from groundwater, called *phreatophytes*, often have root systems extending to depths of 40 ft or more. This invisible evapotranspiration loss may be quite large. At a rate of 3 ft/yr the loss would be 1920 acre-ft/sq mi/yr.

The various channels of groundwater discharge may be viewed as spillways of the groundwater reservoir. When groundwater is high, discharge through the natural spillways tends to maintain a balance between inflow and outflow. During dry periods the natural discharge is reduced as groundwater levels fall and outflow may even cease. Artesian aquifers may not reflect this natural balance as rapidly as water-table aquifers, but sustained drought will decrease water levels in the recharge area and decrease discharge from the aquifer.

6-11. Equilibrium hydraulics of wells. Figure 6-8 shows a well in a homogeneous aquifer of infinite extent with initially horizontal water table. For flow to occur to the well there must be a gradient toward the well. The resulting water-table form is called a *cone of depression*. If the decrease in water level at the well (*drawdown*) is small with respect to the total thickness of the aquifer and if the well completely penetrates the aquifer, the streamlines of flow to the well may be assumed to be horizontal.   In this case an approximate formula relating well discharge and aquifer characteristics may be derived.

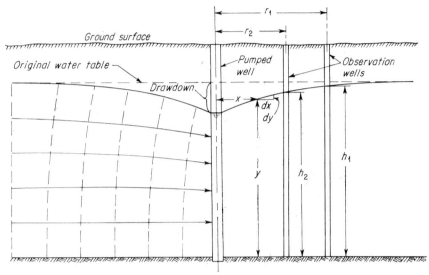

FIG. 6-8. Definition sketch and flow net for equilibrium flow conditions at a well.

Flow toward the well through a cylindrical surface at radius x_1 must equal the discharge of the well, and from Darcy's law [Eq. (6-4)]

$$q = 2\pi xy K_p \frac{dy}{dx} \tag{6-9}$$

where $2\pi xy$ is the area of the cylinder and dy/dx the slope of the water table.   Integrating with respect to x from r_1 to r_2 and y from h_1 to h_2 yields

$$q = \frac{\pi K_p(h_1{}^2 - h_2{}^2)}{\log_e (r_1/r_2)} \tag{6-10}$$

where h is the height of the water table above the base of the aquifer at distance r from the pumped well.

This equation was first proposed by Dupuit in 1863 and subsequently modified by Thiem[1] in 1906.   It suffers from the restrictive assumptions required for its derivation and is now rarely used.   A further serious restriction is the fact that, because of the low velocities of groundwater flow, true equilibrium conditions occur only after a very long period of pumping at constant rate.

[1] G. Thiem, "Hydrologische Methoden," J. M. Gebhardt's Verlag, Leipzig, 1906.

6-12. Nonequilibrium hydraulics of wells. During the initial period of pumping from a new well, much of the discharge is derived from storage in the portion of the aquifer unwatered as the cone of depression develops. Equilibrium analysis indicates a permeability which is too high because only part of the discharge comes from flow through the aquifer to the well. This leads to an overestimate of the potential yield of the well.

In 1935 Theis[1] presented a formula derived from a consideration of the

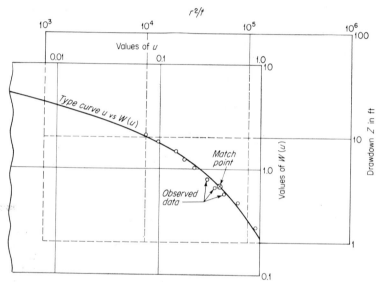

FIG. 6-9. Use of the Theis method for solution of a well problem.   Match point coordinates $u = 0.4$, $W(u) = 0.7$, $Z = 3.4$, $r^2/t = 5.3 \times 10^4$.

heat-flow analogy which accounts for the effect of time and the storage characteristics of the aquifer. His formula is

$$Z_r = \frac{q}{4\pi T} \int_u^\infty \frac{e^{-u}}{u}\, du \tag{6-11}$$

where Z_r is the drawdown in an observation well at distance r from the pumped well, T is transmissibility, and u is given by

$$u = \frac{1.87 r^2 S_c}{Tt} \tag{6-12}$$

In Eq. (6-12) t is the time in days since pumping began, and S_c is the

[1] C. V. Theis, The Relation between the Lowering of the Piezometric Surface and the Rate and Duration of Discharge of a Well Using Ground-water Storage, *Trans. Am. Geophys. Union*, Vol. 16, pp. 519–524, 1935.

storage constant of the aquifer, or the volume of water removed from a column of aquifer 1 ft square when the water table or piezometric surface is lowered 1 ft. For water-table aquifers it is essentially the specific yield. The integral in Eq. (6-11) is commonly written as $W(u)$, called the "well function of u." It may be evaluated from the series

$$W(u) = -0.5772 - \log_e u + u - \frac{u^2}{2 \cdot 2!} + \frac{u^3}{3 \cdot 3!} \cdots \quad (6\text{-}13)$$

Values of $W(u)$ for various values of u are given in Table 6-3 adapted from a more complete table by Wenzel.[1]

Equation (6-11) is usually solved graphically by first plotting a "type curve" of u vs. $W(u)$ on logarithmic paper (Fig. 6-9). From Eq. (6-12),

$$\frac{r^2}{t} = \frac{T}{1.87 S_c} u \qquad (6\text{-}14)$$

TABLE 6-3. Values of $W(u)$ for Various Values of u
(After Wenzel)

u	1.0	2.0	3.0	4.0	5.0	6.0	7.0	8.0	9.0
$\times 1$	0.219	0.049	0.013	0.0038	0.00114	0.00036	0.00012	0.000038	0.000012
$\times 10^{-1}$	1.82	1.22	0.91	0.70	0.56	0.45	0.37	0.31	0.26
$\times 10^{-2}$	4.04	3.35	2.96	2.68	2.48	2.30	2.15	2.03	1.92
$\times 10^{-3}$	6.33	5.64	5.23	4.95	4.73	4.54	4.39	4.26	4.14
$\times 10^{-4}$	8.63	7.94	7.53	7.25	7.02	6.84	6.69	6.55	6.44
$\times 10^{-5}$	10.95	10.24	9.84	9.55	9.33	9.14	8.99	8.86	8.74
$\times 10^{-6}$	13.24	12.55	12.14	11.85	11.63	11.45	11.29	11.16	11.04
$\times 10^{-7}$	15.54	14.85	14.44	14.15	13.93	13.75	13.60	13.46	13.34
$\times 10^{-8}$	17.84	17.15	16.74	16.46	16.23	16.05	15.90	15.76	15.65
$\times 10^{-9}$	20.15	19.45	19.05	18.76	18.54	18.35	18.20	18.07	17.95
$\times 10^{-10}$	22.45	21.76	21.35	21.06	20.84	20.66	20.50	20.37	20.25
$\times 10^{-11}$	24.75	24.06	23.65	23.36	23.14	22.96	22.81	22.67	22.55
$\times 10^{-12}$	27.05	26.36	25.95	25.66	25.44	25.26	25.11	24.97	24.86
$\times 10^{-13}$	29.36	28.66	28.26	27.97	27.75	27.56	27.41	27.28	27.16
$\times 10^{-14}$	31.66	30.97	30.56	30.27	30.05	29.87	29.71	29.58	29.46
$\times 10^{-15}$	33.96	33.27	32.86	32.58	32.35	32.17	32.02	31.88	31.76

If q is constant, Eq. (6-11) indicates that Z_r equals a constant times $W(u)$. Thus a curve of r^2/t vs. Z_r should be similar to the type curve of u vs. $W(u)$. After the field observations are plotted, the two curves are superimposed with their axes parallel and adjusted until some portions of the two curves coincide. The coordinates of a common point taken from the region where the curves coincide are used to solve for T and S_c, using Eqs. (6-11) and (6-14). Values of Z_r and r^2/t may come from one

[1] L. K. Wenzel, Methods for Determining the Permeability of Water-bearing Materials, *U.S. Geol. Survey Water-supply Paper* 887, 1942.

well with various values of t, from several wells with different values of r, or a combination of both.

When u is small, the terms of Eq. (6-13) following $\log_e u$ are small and may be neglected. Equation (6-12) indicates that u will be small when t is large, and in this case a modified solution of the Theis method is possible[1] by writing

$$T = \frac{2.3q}{4\pi\,\Delta Z}\log_{10}\frac{t_2}{t_1} \tag{6-15}$$

where ΔZ is the change in drawdown between times t_1 and t_2. The

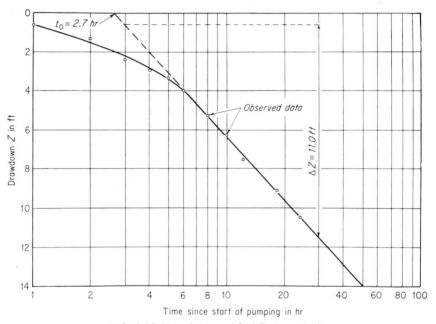

FIG. 6-10. Use of the modified Theis method.

drawdown Z is plotted on an arithmetic scale against time t on a logarithmic scale (Fig. 6-10). If ΔZ is taken as the change in drawdown during one log cycle, $\log_{10}(t_2/t_1) = 1$ and T is easily determined from Eq. (6-15). When $Z = 0$,

$$S_c = \frac{0.3Tt_0}{r^2} \tag{6-16}$$

where t_0 is the intercept (in days) obtained if the straight-line portion of the curve is extended to $Z = 0$.

[1] C. E. Jacob, Drawdown Test to Determine the Effective Radius of Artesian Well, *Trans. ASCE*, Vol. 112, pp. 1047–1070, 1947.

As in the Thiem equation, Theis assumes parallel streamlines, i.e., small drawdown and full penetration of the well. While Theis adjusts for the effect of storage in the aquifer, he does assume instantaneous unwatering of the aquifer material as the water table drops. These conditions are reasonably well satisfied in artesian aquifers. However, the procedure should be used with caution in thin or poorly permeable water-table aquifers.

6-13. Boundary effects. The assumption of a symmetrical cone of depression implies a homogeneous aquifer of great extent. Such an ideal aquifer is rarely encountered, although in many cases the condition is approximated closely enough for reasonable accuracy. When several wells are close together, their cones of depression may overlap or *interfere*

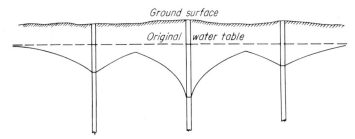

FIG. 6-11. Effect of interference between wells.

and the water table appears as in Fig. 6-11. Where the cones of depression overlap, the drawdown at a point is the sum of the drawdowns caused by the individual wells. The two-dimensional analysis is greatly simplified, but it should be evident that, when wells are located too close together, the flow from the wells is impaired and the drawdowns increased.

Figure 6-12 shows an aquifer with a positive boundary in the form of an intersecting surface stream. The gradient from the stream to the well causes influent seepage from the stream. If the streamflow is more than the seepage, so that flow continues in the stream, the cone of depression of the well must coincide with the water surface in the stream. A rigorous analysis would require that the channel be the full depth of the aquifer to avoid vertical flow components. However, if the well is not too close to the stream no serious error is introduced if this condition is not satisfied. The method of images devised by Lord Kelvin for electrostatic theory is a convenient way to treat boundary problems. An image well is assumed to have all the properties of the real well but to be located on the opposite side of the stream and at the same distance from it as the real well. Since the stream adds water to the aquifer, the image well is assumed to be a recharge well, i.e., one that adds water to the aquifer. Its cone of depression is the same as that of the real well but is inverted (Fig. 6-12).   The resultant cone of depression for the real well is found by subtracting the drawdown caused by the image well from that caused by the real well (assuming no boundary).   The corrected water table between the real well and the stream is, therefore, higher than without the effect of the stream.   At the stream, the two drawdowns are equal and the net drawdown is zero.   Thus the image well satisfies the conditions first set up for this problem.

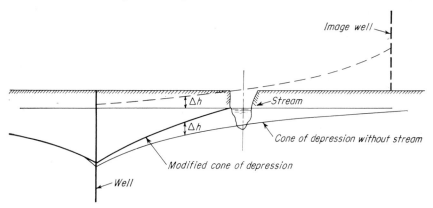

FIG. 6-12. Image well simulating the effect of seepage from a stream on water levels adjacent to a pumped well.

Negative boundaries, i.e., faults and similar structures across which no groundwater is transmitted, can be analyzed in a similar manner.   More complicated boundary problems require judicious selection of multiple image wells.   Most geologic boundaries are neither abrupt nor straight. Unless the aquifer is very small relative to the zone of influence of the well, the assumption of sharp discontinuities is not serious.   Relaxation methods and electrical and membrane analogies have also been used in the solution of boundary problems.

THE POTENTIAL OF A GROUNDWATER RESERVOIR

A basic problem in engineering groundwater studies is the question of the permissible rate of withdrawal from a groundwater basin.   This quantity, commonly called the *safe yield*, is defined by Meinzer[1] as:

. . . the rate at which water can be withdrawn for human use without depleting the supply to such an extent that withdrawal at this rate is no longer economically feasible.

Many other definitions of safe yield have been suggested and alternative terms such as sustained yield, feasible rate of withdrawal, and optimum yield have been proposed.   The concept of safe yield has been misused

[1] O. E. Meinzer, Outline of Ground-wate Hydrology, with Definitions, *U.S. Geol. Survey Water-supply Paper* 494, p. 55, 1923.

and has received considerable criticism. Kazmann[1] has suggested that it be abandoned because of its frequent interpretation as a permanent limitation on the permissible withdrawal. It is important, therefore, that the safe yield be recognized as a quantity determined for a specific set of controlling conditions and subject to change as a result of changing economic or physical conditions. It should also be recognized that the concept can be applied only to a complete groundwater unit. The possible withdrawal from a single well or group of wells in a field is affected by a variety of factors such as size, construction, and spacing of wells as well as by any controls on the flow of groundwater toward the particular field.

6-14. Safe yield. The safe yield of a groundwater basin is governed by many factors, one of the most important being the quantity of water available. This hydrologic limitation is often expressed by the equation

$$G = P - Q_S - E_T + Q_g - \Delta S_g - \Delta S_s \qquad (6\text{-}17)$$

where G is safe yield; P, precipitation on the area tributary to the aquifer; Q_S, surface streamflow from the same area; E_T, evapotranspiration; Q_g, net groundwater inflow to the area; ΔS_g, change in groundwater storage; and ΔS_s, change in surface storage. If the equation is evaluated on a mean annual basis, ΔS_s will usually be zero.

With the exception of precipitation, all terms of Eq. (6-17) are subject to artificial change and G may be computed only by assuming the conditions regarding each item. Artificial-recharge operations can reduce Q_S. Irrigation diversion from influent streams may increase evapotranspiration. Lowering of the water table by pumping may increase groundwater inflow (or reduce groundwater outflow) and may make otherwise effluent streams into influent streams.

The permanent withdrawal of groundwater from storage is called *mining*, the term being used in the same sense as for mineral resources. If the storage in the aquifer is small, excessive mining may be disastrous to any economy dependent on the aquifer for water. On the other hand, many large groundwater basins contain vast reserves of water, and planned withdrawal of this water at a rate that can be sustained over a long period may be a wise use of this resource. The annual increment of mined water, ΔS_g of Eq. (6-17), increases the safe yield. Thus Eq. (6-17) cannot properly be considered an equilibrium equation or solved in terms of mean annual values. It can be solved correctly only on the basis of specified assumptions for a stated period of years.

The factors which control the assumptions on which Eq. (6-17) is solved are primarily economic. The feasibility of artificial recharge or

[1] R. G. Kazmann, "Safe Yield" in Ground-water Development, Reality or Illusion?, *J. Irrigation and Drainage Div. ASCE*, Vol. 82, November, 1956. See also discussion by McGuinness, Ferris, and Kramsky, Vol. 82, May, 1957.

surface diversion is usually determined by economics. If water levels
in the aquifer are lowered, pumping costs are increased. Theoretically,
there is a water-table elevation at which pumping costs equal the value
of the water pumped and below which water levels should not be lowered.
Practically, the increased cost is often passed on to the ultimate consumer
and the minimum level is never attained. Excessive lowering of the
water table may result in contamination of the groundwater by inflow of

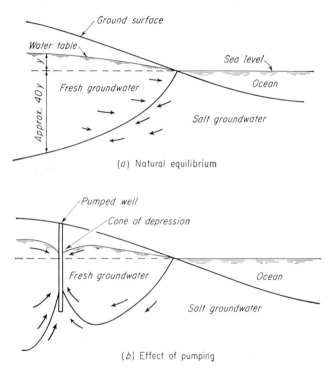

FIG. 6-13. Salt-water–fresh-water relations adjacent to a coastline.

undesirable waters. This hazard is especially prevalent near seacoasts
where sea-water intrusion (Sec. 6-15) may occur. A similar problem may
develop wherever an aquifer is adjacent to a source of saline groundwater.

Transmissibility of an aquifer may also place a limit on safe yield.
Although Eq. (6-17) may indicate a potentially large draft, this can be
realized only if the aquifer is capable of transmitting the water from the
source area to the wells at a rate which is high enough to sustain the draft.
This problem is especially likely to develop in long artesian aquifers.

6-15. Sea-water intrusion. Since sea water (specific gravity about
1.025) is heavier than fresh water, the groundwater under a uniformly
permeable circular island would appear as shown in Fig. 6-13. The lens
of fresh water floating on salt water is known as a *Ghyben-Herzberg lens*,

after the codiscoverers of the principle.   About 40 ft of fresh water is
required below sea level for each foot of fresh water above sea level to
maintain hydrostatic equilibrium.   If a cone of depression is formed
about a well in the fresh water, salt water will rise 40 ft for each foot of
drawdown.   Because of this, horizontal skimming wells with small
drawdown are common in the Pacific islands.   Similar intrusion can
develop along any coastline if the water table or piezometric level drops
sufficiently low.

The best means of controlling salt-water intrusion is to manage the
aquifer so that adequate water-table or piezometric levels are maintained

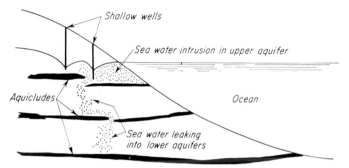

FIG. 6-14. Contamination of deep aquifers from above.

at the coast.   This requires a continuous flow of fresh water into the ocean.
This flow is part of Q_g, the net groundwater exchange of the aquifer.   It
has been suggested that an impermeable barrier might be constructed
across the seaward end of the aquifer to prevent intrusion without loss
of fresh water.   Such a barrier will be a major construction project if
ever attempted.   An alternative barrier is a water mound formed by
injection of fresh water into wells near the coast.   If the injection is
seaward of the salt-water front some sea water will be trapped in the
aquifer, but this will not be serious if sufficient fresh water exists to
dilute it.   Injection of treated sewage effluent has proved effective in
southern California.

Salt water sometimes enters an aquifer through damaged or corroded
well casings.   If a well passes through an aquifer containing undesirable
water or through salt water into an underlying fresh-water aquifer, the salt
water can enter through the leaky casing and drop down to the fresh water.[1]
Jacob[2] has pointed out that several aquifers may exist at a coastline
(Fig. 6-14).   Development of the upper aquifer first permits salt-water
intrusion, and leakage through the underlying aquiclude results in

[1] R. R. Bennett, Ground-water Situation at Baltimore Badly Confused, *Water
Works Eng.*, Vol. 98, pp. 891, 904–907, August, 1945.

[2] C. E. Jacob, Full Utilization of Groundwater Reservoirs, *Trans. Am. Geophys.
Union*, Vol. 38, p. 417, June, 1957.

contamination of the deeper aquifers. In such a case withdrawal should begin from the lower aquifers.

6-16. Artificial recharge. The safe yield of an aquifer can be increased if additional water can be introduced into it. In some cases[1] floodwaters are retained in surface reservoirs until they can be released at rates at or below the percolation capacity of the stream channels. In other instances floodwaters are diverted to spreading grounds where they are ponded until they infiltrate. Infiltration rates have generally been less than 5 ft/day, and considerable effort[2] has been exerted to find ways to increase infiltration rates by furrowing the spreading area, use of chemicals or organic additives, etc. Suter[3] has reported rates as high as 75 ft/day in a recharge pit near Peoria, Illinois. The problems of infiltration are most complex, and the development of a spreading program should be preceded by careful site surveys and tests.

Where recharge by spreading is not feasible because of low permeability or lack of adequate area for spreading grounds, recharge by wells may be attempted. The hydraulics of the operation is similar to that of a discharge well except that a groundwater mound builds up around the well and the rate of recharge is dependent on the rate at which this water moves away from the well. Recharge wells are usually successful when the water is reasonably clean, but suspended solids or bacterial slimes may clog the well screen or the adjacent aquifer. Storm water should be settled to remove suspended matter before recharging. The capacity of a single recharge well is generally small and the cost relatively high compared with spreading unless producing wells are used for recharge on a seasonal basis. This may be prohibited by health authorities unless the water is chlorinated, because pollutants may be injected directly into the aquifer.

To offset the large withdrawal of water for air conditioning on Long Island, groundwater users are required to return an equal amount of water to the aquifer. This is usually done through recharge wells. An interesting result has been a steady increase in groundwater temperature[4] resulting from the recharge of warmer water than that which was withdrawn.

[1] H. Conkling, Utilization of Ground-water Storage in Stream-system Development, *Trans. ASCE*, Vol. 111, pp. 275–354, 1946.
F. B. Laverty, Correlating Flood Control and Water Supply, *Trans. ASCE*, Vol. 111, pp. 1127–1174, 1946.
[2] L. Schiff, Water Spreading for Storage Underground, *Agr. Eng.*, Vol. 55, pp. 794–800, 1954.
[3] M. Suter, The Peoria Recharge Pit: Its Development and Results, *J. Irrigation and Drainage Div. ASCE*, Vol. 82, November, 1956.
[4] M. L. Brashears, Ground-water Temperature on Long Island, N. Y., as Affected by Recharge of Warm Water, *Econ. Geol.*, Vol. 36, pp. 811–828, December, 1941.

A well constructed close to a stream increases the percolation to ground-water and is a form of artificial recharge. Because the water is filtered as it moves through the ground, the well becomes a natural filter plant, allowing development of pure water from a polluted stream at minimum expense for treatment. The process, known as *induced percolation*,[1] has been extensively employed along the Ohio River. Horizontal *infiltration galleries* may be constructed adjacent to a stream for the same purpose.

6-17. Artesian aquifers. The evaluation of the potential of an artesian aquifer involves some special factors. The confining strata are commonly assumed to be watertight. If the permeability of the aquiclude is one Meinzer unit and the hydraulic gradient is unity, the daily seepage would amount to about 28 mgd (80 acre-ft)/sq mi. A quantity of this magnitude would be quite significant in the groundwater exchange of an aquifer. Hantush[2] has demonstrated a procedure which accounts for such leakage in the analysis of pumping tests on artesian aquifers.

Artesian aquifers demonstrate considerable compressibility. This is evident from numerous cases where fluctuations in tide level, barometric pressure, or even the superimposed load of trains are reflected in fluctuations of water level in wells penetrating the aquifer. If the pressure in an artesian aquifer is relieved locally by removal of water, compression of the aquifer may result with subsidence of the ground above it. Such subsidence has been observed[3] in areas subject to heavy withdrawal of groundwater, with ground-surface elevations declining more than 10 ft. The observations are not completely explained but it seems likely that much of the compression is in the clays of the overlying aquicludes. Aside from the disrupting effects of the surface subsidence, the phenom-enon suggests that pumping tests on such aquifers may be misleading because of the flow derived from storage as a result of the compression. Although the small fluctuations appear to exhibit elastic behavior, there is no evidence that the ground levels in regions of pronounced subsidence will be recovered if the aquifers are repressurized.

6-18. Time effects in groundwater. Flow rates in the groundwater are normally extremely slow, and considerable time may be involved in groundwater phenomena. A critical lowering of the water table adjacent to a coast may not bring immediate salt-water intrusion because of the

---

[1] R. G. Kazmann, Induced Infiltration Supplies Most Productive Well Field, *Civil Eng.*, Vol. 16, pp. 544–546, December, 1946.

[2] M. S. Hantush, Analysis of Data from Pumping Tests in Leaky Aquifers, *Trans. Am. Geophys. Union*, Vol. 37, pp. 702–714, December, 1956.

[3] J. F. Poland and G. H. Davis, Subsidence of the Land Surface in the Tulare-Wasco (Delano) and Los Banos-Kettleman City Area, San Joaquin Valley, California, *Trans. Am. Geophys. Union*, Vol. 37, pp. 287–296, June, 1956.

time required for the salt water to move inland. Werner[1] suggests that several hundred years might be required for a sudden increase in water level in the recharge area of an extensive artesian aquifer to be transmitted through the aquifer. Jacob[2] found that water levels on Long Island were related to an effective precipitation which was the sum of the rainfalls for the previous 25 yr, each weighted by a factor which decreased with time. McDonald and Langbein[3] found long-term fluctuations in streamflow in the Columbia Basin which they believe are related to groundwater fluctuations. Thus in interpreting groundwater data it is important to give full weight to the influence of time. Observed variations in groundwater levels must be correctly related to causal factors or serious misconceptions may result.

BIBLIOGRAPHY

Ferris, J. G.: Ground Water, Chap. VII, in C. O. Wisler and E. F. Brater, "Hydrology," pp. 198–272, Wiley, New York, 1949.

Hubbert, M. K.: The Theory of Ground-water Motion, *J. Geol.*, Vol. 48, pp. 785–944, 1940.

Jacob, C. E.: Flow of Ground Water, Chap. V, in H. Rouse (ed.), "Engineering Hydraulics," pp. 321–386, Wiley, New York, 1950.

Meinzer, O. E.: Ground Water, Chap. X, in "Hydrology," Vol. IX, Physics of the Earth Series, pp. 385–476, McGraw-Hill, New York, 1942 (reprinted Dover Publications, New York, 1949).

Muskat, M.: "The Flow of Homogeneous Fluids through Porous Media," Edwards, Ann Arbor, Mich., 1946.

Thomas, H. E.: "The Conservation of Ground Water," McGraw-Hill, New York, 1951.

Tolman, C. F.: "Ground Water," McGraw-Hill, New York, 1937.

DATA SOURCES

The primary source of groundwater data is the bulletins Water Levels and Artesian Pressures in the United States which are published annually as *Water-supply Papers* of the U.S. Geological Survey. Many states also publish groundwater data.

PROBLEMS

6-1. An undisturbed rock sample has an oven-dry weight of 652.47 g. After saturation with kerosene its weight is 731.51 g. It is then immersed in kerosene and displaces 300.66 g. What is the porosity of the sample?

6-2. At Station A the water-table elevation is 642 ft above sea level and at B the elevation is 629 ft. The stations are 1100 ft apart. The aquifer has a permeability

[1] P. W. Werner, Notes on Flow-time Effects in the Great Artesian Aquifers of the Earth, *Trans. Am. Geophys. Union*, Vol. 27, pp. 687–708, October, 1946.

[2] C. E. Jacob, Correlation of Ground-water Levels and Precipitation on Long Island, New York, *Trans. Am. Geophys. Union*, Vol. 24, Part 2, pp. 564–580, 1943, and Vol. 25, Part 6, pp. 928–939, 1944.

[3] C. C. McDonald and W. B. Langbein, Trends in Runoff in the Pacific Northwest, *Trans. Am. Geophys. Union*, Vol. 29, pp. 387–397, June, 1948.

of 300 Meinzer units and a porosity of 14 per cent. What is the actual velocity of flow in the aquifer?

6-3. If the root zone in clay-loam soil is 3 ft thick, what quantity of available moisture (in inches depth) should it hold? Use Table 6-1.

6-4. A soil sample has a coefficient of permeability of 250 Meinzer units. What would be its permeability at 50°F?

6-5. A 12-in.-diameter well penetrates 80 ft below the static water table. After 24 hr of pumping at 1100 gpm the water level in a test well at 320 ft is lowered 1.77 ft and in a well 110 ft away the drawdown is 3.65 ft. What is the transmissibility of the aquifer? Use Eq. (6-10).

6-6. The time-drawdown data for an observation well 296 ft from a pumped well (500 gpm) are tabulated below. Find the transmissibility and storage constant of the aquifer. Use the Theis method.

Time, hr	Drawdown, ft	Time, hr	Drawdown, ft
1.9	0.28	9.8	1.09
2.1	0.30	12.2	1.25
2.4	0.37	14.7	1.40
2.9	0.42	16.3	1.50
3.7	0.50	18.4	1.60
4.9	0.61	21.0	1.70
7.3	0.82	24.4	1.80

6-7. Tabulated below are the time-drawdown data for an observation well 150 ft from a well pumped at 350 gpm. Find the transmissibility and storage constant by the modified Theis method.

Time, hr....................	1.8	2.7	5.4	9.0	18.0	54.0
Drawdown, ft................	1.8	2.4	3.6	4.3	5.8	8.1

6-8. A well 250 ft deep is planned in an aquifer having a transmissibility of 10,000 gpd per foot width and a storage coefficient of 0.010. The well is expected to yield 500 gpm and will be 12 in. in diameter. If the static water level is 50 ft below the ground surface, estimate the pumping lift at the end of 1 yr and 3 yr of operation.

6-9. After pumping a new 12-in. well for 24 hr at 150 gpm, the drawdowns in a number of nearby observation wells are as given below. Find the storage coefficient and transmissibility of the aquifer.

Well number..........	1	2	3	4	5	6	7
Distance, ft...........	100	141	190	200	283	347	490
Drawdown, ft.........	10.5	7.5	6.2	4.0	2.4	1.4	0.6

6-10. An 18-in. well is in an aquifer with a transmissibility of 8000 gpd per foot width and a storage coefficient of 0.07. What pumping rate can be adopted so that the maximum drawdown after 2 yr will not exceed 20 ft?

6-11. A 24-in. well is in an aquifer with a transmissibility of 10,000 gpd per foot width and a storage coefficient of 0.05. Draw the profile of the cone of depression after 1 yr of pumping at 500 gpm. If a fault is located 1000 ft from this well, what would be the profile of the cone of depression?

6-12. The well of Prob. 6-11 is 800 ft from a stream which flows all year. How much is the drawdown midway between the well and the stream decreased because of this seepage?

6-13. Using data from the *Water-supply Papers* or other source, find out what you can about the trend of groundwater levels in your area. What explanation can you see for the observed trends? What is the source of the groundwater? Is an overdraft of the available supply indicated? Are there any possible ways of improving the yield?

6-14. For a basin selected by your instructor, make an estimate of the safe yield, assuming no change in present conditions.

7

CHARACTERISTICS OF THE HYDROGRAPH

The water which constitutes streamflow may reach the stream channel by any of several paths from the point where it first reaches the earth as precipitation. Some water flows over the soil surface as *surface runoff* and reaches the stream soon after its occurrence as rainfall. Other water infiltrates through the soil surface and flows beneath the surface to the stream. This water moves more slowly than the surface runoff and contributes to the sustained flow of the stream during periods of dry weather. In hydrologic studies involving rate of flow in streams it is usually necessary to distinguish between these components of total flow. The first step in such studies is often the division of the observed hydrographs of streamflow into components, preliminary to the analysis of the relation between rainfall and runoff (Chap. 8), the determination of the characteristic shape of hydrographs for a basin (Chap. 9), or a study of drought conditions (Sec. 11-10).

7-1. The components of runoff. The actual route followed by a specific water particle from the time it reaches the ground until it enters a stream channel is devious. It is convenient to visualize three main routes of travel: overland flow, interflow, and groundwater flow.

Overland flow or *surface runoff* is that water which travels over the ground surface to a channel. The word "channel" as used here refers to any of the depressions which may carry small rivulets of water in turbulent flow during and for a short while after a rain. Such channels are numerous, and the distance water must travel as overland flow is relatively short, rarely more than 200 ft and commonly much less. Therefore overland flow soon reaches a channel and, if it occurs in sufficient quantity, is an important element in the formation of flood peaks. The amount of surface runoff may, however, be quite small, for surface flow over a permeable soil surface can occur only when the rainfall rate exceeds the infiltration capacity (Chap. 8). In many small and moderate storms, surface runoff may occur only from impermeable surfaces within the basin or from precipitation which falls directly on the water surface of the basin. Except in urban areas, the total of impermeable area and water surface is usually a small part of the basin area. Hence, surface runoff is an important factor in streamflow only as the result of heavy or high-intensity rains.

Some of the water which infiltrates the soil surface may move laterally through the upper soil layers until it enters a stream channel. This water, called *interflow* or *subsurface flow*, moves more slowly than the surface runoff and reaches the streams somewhat later. The proportion of the total runoff which occurs as interflow is dependent on the geology of the basin. A thin soil cover overlying rock or a hardpan or plowbed a short distance below the soil surface favors substantial quantities of interflow, whereas uniformly permeable soil encourages downward percolation to groundwater. Although traveling more slowly than overland flow, interflow may be much larger in quantity, especially in storms of moderate intensity, and hence may be the principal source of water for the smaller rises of streamflow. There is evidence that interflow in the Coweeta Forest, North Carolina, may account for 85 per cent of the total runoff.[1]

Some precipitation may percolate downward until it reaches the water table (Chap. 6). This groundwater accretion may eventually discharge into the streams as *groundwater flow*, also called *base flow* and *dry-weather flow*, if the water table intersects the stream channels of the basin. In this event the streams are said to be *effluent*. The groundwater contribution to streamflow cannot fluctuate rapidly because of the devious path followed and the lower velocity. In some regions more than 2 yr is required[2] for the effect of a given accretion to groundwater to be discharged into the streams.

Basins having permeable surface soils and large, effluent groundwater bodies show sustained high flow throughout the year, with a relatively small ratio between flood flow and mean flow. Basins with surface soils of low permeability or influent groundwater bodies will have higher ratios of peak to average flows and very low or zero flows between floods. Hydrographs for each type of basin are shown in Fig. 7-1. Hat Creek drains volcanic terrain with a large groundwater contribution, while the Santa Ynez River is influent throughout most of its length.

The distinctions which have been drawn between the three components of flow are arbitrary and, to some degree, artificial. Water may start out as surface runoff, infiltrate from the sheet of overland flow, and complete its trip to the stream as interflow. On the other hand, interflow

---

[1] R. A. Hertzler, Engineering Aspects of the Influence of Forests on Mountain Streams, *Civil Eng.*, Vol. 9, pp. 487–489, 1939.

[2] C. C. McDonald and W. B. Langbein, Trends in Runoff in the Pacific Northwest, *Trans. Am. Geophys. Union*, Vol. 29, pp. 387–397, June, 1948.

may come to the surface where a relatively impervious stratum intersects a hillside and finish its journey to the stream as overland flow. The description of interflow is similar in many ways to what was called "perched groundwater" in Chap. 6. Certainly what is described as interflow varies from groundwater only in speed of travel. In limestone terrain, groundwater frequently moves at relatively high velocities as turbulent flow through solution channels and fractures in the limestone.

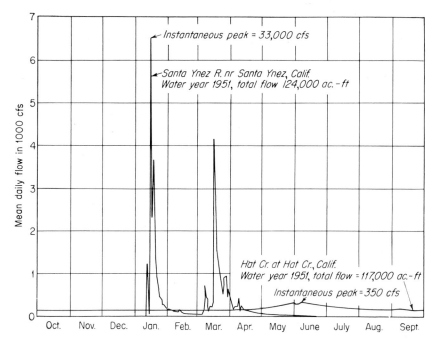

FIG. 7-1. Comparison of hydrographs from two streams of differing geologic characteristics

Streams in limestone country often exhibit a high ratio of flood-peak flows to average flow, a condition characteristic of streams having small groundwater contributions. In such terrain, groundwater flow actually has some of the characteristics ascribed to interflow. In practice, therefore, it is customary to consider the total flow to be divided into only two parts: *storm*, or *direct, runoff* and *base flow*. The distinction is actually on the basis of time of arrival in the stream rather than on the path followed. Direct runoff is presumed to consist of overland flow and a substantial portion of the interflow, whereas base flow is considered to be largely groundwater.

7-2. Streamflow recessions. A typical hydrograph resulting from an isolated period of rainfall is shown in Fig. 7-2. The hydrograph consists of a *rising limb, crest segment,* and *falling limb* or *recession.* The shape of the rising limb is influenced mainly by the character of the storm which caused the rise.   Storm factors are discussed in detail in Chap. 9. The point of inflection on the falling side of the hydrograph is commonly assumed to mark the time at which surface inflow to the channel system ceases.   Thereafter, the recession curve represents withdrawal of water from storage within the basin.   The shape of the recession is largely independent of the characteristics of the storm causing the rise.   On large basins subject to runoff-producing rainfall over only a part of the

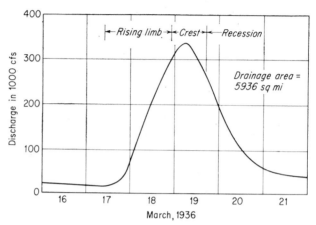

FIG. 7-2. A typical hydrograph showing the nomenclature for its components.   (Potomac River at Shepherdstown, West Virginia.)

basin, the recession may vary from storm to storm, depending on the particular area of runoff generation.   If rainfall occurs while the recession from a previous storm is in progress, the recession will naturally be distorted.   However, the recession curve for a basin is a useful tool in hydrology.

The recession curve, sometimes called a *depletion curve* because it represents depletion from storage, is described by a characteristic depletion equation

$$q_1 = q_0 K_r \qquad (7\text{-}1)$$

where q_0 is the flow at any time, q_1 is the flow one time unit later, and K_r is a recession constant which is less than unity.   Equation (7-1) can be written in the more general form as

$$q_t = q_0 K_r{}^t \qquad (7\text{-}2)$$

where q_t is the flow t time units after q_0.   The time unit is frequently taken as 24 hr although on small basins a shorter unit may be necessary. The numerical value of K_r depends on the time unit selected.   Integrating

Eq. (7-2) and remembering that the volume of water discharged during time dt is $q\,dt$ and is equal to the decrease in storage $-dS$ during the same interval, the storage S_t remaining in the basin at time t is

$$S_t = -\frac{q_t}{\log_e K_r} \tag{7-3}$$

Equation (7-2) will plot as a straight line on semilogarithmic paper with q on the logarithmic scale. If the recession of a stream rise is

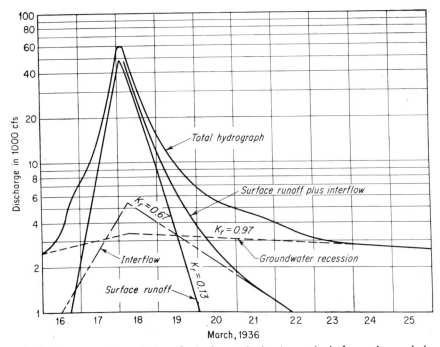

FIG. 7-3. Semilogarithmic plotting of a hydrograph, showing method of recession analysis.

plotted on semilogarithmic paper (Fig. 7-3) the result is usually not a straight line but a curve with gradually decreasing slope (i.e., increasing values of K_r). The reason for this is that the water is coming from three different types of storage—stream channels, surface soil, and the groundwater—each having different lag characteristics. Barnes[1] suggests that the recession can be approximated by three straight lines on a semilogarithmic plot. Often, however, the transition from one line to the next is so gradual that it is difficult to select the points of change in slope. The slope of the last portion of the recession should represent the char-

[1] B. S. Barnes, Discussion of Analysis of Runoff Characteristics, *Trans. ASCE*, Vol. 105, p. 106, 1940.

acteristic K_r for groundwater since, presumably, both interflow and surface runoff have ceased. By projecting this slope backward in time (Fig. 7-3) and replotting the difference between the projected line and the total hydrograph, a recession which for a time consists largely of interflow is obtained. With the slope applicable to interflow thus determined, the process can be repeated to establish the recession characteristics of surface runoff.

The technique described above represents a degree of refinement rarely necessary for engineering problems. The base-flow recession curve is most frequently used, and one method for developing such a curve is to

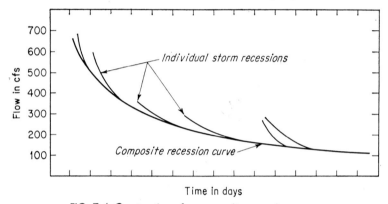

Time in days

FIG. 7-4. Construction of a composite recession curve.

piece together sections of recession from various storms until a composite curve (Fig. 7-4) is obtained which covers the necessary range of flow rates. A template conforming to this curve is often convenient.

A recession curve may also be developed[1] by plotting values of q_0 against q_t some fixed time t later (Fig. 7-5). If Eq. (7-1) were strictly correct, the plotted data would indicate a straight line. Normally, however, a curve indicating a gradual change in the value of K_r results. This curve becomes asymptotic to a 45° line as q approaches zero.

The methods illustrated in Figs. 7-4 and 7-5 may be used to construct recessions for base flow, direct runoff, or total flow. For a base-flow recession, data should be selected from periods several days after the peak of a flood so that it is reasonably certain that no direct runoff is included. After the base-flow recession has been established, it may be projected back under the hydrograph immediately following a flood peak, and the difference between the projected base flow and the total hydrograph used to develop a direct-runoff recession curve. When the method of Fig. 7-5 is used, it is customary to draw the base-flow curve

[1] W. B. Langbein, Some Channel Storage and Unit Hydrograph Studies, *Trans. Am. Geophys. Union*, Vol. 21, Part 2, pp. 620–627, 1940.

to envelop the plotted data on the right.   The argument for this is that such a curve represents the slowest recession (high K_r) and that points deviating to the left may include direct runoff.   By a similar argument it is common to envelop the data for the direct-runoff recession on the left.

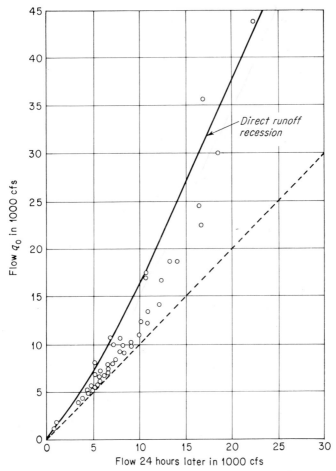

FIG. 7-5. Recession curves in the form q_0 vs. q_1 for the American River at Fair Oaks, California.

A total-flow recession will show more variation from storm to storm because of the varying quantities of direct and base flow.   Total-flow recessions can be derived by either of the methods just described.   At high flows when the relative base-flow contribution is small, the total-flow recession approaches the direct-runoff recession.

7-3. Hydrograph separation. Because of the differing characteristics of direct and groundwater runoff, it is common practice to divide the hydrograph into two components as a basis for subsequent analysis. This process is known as *hydrograph separation* or *hydrograph analysis*. Since there is no real basis for distinguishing between the direct and groundwater flow in the stream at any instant and since the definitions

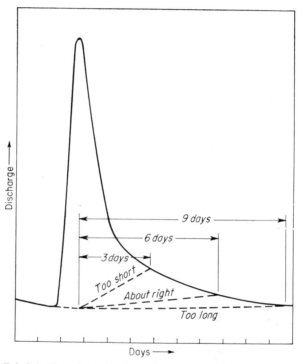

FIG. 7-6. Selection of the time base for the surface-runoff hydrograph.

of these two components are relatively arbitrary, the method of separation is usually equally arbitrary.

Practically, the method of separation should be such that the time base of direct runoff remains relatively constant from storm to storm. This is usually provided by terminating the direct runoff at a fixed time after the peak of the hydrograph. As a rule of thumb, the time in days N may be approximated by

$$N = A^{0.2} \qquad (7\text{-}4)$$

where A is the drainage area in square miles. However, N is probably better determined by inspection of a number of hydrographs, keeping in mind that the total time base should not be excessively long and the rise of the groundwater should not be too great.   Figure 7-6 illustrates some reasonable and unreasonable assumptions regarding N.

The most widely used separation procedure consists of extending the recession existing prior to the storm to a point under the peak of the hydrograph (AB, Fig. 7-7).   From this point a straight line is drawn to the hydrograph at a point N days after the peak.   The reasoning behind this procedure is that, as the stream rises, there is flow from the stream

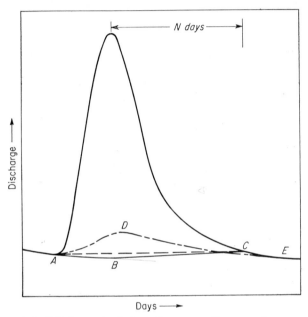

FIG. 7-7. Some simple base-flow separation procedures.

into the banks (Fig. 7-8).   Hence, the base flow should decrease until stages in the stream begin to drop and the bank storage returns to the channel.   While there is some support for this reasoning, there is no justification for assuming that the decrease in base flow conforms to the usual recession.   Actually, if the increment of bank storage is greater than the inflow from the groundwater, the base flow is effectively negative. Hence, this procedure is quite arbitrary and no better than line AC (Fig. 7-7), which is simply a straight line from the point of rise to the hydrograph N days after the peak.   The difference in volume of base flow by these two methods is quite small and probably unimportant as long as one method is used consistently.

A third method of separation is illustrated by line ADE (Fig. 7-7). This line is constructed by projecting the recession of the groundwater after the storm back under the hydrograph to a point under the inflection

point of the falling limb.   An arbitrary rising limb is sketched from the
point of rise of the hydrograph to connect with the projected base-flow
recession.   This type of separation may have some advantages where
groundwater is relatively large in quantity and reaches the stream fairly
rapidly, as in limestone terrain.

7-4. Analysis of complex hydrographs.   The discussion of hydrograph separation in Sec. 7-3 assumed an isolated streamflow event without
subsequent rainfall until after the direct runoff had left the basin.   This
type of event is easier to analyze than the complex hydrographs resulting

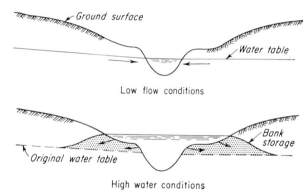

Low flow conditions

High water conditions

FIG. 7-8. Bank-storage variations during a flood.

from two or more closely spaced bursts of rainfall (Fig. 7-9).   Often,
however, analysis of the more complex cases cannot be avoided.   In
these cases it is necessary to separate the runoff caused by the individual
bursts of rainfall in addition to separating direct runoff from base flow.

If a simple base-flow separation such as line ABC or AC of Fig. 7-7 is
to be used, the division between bursts of rain is usually accomplished
by projecting the small segment of recession between peaks, using a
total-flow recession curve for the basin (line AB, Fig. 7-9).   The base-
flow separation is then completed by drawing CDB and EF.   The
direct runoff for the two periods of rain is given by the shaded areas
marked I and II.   Note that a separation of this type is impracticable
unless there are two clearly defined peaks with a short segment of recession following the first peak.

A separation of the type illustrated by ADE in Fig. 7-7 can also be used
for complex storms.[1]   The base-flow recession DE of the second rise (Fig.
7-10) is constructed by projecting the base-flow recession backward.
The base flow during the period of recession after the first peak can be

[1] R. K. Linsley and W. C. Ackermann, A Method of Predicting the Runoff from
Rainfall, *Trans. ASCE*, Vol. 107, pp. 825–835, 1942.

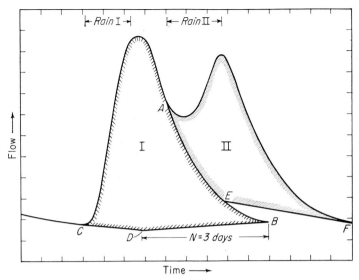

FIG. 7-9. Separation of complex hydrographs, using recession curves.

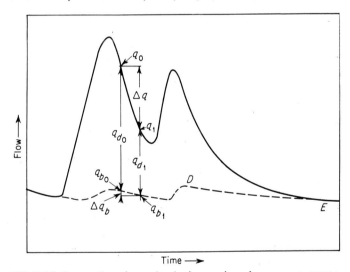

FIG. 7-10. Separation of complex hydrographs, using q_0 vs. q_1 curves.

determined by noting that

$$\Delta q = \Delta q_d + \Delta q_b \tag{7-5}$$

where Δq_d is the change in direct runoff in a unit of time, Δq_b is the change in base flow during the same time unit, and Δq is the change in total flow during the period. If Eq. (7-1) applies to both direct and base flow, then

$$q_1 = K_b q_{b_0} + K_d q_{d_0} \qquad (7\text{-}6)$$

where K_d and K_b are the direct- and base-flow recession coefficients and q_1 is the total flow at the end of the period. Remembering that $q_{d_0} = q_0 - q_{b_0}$, then

$$q_{b_0} = \frac{K_d q_0 - q_1}{K_d - K_b} \qquad (7\text{-}7)$$

Even though the recession constants cannot be determined, a graphical relation between q_0, q_1, and q_{b_0} can be derived by trial, using the recession

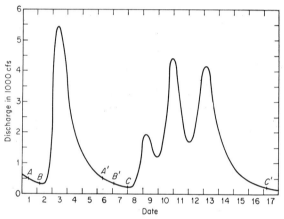

FIG. 7-11. Determination of total-runoff volume.

curves. To do this, a value of q_{b_0} is estimated and the corresponding value of Δq_b determined from the recession. Since Δq is known, Δq_d can be computed from Eq. (7-5). This value of Δq_d should conform to that indicated by the direct-runoff recession curve for a value of $q_{d_0} = q_0 - q_{b_0}$. If it does not, a second trial is indicated. A relation between Δq_d and q_{d_0} is helpful and can easily be constructed from the recession curve.

After the position of the groundwater recession has been established, the balance of the groundwater hydrograph is drawn to conform to these values. The direct runoff for the two storms can then be separated by extending the total recession between the two until it intersects the corresponding base-flow curve (extended).

7-5. Determination of total runoff. In some types of analysis (see Sec. 5-10) there is need to determine the total streamflow (direct runoff plus groundwater) resulting from a particular storm or group of storms. This can be done by computing the total volume of flow occurring during a period beginning and ending with the same discharge and encompassing the rise under consideration, provided that groundwater-recession conditions prevail at both times. In Fig. 7-11, the area under the hydrograph between times A and A', or B and B', represents the total runoff from the storm causing the first rise. Similarly, that between times C and C' constitutes the total runoff produced by the last three storms. If groundwater-recession conditions do not prevail at the beginning and end of the rise under study, the recession must be extended as described earlier. Proof of the foregoing is found in the fact that, from continuity, total runoff for the period AA' must equal the observed streamflow plus any change in storage between A and A'. But from Eq. (7-3) the storage is a function of the flow, and since the flows at A and A' are equal, the change in storage must be zero. Hence the observed streamflow must equal total runoff.

BIBLIOGRAPHY

Linsley, R. K., M. A. Kohler, and J. L. H. Paulhus: "Applied Hydrology," Chap. 15, pp. 387–444, McGraw-Hill, New York, 1949.

PROBLEMS

7-1. Using the sample page from a *Water-supply Paper* which appears as Fig. 4-18, construct direct- and base-flow recession curves of the type illustrated by Fig. 7-5. Are the values of K_r constant for these curves? What are the average values of K_r for direct and base flow? Using an average value of K_r, find the volume of groundwater storage when the flow is 1100 cfs.

7-2. Tabulated below are ordinates at 24-hr intervals for a hydrograph. Assuming these ordinates are for the basin analyzed in Prob. 7-1, separate the base flow from the direct runoff by each of the three methods illustrated in Fig. 7-7. Compute the volume of direct runoff in each case.

Time, days	Flow, cfs	Time, days	Flow, cfs
1	2,340	8	3,230
2	34,300	9	2,760
3	25,000	10	2,390
4	14,000	11	2,060
5	8,960	12	1,770
6	5,740	13	1,520
7	4,300	14	1,320

7-3. Plot the data of Prob. 7-2 on semilogarithmic paper and determine recession constants for surface runoff, interflow, and groundwater flow. What volume of each of the three components is present?

8

RUNOFF RELATIONS

Precipitation is the primary factor determining streamflow. The sequence of events is such that runoff lags behind the precipitation producing it, the amount of the lag depending upon the characteristics of the drainage area. Reliable rainfall-runoff relations and techniques for distributing runoff through time are the basis of efficient design and operation of hydraulic projects. They are also important tools in river forecasting.

THE PHENOMENA OF RUNOFF

8-1. Surface retention. Much of the rain falling during the first part of a storm is stored on the vegetal cover as *interception* and in surface puddles as *depression storage*. As rain continues, the soil surface becomes covered with a film of water, known as *surface detention*, and flow begins downslope toward an established surface channel. En route to a channel, the water is designated as *overland flow* and, upon entering a channel, it becomes *surface runoff*. That part of storm precipitation which does not appear either as infiltration or as surface runoff during or immediately following the storm is *surface retention*. In other words, surface retention includes interception, depression storage, and evaporation during the storm but does not include that water which is temporarily stored en route to the streams.

Although the effect of vegetal cover is unimportant in major floods, interception by some types of cover may be a considerable portion of the annual rainfall. Interception storage capacity is usually satisfied early in a storm so that a large percentage of the rain in the numerous small storms is intercepted. After the vegetation is saturated, interception would cease were it not for the fact that appreciable water may evaporate from the enormous wetted surface of the foliage. Once interception storage is filled, the amount of water reaching the soil surface is equal to the rainfall less evaporation from the vegetation. Interception storage capacity is reduced as wind speed increases, but the rate of evaporation is increased. Apparently, high wind speeds tend to augment total interception during a long storm and to decrease it for a short storm.

Extensive experimental interception data have been accumulated by numerous investigators,[1] but evaluation and application of the data to specific problems are made difficult because of varied experimental techniques employed. Data for forest cover, relatively more plentiful than those for crops and other low-level vegetation, are usually obtained by placing several rain gages on the ground under the canopy and comparing the average of their catch with that in the open. Sometimes the gages (*interceptometers*) are placed at random in an attempt to measure average interception for an area. In other cases, the interceptometers are placed at carefully selected points under the tree crown to measure interception on its projected area. In either case, application of the data requires detailed knowledge of the cover density over the area of interest. Most data for forests have been collected by placing interceptometers free of underbrush, grass, etc., and little is known of total interception as required in most hydrologic problems.

Trimble and Weitzman[2] found that mixed hardwood about 50 yr old and typical of considerable area in the southern Appalachian Mountains intercepts about 20 per cent of the rainfall both in summer and winter. No measurements were made of flow down the tree trunks, but it is likely that net interception is nearer 18 per cent for storms with rainfall in the order of 0.5 in. Qualitatively, it can be said that annual interception by a well-developed forest canopy is about 10 to 20 per cent of the rainfall and that the storage capacity of the canopy ranges from 0.03 to 0.06 in.

Horton[3] derived a series of empirical formulas for estimating interception (per storm) by various types of vegetal cover. Applying these formulas to 1-in. storms and assuming normal cover density give the following values of interception:

[1] R. K. Linsley, M. A. Kohler, and J. L. H. Paulhus, "Applied Hydrology," pp. 263–268, McGraw-Hill, New York, 1949.

P. B. Rowe and T. M. Hendrix, Interception of Rain and Snow by Second-growth Ponderosa Pine, *Trans. Am. Geophys. Union*, Vol. 32, pp. 903–908, December, 1951.

W. M. Johnson, The Interception of Rain and Snow by a Forest of Young Ponderosa Pine, *Trans. Am. Geophys. Union*, Vol. 23, Part 2, pp. 566–570, 1942.

J. Kittredge, H. J. Loughead, and A. Mazurak, Interception and Stem Flow in a Pine Plantation, *J. Forestry*, Vol. 39, pp. 505–522, June, 1941.

N. L. Stoltenberg and C. W. Lauritzen, Interception Storage of Rainfall by Corn Plants, *Trans. Am. Geophys. Union*, Vol. 31, pp. 443–448, April, 1948.

[2] G. R. Trimble, Jr., and S. Weitzman, Effect of a Hardwood Forest Canopy on Rainfall Intensities, *Trans. Am. Geophys. Union*, Vol. 35, pp. 226–234, April, 1954.

[3] R. E. Horton, Rainfall Interception, *Monthly Weather Rev.*, Vol. 47, pp. 603–623, September, 1919.

Crop	Height, ft	Interception, in.
Corn....................	6	0.03
Cotton................	4	0.33
Tobacco...............	4	0.07
Small grains...........	3	0.16
Meadow grass..........	1	0.08
Alfalfa................	1	0.11

Rainwater retained in puddles, ditches, and other depressions in the soil surface is termed *depression storage*. These depressions vary widely in area and depth; their size depends to a considerable degree on the definition of a depression. As soon as rainfall intensity exceeds the infiltration capacity (Sec. 8-2), the rainfall excess begins to fill surface depressions. Each depression has its own capacity and, when filled, further inflow is balanced by outflow plus infiltration and evaporation. Depressions of various sizes are both superimposed and interconnected. Almost immediately after the beginning of rainfall excess, the smallest depressions become filled and overland flow begins. Most of this water in turn fills larger depressions, but some of it follows an unobstructed path to the stream channel. This chain of events continues, with successively larger portions of overland flow contributing to the streams. Water held in depressions at the end of rain is either evaporated or absorbed by the soil through infiltration.

Virtually nothing can be said of the magnitude of depression storage, since meaningful observations cannot be easily obtained, and values are highly dependent on definition of terms. Individual depressions of appreciable area relative to the drainage basin under consideration are usually called *blind drainage* and excluded from hydrologic analysis. The remaining depression storage is usually lumped with interception and treated as *initial loss* with respect to storm runoff. Nevertheless, depression storage may be of considerable magnitude and may play an important role in the hydrologic cycle. Stock ponds, terraces, and contour farming all tend to moderate the flood hydrograph by increasing depression storage, while land leveling and drainage reduce depression storage. Because most basins have some very large depressions, it is likely that the depression-storage capacity of the basin is never completely filled.

8-2. Infiltration. *Infiltration* is the passage of water through the soil surface into the soil. Although a distinction is made between infiltration and *percolation*, the movement of water within the soil, the two phenomena are closely related since infiltration cannot continue unimpeded unless percolation removes infiltered water from the surface soil. The soil is permeated by noncapillary channels through which gravity water flows downward toward the groundwater, following the path of least resistance.   Capillary forces continuously divert gravity water into capillary pore spaces, so that the quantity of gravity water passing successively lower horizons is steadily diminished.   This leads to increasing resistance to gravity flow in the surface layer and a decreasing rate of infiltration as a storm progresses.   The rate of infiltration in the early

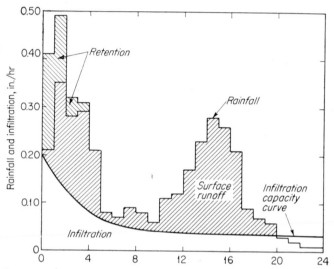

FIG. 8-1. Simple separation of infiltration and surface runoff, using hourly rainfall data, estimated retention, and an infiltration-capacity curve.

phases of a storm is less if the capillary pores are filled from a previous storm.

There is a maximum rate at which water can enter the soil at a particular point under a given set of conditions; this rate is called the *infiltration capacity*.   The actual infiltration rate f_i equals the infiltration capacity f_p only when the supply rate i_s (rainfall intensity less rate of retention) equals or exceeds f_p.   Theoretical concepts presume that actual infiltration rates equal the supply rate when $i_s \leq f_p$ and are otherwise at the capacity rate (Fig. 8-1).   The value of f_p is at a maximum f_0 at the beginning of a storm and approaches a low, constant rate f_c as the soil profile becomes saturated.   The limiting value is controlled by subsoil permeability.   Horton[1] found that infiltration-capacity curves approxi-

---

[1] R. E. Horton, The Role of Infiltration in the Hydrologic Cycle, *Trans. Am. Geophys. Union*, Vol. 14, pp. 446–460, 1933.

mate the form

$$f_p = f_c + (f_0 - f_c)e^{-kt} \tag{8-1}$$

where e is the Napierian base, k is an empirical constant, and t is time from beginning of rainfall. The equation is applicable only when $i_s \geq f_p$ throughout the storm.

Infiltration capacity depends on many factors such as soil type, moisture content, organic matter, vegetative cover, and season. Of the soil characteristics affecting infiltration, noncapillary porosity is perhaps the most important. Porosity determines storage capacity and also

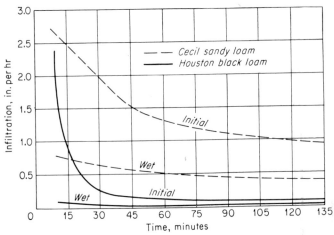

FIG. 8-2. Comparative infiltration rates during initial and wet runs. (After Free, Browning, and Musgrave.)

affects resistance to flow. Thus, infiltration tends to increase with porosity. An increase in organic matter also results in increased infiltration capacity, largely because of a corresponding change in porosity.[1]

Figure 8-2 demonstrates the effect of initial moisture content and the variations to be expected from soil to soil. The effect of vegetation on infiltration capacity is difficult to determine, for it also influences interception. Nevertheless, vegetal cover does increase infiltration as compared with barren soil because (1) it retards surface flow, giving the water additional time to enter the soil; (2) the root systems make the soil more pervious; and (3) the foliage shields the soil from raindrop impact and reduces rain packing of the surface soil.

Most data on infiltration rates are derived from infiltrometer tests.[2]

[1] G. R. Free, G. M. Browning, and G. W. Musgrave, Relative Infiltration and Related Physical Characteristics of Certain Soils, U.S. Dept. Agr. Tech. Bull. 729, 1940.

[2] Hydrology Handbook, ASCE Manual 28, pp. 47–51, 1949.

An *infiltrometer* is a tube, or other boundary, designed to isolate a section of soil. The effective area varies from less than one square foot to several hundred square feet. Although many of the earlier tests were made by flooding the infiltrometer, this method is no longer recommended and has been supplanted by sprinkling techniques.[1] Since it is impossible to measure directly the quantity of water penetrating the soil surface, infiltration is computed by assuming it to equal the difference between water applied and measured surface runoff. In addition to the difficulties inherent in simulating raindrop size and velocity of fall with sprinklers, experiments using artificial rainfall have other features tending to cause higher infiltration rates in tests than under natural conditions.

Attempts have been made to derive infiltration data by analyzing rainfall and runoff data from small drainage basins with homogeneous soils,[2] and Horton,[3] Sherman,[4] and others have presented techniques for deriving average "equivalent" infiltration-capacity data from records of heterogeneous basins. On natural basins allowance must be made for subsurface flow and surface retention. Since present methods of hydrograph analysis do not permit reliable separation of surface and subsurface flow, it is extremely difficult to obtain reliable infiltration data by analysis of data from natural basins.

8-3. The runoff cycle. The *runoff cycle* is the descriptive term applied to that portion of the hydrologic cycle between incident precipitation over land areas and subsequent discharge of this water through stream channels or evapotranspiration. Hoyt[5] has presented a comprehensive description of the hydrologic phenomena occurring at selected times during the runoff cycle by considering an idealized cross section of a basin. In the discussion here, it appears more instructive to consider the time variations of the hydrologic factors during an extensive storm on a relatively dry basin.

Figure 8-3 shows schematically the disposition of a steady, moderate-intensity rainfall. The dotted area of the figure represents the portion of total precipitation which eventually becomes streamflow measured at the basin outlet. Channel precipitation is the only increment of stream-

---

[1] Tests to determine infiltration rates during irrigation are customarily made by flooding.

[2] A. W. Zingg, The Determination of Infiltration Rates on Small Agricultural Watersheds, *Trans. Am. Geophys. Union*, Vol. 24, Part 2, pp. 476–480, 1943.

[3] R. E. Horton, Determination of Infiltration Capacity for Large Drainage Basins, *Trans. Am. Geophys. Union*, Vol. 18, pp. 371–385, 1937.

[4] L. K. Sherman, Comparison of F-curves Derived by the Methods of Sharp and Holtan and of Sherman and Mayer, *Trans. Am. Geophys. Union*, Vol. 24, Part 2, pp. 465–467, 1943.

[5] W. G. Hoyt, An Outline of the Runoff Cycle, *Penn. State Coll. School of Eng., Tech. Bull.* 27, pp. 57–67, 1942.

flow during the initial period of rainfall. As the streams rise, their total surface area increases and, consequently, the volume rate of channel precipitation increases.

The rate of interception is high at the beginning of rain, especially during summer and with dense vegetal cover. However, the available storage capacity is depleted rather quickly, so that the interception rate decreases to that required to replace water evaporated from the vegetation. Most of the interception is eventually returned to the atmosphere by evaporation.

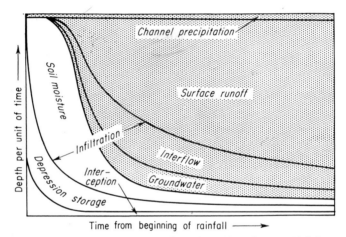

FIG. 8-3. Schematic diagram of the disposition of storm rainfall.

The rate at which depression storage is filled by incident precipitation decreases rapidly from a high initial value as the smaller depressions become filled. It approaches zero at a relatively high value of total-storm rainfall, depending on land slope, basin area, and other factors. While depression storage is shown as a total loss to streamflow in the simplified figure, a portion of this water does infiltrate and reach the stream as groundwater or interflow. The remainder is returned to the atmosphere through evaporation.

Except in very intense storms, the greater portion of the soil-moisture deficiency is satisfied before appreciable surface runoff takes place. However, some of the rain occurring late in the storm undoubtedly becomes soil moisture, since the downward movement of this water is relatively slow.

Water infiltrating the soil surface and not retained as soil moisture either moves to the stream as interflow or penetrates to the water table and eventually reaches the stream as groundwater. There is a difference of opinion on the quantitative division of this water between interflow and groundwater.   Figure 8-3 shows a gradual decrease in the contribution to interflow but this may not be true in every case.

The rate of surface runoff starts at zero, increases slowly at first and then more rapidly, eventually approaching a relatively constant percentage of the rainfall rate.   Both the percentage and the rate of runoff are dependent upon rainfall intensity.   Because the exact division between surface runoff and interflow is uncertain, the details of the diagram are not precise in this respect.

Figure 8-3 illustrates only one of an infinite number of possible cases. A change in rainfall intensity would change the relative magnitude of all the factors.   Further complications are introduced by varying rainfall intensity during the storm or by occurrence of snow or frozen ground. To appreciate further the complexity of the process in a natural basin, remember that all the factors of Fig. 8-3 vary from point to point within the basin during a storm.   Nevertheless, the foregoing description should aid in understanding the relative time variations of hydrologic phenomena which are important in considering the runoff relations discussed later in the chapter.

ESTIMATING THE VOLUME OF STORM RUNOFF

8-4. Rainfall vs. storm runoff.   Until recently, the estimation of runoff as a percentage of storm rainfall was standard practice.   The applicable coefficient varies from near zero for a small storm to a relatively high value for a major storm and is dependent upon initial moisture conditions.   Although the experienced hydrologist may be reasonably successful in selecting the proper coefficient for each storm, the method is extremely subjective, and its use cannot be advocated for estimating the runoff from specific storms.   The coefficient method is still widely used in the design of storm-drainage and small water-control structures (Sec. 9-10) and is the basis of design required by many city and county codes.

The variation in runoff coefficient with magnitude of storm can be taken into account by graphical correlation (Sec. A-1) of rainfall and runoff (Fig. 8-4).   Such relations are typically curved, indicating an increasing percentage of runoff with increasing rainfall.   Only a moderate degree of correlation can be expected, however, since variations in initial moisture conditions are not considered.

8-5. Initial moisture conditions.   The quantity of runoff produced by a storm depends on (1) the moisture deficiency of the basin at the onset of rain and (2) the storm characteristics, such as rainfall amount, intensity, and duration.   The storm characteristics can be determined from an adequate network of precipitation gages, but the direct determination of moisture conditions throughout the basin at the beginning of the storm is not feasible. While reliable observations of soil moisture can be made at a point, three-dimensional measurements are required in a medium recognized for its marked physical discontinuities. Also, any complete accountability of moisture within a basin must include consideration of depression and interception storage.

In humid and subhumid areas where streams flow continuously, groundwater discharge at the beginning of the storm has been found to be a good index to initial moisture conditions (Fig. 8-5). Since recent rains affect

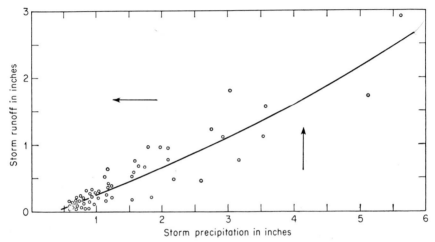

FIG. 8-4. Rainfall-runoff relation for Monocacy River at Jug Bridge, Maryland (817 sq mi).

current moisture deficiency, even though they have no effect on streamflow, this index should be supplemented by a weighted index of the rainfall for several days preceding.

Pan-evaporation data are sometimes used in the computation of a moisture index. In a study of the Valley River, North Carolina, Linsley and Ackermann[1] found that field-moisture deficiency at any time was approximately equal to 90 per cent of the total Class A pan evaporation since the ground was last saturated, less any additions made to field moisture by intervening rains. Basin-accounting techniques (Sec. 5-14) applied on a daily basis provide a reasonably accurate estimate of moisture deficiency which can be used as an index to runoff.[2] This approach is laborious but should yield excellent results.

The most common index is based on antecedent precipitation. The

[1] R. K. Linsley and W. C. Ackermann, Method of Predicting the Runoff from Rainfall, *Trans. ASCE*, Vol. 107, pp. 825–846, 1942.

[2] M. A. Kohler, Computation of Evaporation and Evapotranspiration from Meteorological Observations, *U.S. Weather Bur. Rept.*, 1957 (mimeographed).

rate at which moisture is depleted from a particular basin under specified meteorological conditions is roughly proportional to the amount in storage (Sec. 5-14). In other words, the soil moisture should decrease logarithmically (Appendix B) with time during periods of no precipitation,[1]

$$I_t = I_0 k^t \tag{8-2}$$

where I_0 is the initia' value of *antecedent-precipitation index*, I_t is the

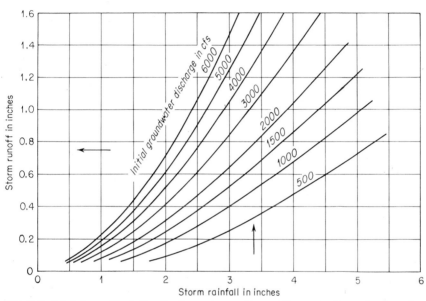

FIG. 8-5. Rainfall-runoff relation for Susquehanna River at Towanda, Pennsylvania, using groundwater flow as a parameter (7797 sq mi).

reduced value t days later, and k is a recession factor ranging normally between 0.85 and 0.98. Letting t equal unity,

$$I_1 = kI_0 \tag{8-3}$$

Thus, the index for any day is equal to that of the previous day multiplied by the factor k (Appendix B). If rain occurs on any day, the amount of rain is added to the index (Fig. 8-6). Since storm runoff does not add to the residual moisture of the basin, an index of precipitation minus runoff, i.e., basin recharge, should be more satisfactory than the precipitation index alone. Commonly, however, the minor improvements gained do not justify the added computation.

Equation (8-2) assumes that the daily depletion of soil moisture

[1] M. A. Kohler and R. K. Linsley, Predicting the Runoff from Storm Rainfall, *U.S. Weather Bur. Research Paper* 34, 1951.

(primarily evapotranspiration) is

$$I_0 - I_1 = I_0(1 - k) \qquad (8\text{-}4)$$

Since actual evapotranspiration is a function of the potential value and the available moisture (I_0), k should be a function of potential evapotranspiration. The variation in potential evapotranspiration is largely seasonal, and Eq. (8-2) has been found to be reasonably satisfactory when

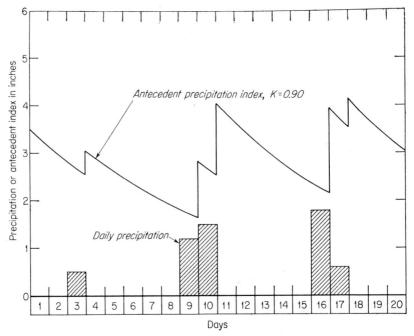

FIG. 8-6. Variation of antecedent index with daily precipitation.

used jointly with calendar date (Sec. 8-7). There is an added advantage in using the date as a parameter because it also reflects variations in surface conditions related to farming practices, vegetation, etc.

The value of the index on any day theoretically depends on precipitation over an infinite antecedent period, but if a reasonable initial value is assumed, the computed index will closely approach the true value within a few weeks. The index value applicable to a particular storm is taken as that at the beginning of the first day of rain. Thus a value of 1.8 in. would be used for the storm of the 9th and 10th in Fig. 8-6.

8-6. Storm analysis. In any statistical correlation, it is extremely important that the basic data be as consistent and reliable as possible. Methods of storm analysis should be rigorous and objective. Only that storm rainfall which produced the runoff being considered should be included. Small showers occurring after the hydrograph had started to recede should not be included if they had little effect upon the amount of runoff. Similarly, showers occurring before the main storm should be excluded from the storm rainfall and included in the antecedent-precipitation index. Long, complex storms should be separated into as many short storm periods as possible by hydrograph analysis. Average basin rainfall for the selected storm period is computed by one of the methods described in Chap. 3.

Runoff also depends upon rainfall intensity, but for basins of 100 sq mi or more, an average intensity as reflected by amount and duration is usually adequate. In this case duration can be estimated with sufficient accuracy from 6-hr rainfall data. An objective rule is preferable, such as "the sum in hours of those 6-hr periods with more than 0.2 in. of rain plus one-half the intervening periods with less than 0.2 in." Although experimental infiltration data indicate rates commonly in excess of 0.1 in./hr, relations such as Fig. 8-8 consistently show the effect of duration on storm runoff to be in the order of 0.01 in./hr. The difference is largely caused by intercorrelations and the inclusion of interflow with surface runoff.

Surface runoff is the residual after interception, depression storage, and infiltration are taken from rainfall. Hence, it is not uncommon to use the difference between rainfall and runoff (basin recharge) as the dependent variable in correlations. The definition of recharge is contingent on that used for runoff. The contribution to groundwater may be treated as part of total runoff[1] or it may be considered as groundwater recharge if one is interested in estimating only storm runoff.

8-7. Coaxial relations for total storm runoff or basin recharge. If storm characteristics and basin conditions are to be adequately represented in a runoff relation, the correlation must include a number of independent factors as well as the dependent variable (either runoff or recharge). The coaxial method (Sec. A-3) of graphical correlation is particularly suited for this work.[2]

To illustrate, assume that a relation for estimating basin recharge is desired, using antecedent precipitation, date (or week number), and rainfall amount and duration as parameters. Values of each of these parameters are compiled for 50 or more storms. A three-variable relation is developed first (Fig. 8-7, chart A) by (1) plotting antecedent precipitation vs. recharge, (2) labeling the points with week number, and (3) fitting a smooth family of curves representing the various weeks. Chart

---

[1] R. K. Linsley and J. B. Franzini, "Elements of Hydraulic Engineering," p. 35, McGraw-Hill, New York, 1955.

[2] M. A. Kohler and R. K. Linsley, Predicting the Runoff from Storm Rainfall, *U.S. Weather Bur. Research Paper* 34, 1951.

B is placed with its horizontal scale matching that of chart A to facilitate plotting. Points are plotted in chart B with observed recharge as ordinate and recharge computed from chart A as abscissa, and these points are labeled with duration. A family of smooth curves is drawn to represent the effect of duration on recharge. Charts A and B together

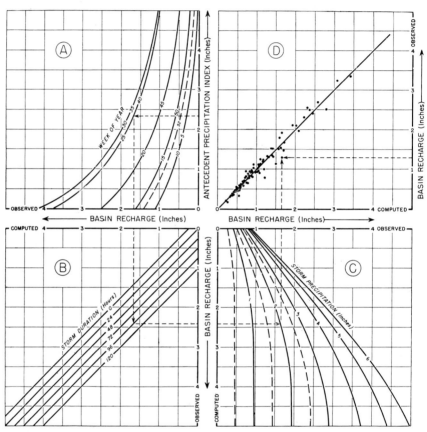

FIG. 8-7. Basin-recharge relation for the Monocacy River at Jug Bridge, Maryland. (After U.S. Weather Bureau.)

are a graphical relation for estimating recharge from antecedent index, week, and duration. Storm precipitation is then introduced (chart C) by (1) plotting recharge computed from charts A and B against observed recharge, (2) labeling the points with rainfall amount, and (3) fitting a family of curves. Charts A, B, and C constitute the *first approximation* to the desired relation. Chart D indicates the over-all accuracy of the derived charts.

Since the parameters are intercorrelated and the first charts are developed independently of factors subsequently introduced, revision of the charts may improve the over-all relation.   In other words, the process is one of successive approximations.   To check the week curves, the other curve families are assumed to be correct and the adjusted abscissa for a point in chart A is determined by entering charts B and C in reverse order with observed recharge, rainfall amount, and duration.   The ordinate for the adjusted point is the observed antecedent-precipitation index.   In other words, the week curves should be revised to fit this adjusted point if the relation is to yield a computed recharge equal to the observed recharge.   The second (and subsequent) approximations for duration and rainfall are made in the same manner.   In each case the points are plotted by entering the chart sequence from both ends with observed values to determine the adjusted coordinates.

Although the method presented in the previous paragraphs is general and can be used as described, certain modifications simplify the procedure and require fewer approximations.   Since storm rainfall is extremely important, the first plotting of chart A may show little correlation, and the construction of the curves will be difficult.   However, an important advantage in having the rainfall parameter in the last chart is that the possibility of computing runoff in excess of rainfall or of computing negative values of runoff is eliminated.   Moreover, the arrangement of Fig. 8-7 results in the determination of a unified index of moisture conditions in the first chart, which is a decided advantage in river forecasting. If the plotting of chart A is limited to storms having rainfall within a specified class interval (2 to 4 in., for example), the construction of the curves is simplified, provided that there are sufficient data.   Only limited data are required since the general curvature and convergence are always as shown in the example.   The relations are quite similar throughout a geographic region, and charts A and B for one basin may be used as a first approximation for another basin in the area.

Figure 8-7 shows that errors for points with negligible runoff are considerably magnified when routed back through the chart sequence to derive second-approximation curves.   Hence, low-runoff points may well be omitted from this step.

When basin recharge for a storm has been computed from Fig. 8-7, the runoff is estimated by subtracting recharge from observed rainfall. Since both rainfall and recharge appear on chart C, this subtraction can be eliminated by reorientation of the curves to read runoff directly (Fig. 8-8).   The charts can also be superimposed (Fig. 8-9) to conserve space without reducing scale.

To use the runoff volume computed from a relation such as Fig. 8-8 with a unit hydrograph (Chap. 9) to synthesize an extended-storm hydrograph requires that runoff increments be estimated for successive time periods. This is done by computing runoff from accumulated rainfall up to the end of each period and subtracting these successive values to obtain increments.

Since it is impossible to segregate the water passing a gaging station according to the portion of the basin in which it fell, statistical runoff

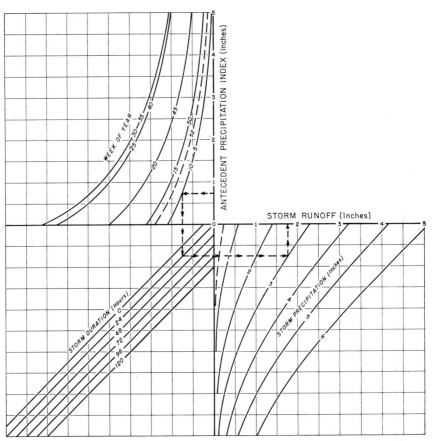

FIG. 8-8. Storm-runoff relation for Monocacy River at Jug Bridge, Maryland. (After U.S. Weather Bureau.)

relations must be based on basin averages of the parameters. Unfortunately, a relation which is based on storms of uniform areal distribution will yield runoff values which are too low when applied to storms with extremely uneven distributions. This can be demonstrated by computing the runoff for 4, 6, and 8 in. of rainfall, assuming all other factors to remain fixed. While 6 is the average of 4 and 8, the average runoff from the 4- and 8-in. rainfalls is not equal to that from a 6-in. rain. An uneven distribution of antecedent precipitation produces similar results. Runoff relations based on uniform areal conditions can properly be used to compute the runoff in the vicinity of each rainfall station, and the average of these runoff values will, in general, more nearly approach the observed runoff from the basin when either the storm or the antecedent precipitation is quite variable.

8-8. Coaxial relations for incremental storm runoff. When relations of the type shown in Fig. 8-8 are applied to very small basins, there is a decided tendency to undercompute the peaks of the larger floods. These rare events are often the result of high-intensity, short-duration storms which cannot be reproduced without taking into account the time distribution of the rainfall. This difficulty can be overcome[1] by revising the curves to permit estimates of hourly increments of runoff from corresponding hourly rainfall.

The chief difficulty in developing an hourly (increment) relation lies in the fact that one cannot determine increments of runoff for storms of record by hydrograph analysis. Thus, values of the dependent factor in the correlation cannot be obtained directly from the streamflow record. In practice, the runoff increments must first be estimated from a total storm relation (Fig. 8-8) as described in Sec. 8-7. The correlation process permits successive revision of the derived runoff increments, always maintaining the correct total-storm runoff. The derived increments can be checked qualitatively by application of a unit hydrograph (Sec. 9-8).

Still another problem is the derivation of a soil-moisture index which is representative of conditions at any time during a storm. Although not as sensitive as might be desired, a relation such as that of chart *A*, Fig. 8-7, is reasonably satisfactory, if storm precipitation up to the beginning of the time increment under consideration is included in the antecedent-precipitation index.

To illustrate, assume that a unit hydrograph and a relation such as Fig. 8-8 are applicable to a small basin and that an incremental relation such as Fig. 8-9 is desired. The analysis would proceed as follows:

1. For each of a number of short storms compute the accumulated storm runoff, hour by hour, with Fig. 8-8. Obtain hourly increments by subtraction of successive accumulated values, and adjust these increments to yield the correct total-storm runoff.

2. Compute storm hydrographs by applying the increments just derived to the 1-hr unit hydrograph (Sec. 9-8). If hydrograph reproduction is not satisfactory, adjust incremental runoff values as required.

3. Derive the antecedent-precipitation index for each hour by adding

[1] J. F. Miller and J. L. H. Paulhus, Rainfall-Runoff Relation for Small Basins, *Trans. Am. Geophys. Union*, Vol. 38, pp. 216–218, April, 1957.

the storm rainfall up to the designated hour to the initial value of the index for the storm.

4. Entering Fig. 8-9[1] with the antecedent index and week number, plot at the corresponding hourly runoff, and label the point with hourly rainfall. Points should be plotted so that those for each storm are readily discernible (color or symbol). Since hourly increments are less reliable

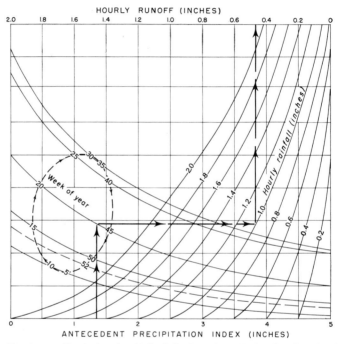

FIG. 8-9. Hourly-runoff relation for Little Falls Branch at Bethesda, Maryland. (*After U.S. Weather Bureau.*)

than total-storm runoff, the analyst may make compensating changes in the points for a given storm to obtain better agreement among storms.

5. Construct hourly-rainfall curves to fit the plotted data.

6. Using the first-approximation curves, compute hourly-runoff values by entering with antecedent index, week, and rainfall, and adjust each set of values to the correct storm total.

7. To check the week curves, enter the relation with hourly runoff (step 6) and rainfall, plot at the corresponding antecedent index, and label each point with the week number. Revise the week curves as indicated by the plotted data.

[1] The curve families of this relation have been superimposed for illustrative purposes. In derivation they should be separated to avoid confusion.

8. If the week curves require revision (step 7), the first-approximation rainfall curves should be checked. Enter the relation with antecedent index and week, plot at the corresponding runoff (step 6), label points with rainfall, and revise the curves as required.

Experience with relations of this type is limited, but results are encouraging. The development process outlined above is cumbersome and time-consuming. With one such relation, however, its modification to fit another basin in the same hydrologic region is achieved rather quickly.

8-9. The infiltration approach to runoff. Basically, the infiltration approach is quite simple. The surface runoff resulting from a given storm is equal to that portion of the rainfall which is not disposed of through (1) interception and depression storage, (2) evaporation during the storm, and (3) infiltration. If items 1 and 2 are invariable or insignificant or can be assigned reasonable values, one need be concerned only with rainfall, infiltration, and runoff. In the simplest case, where the supply rate i_s is at or in excess of the infiltration capacity, surface runoff is equivalent to the storm rainfall less surface retention and the area under the capacity curve. The computations are equally direct if i_s is continuously below f_p at the end of the storm (Fig. 8-1).

Natural rain of varying intensity and intermittently below the infiltration capacity results in a distortion of the capacity curve which is, by definition, applicable only when $i_s \geq f_p$. When $i_s = 0$, capacity must increase with time, and the capacity may either increase or decrease with time when $0 < i_s < f_p$. It is often assumed that the infiltration capacity at any time during a storm is determined by the mass infiltration which has occurred up to that time. If rain begins at a low rate and the rainfall during the first hour is one-half the infiltration capacity, the capacity at the end of the hour would be taken as that at about $\frac{1}{2}$ hr on the applicable capacity curve.

The infiltration approach is frequently applied in deriving the design discharge for airport drainage and similar projects when the drainage area is homogeneous and small, but it is rarely satisfactory in operational problems requiring reliable hydrograph prediction on a continuing basis. Even when applicable, it can be used to compute only one component of flow—surface runoff. Subsurface flow must be computed independently, and this flow may constitute a major portion of the flood flow in some areas. The infiltration concept can be applied to the rational computation of surface runoff from a natural heterogeneous basin only when the area is subdivided with respect to infiltration and storm characteristics and an applicable capacity curve is available for each subarea. The difficulties in applying the theory have led to the use of infiltration indices[1]

[1] H. L. Cook, The Infiltration Approach to the Calculation of Surface Runoff, *Trans. Am. Geophys. Union*, Vol. 27, pp. 726–747, October, 1946.

which must be correlated with factors indicative of initial moisture conditions.

8-10. Infiltration indices.   The Φ *index* is defined as that rate of rainfall above which the rainfall volume equals the runoff volume (Fig. 8-10).   Since Φ represents the combined effects of infiltration, inter-

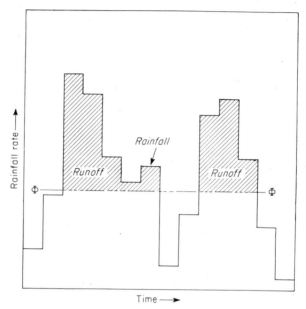

FIG. 8-10. Schematic diagram showing the meaning of the Φ index.

ception, and depression storage, it is equivalent to basin recharge divided by the duration of rainfall, provided that $i \geq \Phi$ throughout the storm.

The *W index* is the average infiltration rate during the time rainfall intensity exceeds the capacity rate; i.e.,

$$W = \frac{F}{t} = \frac{1}{t}(P - Q - S) \qquad (8\text{-}5)$$

where F is total infiltration, t is time during which rainfall intensity exceeds infiltration capacity, P is total precipitation corresponding to t, Q is surface runoff, and S is the effective surface retention.   The W index is essentially equal to the Φ index minus the average rate of retention by interception and depression storage.   While the segregation of infiltration and retention would seem to be a refinement, the task of estimating the retention rate is such that combining it with infiltration is probably equally satisfactory.

With very wet conditions, when the infiltration capacity is at a minimum and the retention rate is very low, the values of W and Φ are almost equal.   Under these conditions, the W index becomes the W_{min} index by definition.   This index is used principally in studies of maximum flood potential.

Values of the indices are easily derived from rainfall and discharge data, using an objective method of hydrograph separation.   To apply the indices the procedure is reversed; runoff is computed from a selected index value.   Since the variability of W and Φ is comparable with that of runoff, correlations are still required between the index and antecedent conditions.   Nevertheless, the approach is used to advantage in the design of projects when the assumption of minimum infiltration is appropriate.[1]

ESTIMATING SNOWMELT RUNOFF

8-11. Physics of snowmelt.   The basic problem of the hydrologist in regard to snow is twofold.   First, he is concerned with estimating the rates of snowmelt from his knowledge of the heat supplied and, second, he must determine how the resulting melt water, perhaps in combination with concurrent rainfall, will affect streamflow.   This section treats the physical aspects of snowmelt; practical solutions to snowmelt problems are covered in Sec. 8-12.

From a physical point of view, the snowmelt and evaporation processes are quite similar.   Both are thermodynamic processes and can be treated by the energy-budget approach.   For each inch of water melted from snow at 32°F, heat must be supplied in the amount of 750 Btu/sq ft or 203 cal/sq cm.   Snowmelt computations are simplified by the fact that the surface is always 32°F during melt and, at the same time, are made more complex by variations in *albedo*, the percentage of solar and diffuse radiation reflected by the surface.   The energy for snowmelt is derived from (1) net radiation, (2) conduction and convective transfer of sensible heat from the overlying air, (3) condensation of water vapor from the overlying air, (4) conduction from the underlying soil, and (5) heat supplied by incident rainfall.

Components of radiation exchange are discussed in Sec. 5-3 in connection with evaporation.   Although only 5 to 10 per cent of incident short-wave radiation is reflected by a free water surface, 80 to 90 per cent is reflected by a clean dry snow surface.   As snow ages, its albedo drops to 50 per cent or less because of changes in crystalline structure, density, and amount of dirt on the surface.   Snow radiates essentially as a black body, and the outgoing long-wave radiation (32°F) during a 24-hr period is equivalent to about 3.3 in. of negative melt.   The net loss by long-wave radiation is materially less than this amount since the

[1] P. Leatham and H. S. Riesbol, Infiltration and Detention Tests as Related to Spillway Design Floods, *Trans. Am. Geophys. Union*, Vol. 31, pp. 234–242, April, 1950.

atmosphere reradiates a portion back to the earth. Net long-wave radiation depends primarily on air and snow temperatures, atmospheric vapor pressure, and extent and type of cloud cover. With clear skies net loss by long-wave radiation is equal to about 0.8 in. of melt per day when dewpoint and air and snow temperatures are near 32°F. Numerous empirical formulas have been derived to estimate this factor[1] and net all-wave radiation, but they are not particularly satisfactory. Radiometer observations of net radiation could provide the needed data if an adequate network of stations was established.

Heat exchange between a snow pack and the atmosphere is also effected by the processes of conduction, convection, condensation, and evaporation. Although it is readily shown that conduction in still air is very small, convective exchange can be an important factor.[2] If the dewpoint of the air is above 32°F, condensation on the snow occurs, with consequent release of latent heat. If the dewpoint is less than the snow-surface temperature, the vapor pressure of the snow is greater than that of the air and evaporation occurs. The rate of transfer of sensible heat (convection) is proportional to the temperature difference between the air T_a and the snow T_s, while vapor transport is proportional to the vapor-pressure gradient $e_a - e_s$. Both processes are proportional to wind velocity v. Since the latent heat of vaporization is about 7.5 times the latent heat of fusion, condensation of 1 in. of water vapor on the snow surface produces 8.5 in. of water, including condensate. The two processes can be described by similar equations

$$M_{\text{convection}} = k_c(T_a - 32)v \tag{8-6}$$

$$M_{\text{condensation}} = k_v(e_a - 6.11)v \tag{8-7}$$

where M is melt, k is an exchange coefficient, and 6.11 is the vapor pressure (millibars) at 32°F.

Temperatures beneath the soil surface do not vary as much or as rapidly as surface temperatures, and there is usually an increase of temperature with depth during the winter and early spring. This results in a transfer of heat from the soil to the snow pack above. While the heat transfer is small on a daily basis, it may be equivalent to several inches of melt during an entire season—sufficient to keep the soil saturated and to permit a prompt response of streamflow when melting from other causes takes place.

[1] E. R. Anderson, Energy-budget Studies, Water-loss Investigations, Vol. 1, Lake Hefner Studies, *U.S. Geol. Survey Profess. Paper* 269 (reprint of *U.S. Geol. Survey Circ.* 229), pp. 71–119, 1954.

"Snow Hydrology, Summary Report of the Snow Investigations," pp. 145–166, North Pacific Division, U.S. Corps of Engineers, Portland, Ore., June, 1956.

[2] P. Light, Analysis of High Rates of Snow Melting, *Trans. Am. Geophys. Union*, Vol. 22, Part 1, pp. 195–205, 1941.

Raindrop temperatures correspond closely to the surface wet-bulb temperature. As the drops enter a snow pack, their temperature is reduced to 32°F and an equivalent amount of heat is imparted to the snow. The melt from rain is given by

$$M_{rain} = \frac{P(T_w - 32)}{144} \tag{8-8}$$

where P is the rainfall in inches, T_w is the wet-bulb temperature (°F), and 144 is the latent heat of fusion in Btu per pound. Thus the heat available in 1 in. of rain at 50°F will melt about ⅛ in. of water from the snow. There has been a tendency to overemphasize the importance of rainfall melt, perhaps because warm rains are accompanied by high humidity and temperature and often by moderate to strong winds.

From a theoretical point of view, it would appear that snowmelt computations could be made by applying the energy-budget approach, and this is basically true for snowmelt at a point. On a natural basin, however, the hydrologist is confronted with numerous complications which have not yet been successfully treated. Among the more obvious complications are the effect of variations in elevation, slope, aspect, forest cover, and albedo on radiation, temperature, wind, and other key factors in snowmelt. The heat required to melt snow is dependent on its thermal quality (Sec. 3-13) which may vary widely within a basin. Finally, since the hydrologist is concerned with the runoff from snowmelt, water retained in the snow pack is not effective. Limited data indicate that snow can retain from 2 to 5 per cent liquid water by weight. These complexities and the scarcity of pertinent data have made the theoretical approach generally inapplicable for operational use. This does not preclude use of these concepts in studying upper limits of snowmelt for design purposes.

8-12. Estimating snowmelt rates and consequent runoff. Of all the pertinent meteorological factors, air temperature is by far the most reliable index to snowmelt. In fact, it so completely reflects radiation, wind, and humidity that residual errors are not materially correlated with these factors. Since snowmelt does not occur with temperatures appreciably below freezing, the data are commonly converted to degree days or degree hours above some base, usually 32°F. A day with a mean temperature of 52°F represents 20 degree days above 32°F. If the minimum temperature for the day is above freezing, then there are 20×24 or 480 degree hours. On the other hand, there are actually more than 480 degree hours in a day with a mean temperature of 52°F if the temperature drops below 32°F for a portion of the day. Degree-day computations are usually based on dry-bulb temperature readings because such data are readily available, but better correlation is sometimes found between snowmelt and wet-bulb readings. Degree days are sometimes computed from a base of 30°F for convenience. In some cases base temperatures as high as 40°F have been used on the argument that the shelter temperature is higher than that at the snow surface. In a few instances degree days have been computed from maximum rather than mean temperatures. Since any value that is used is only an index to the available heat, it is probable that little real difference in utility exists between the various methods of computing degree days.

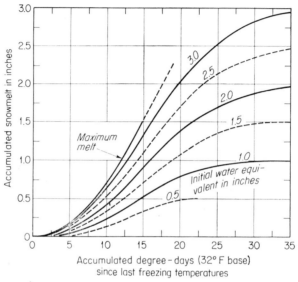

FIG. 8-11. Temperature-snowmelt relation for Pennsylvania. *(After Snyder.)*

Snowmelt relations are generally determined by correlating runoff with degree days and possibly other factors. Sometimes the *degree-day factor*, the ratio of snowmelt (or runoff) to the concurrent number of degree days, is treated as the dependent variable. As originally conceived, the degree-day factor was expected to be relatively constant, but actual variations are often of such magnitude that little advantage is gained from its use. Direct use of degree days in a correlation provides greater flexibility. Average degree-day factors for a melt period range between 0.06 and 0.15 in. per degree day, if the basin is completely snow-covered. The factor increases with time after the beginning of melt if computed from streamflow, largely because of the detention of early melt water in the snow and soil. As the snow cover becomes patchy, the factor again decreases (Fig. 8-13). Slope, aspect, and degree of forest cover cause variations in degree-day factor from basin to basin

and seasonally in mountainous terrain.   In studies of western Pennsylvania, Horton[1] found the factor to vary from 0.09 on thinly covered
basins to 0.06 on heavily forested areas.

   Figure 8-11 shows a snowmelt relation derived for the Susquehanna
River Basin.[2]   This relation tends to account for the ripening and gradual
disappearance of the snow pack, but it provides estimates of snowmelt,

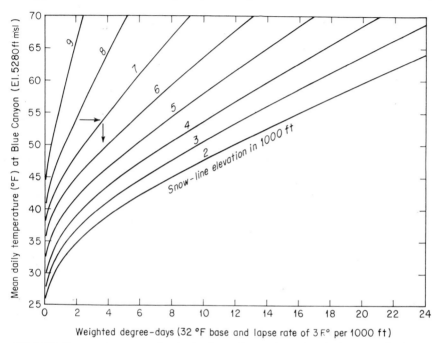

FIG. 8-12. Degree-day curves for the Tuolumne River above Don Pedro Dam, California.

not runoff.   Runoff must be computed by the use of a rainfall-runoff
relation or similar technique.   Similar relations have been used in the
plains area with moderate success.

   In many basins of high relief, winter conditions are typified by semipermanent snow cover in the headwaters while the lower portions of the
basins have only intermittent snow cover.   The lower limit of snow cover
(*snow line*) is a dynamic feature, moving up and down the slope with
passing time.   In practice, the snow line is often considered as a contour
of elevation, a reasonably realistic assumption following a storm.   As
melting proceeds, however, snow cover recedes more rapidly on southerly

   [1] R. E. Horton, Infiltration and Runoff during the Snow Melting Season, with
Forest Cover, *Trans. Am. Geophys. Union*, Vol. 26, Part 1, pp. 59–68, 1945.
   [2] F. F. Snyder, "Cooperative Hydrologic Investigations," Part II, Commonwealth
of Pennsylvania, Harrisburg, Pa., 1939 (mimeo.).

and barren slopes, and the snow line can be defined only as an average elevation of the lower limit of snow. Since surface air temperature is an inverse function of elevation, the rate of snowmelt decreases with elevation. If the freezing isotherm is below the snow line, there is no melting within the basin. Thus, temperature at an index station must be considered in conjunction with the extent of snow cover in estimating snowmelt.

Analysis of mean daily surface air temperature in mountain regions has shown that temperature drops about 3 to 5 F° per 1000-ft increase in elevation. Given the temperature at an index station, an area-elevation curve for the basin, and the average snow-line elevation, one can compute the area subject to melting on the basis of an assumed rate of change of temperature with elevation. The sum ΣDA, where D is the degree days for each small increment of elevation above the snow line and A is the per cent of basin area in each elevation zone, gives a weighted value of degree days over the melting zone. The weighted degree days are thus a function of snow-line elevation and index temperature (Fig. 8-12).

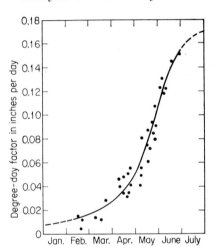

FIG. 8-13. Degree-day-factor curve for the Tuolumne River above Don Pedro Dam, California.

Multiplying the degree days so determined by a degree-day factor gives the snowmelt in inches over the whole basin. In some high-elevation basins of the West, the degree-day factor shows a systematic variation with date during the melting season (Fig. 8-13).[1] It is important that relations such as those of Figs. 8-12 and 8-13 be derived and used as parts of an integrated procedure for synthesizing the hydrograph. The degree-day-factor data of Fig. 8-13 are directly dependent upon the method of deriving degree-day values and the technique for computing snowmelt from the discharge hydrograph.

SEASONAL- AND ANNUAL-RUNOFF RELATIONS

The hydrologist is frequently called upon to estimate seasonal and annual flow volumes, either to synthesize a streamflow record for design or for an operational forecast. In estimating flow volumes for long

[1] R. K. Linsley, A Simple Procedure for the Day-to-day Forecasting of Runoff from Snowmelt, *Trans. Am. Geophys. Union*, Vol. 24, Part 3, pp. 62–67, 1943.

periods, variations in antecedent conditions are not critical, and there is usually no need to distinguish between groundwater and direct runoff. Precipitation is the principal independent factor to be considered.   Inasmuch as the meteorologist cannot yet make reliable predictions of precipitation far in advance, seasonal- or annual-runoff forecasts are feasible only where snow accumulates during the winter and is followed by a characteristic spring thaw.   In the United States such conditions exist

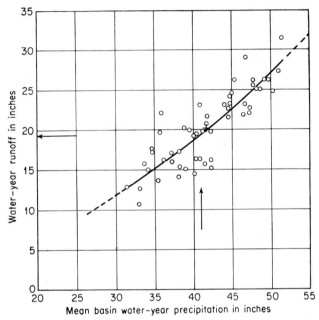

FIG. 8-14. Relation between annual precipitation and runoff for the Merrimack River above Lawrence, Massachusetts (4460 sq mi).

in varying degree throughout the mountainous regions of the West and in the north-central and northeastern states.

8-13. Precipitation-runoff relations.   A simple plotting of annual precipitation vs. annual runoff will often display a high degree of correlation (Fig. 8-14), particularly in areas where the major portion of the precipitation falls in the winter months.   Numerous refinements can be introduced if a moderate increase in reliability justifies the additional effort required in analysis.[1]   First, there is the question of consistent data throughout the period of record under study.   Observed runoff should be adjusted for storage changes in reservoirs.   In addition, construction of reservoirs during the record period may increase evaporation

[1] M. A. Kohler and R. K. Linsley, Recent Developments in Water Supply Forecasting, *Trans. Am. Geophys. Union,* Vol. 30, pp. 427–436, June, 1949.

losses to an extent requiring consideration. Irrigation water use has also been a variable factor in many basins. Finally, changes in observational techniques, discharge section, gage location, and other factors have contributed to discharge records which in some cases show definite time trends unexplained by precipitation. Testing precipitation and runoff data by double-mass analysis (Chaps. 3 and 4) may disclose inconsistencies which can be eliminated through appropriate adjustments.

Figure 8-14 is based on averages of precipitation observed at 30 stations in and near the basin. If records are available for only a few stations, application of station weights may improve results. Summer precipitation, and a portion of that occurring in the fall and spring, is in the form of rain and falls on bare ground. Consequently, a sizable portion of each storm's precipitation goes to basin recharge. Winter snows accumulate as a snow pack, and the portion of each increment utilized as recharge is relatively small. The effectiveness of precipitation in producing streamflow thus depends on when it occurs, and the application of monthly weights will improve the reliability of the relation. Station and monthly weights can be derived through least-squares analysis.[1] The high intercorrelation of precipitation observed at stations within a limited area may result in regression coefficients (weights) which over-emphasize the relative value of the better stations, and, if so, the results should be tempered toward equal weighting. Derived monthly weights may tend to be erratic, particularly if based on a short record, but they can be adjusted to provide a smooth transition throughout the year.

There is often a substantial lag between precipitation and the subsequent discharge of that portion which recharges the groundwater. Where groundwater is an appreciable part of the total flow, introduction of precipitation during the previous year as an additional parameter may improve the reliability of the relation. Streamflow during the previous year and flow during one or more winter months[2] have also been used as indices of groundwater carry-over.

8-14. Use of snow surveys. The application of snow-survey data to the preparation of water-supply forecasts is appealing because of the rather simple relation envisioned. If the seasonal flow results primarily from melting of a mountain snow pack, measurements of the water in the snow pack prior to the beginning of melt should indicate the volume of runoff to be expected. Hence, for many years snow surveys were made near the end of the snow-accumulation season, usually about April 1. While surveys are now made monthly during the snow season at most courses, the April 1 survey is still considered the best index to seasonal

---

[1] M. Ezekiel, "Methods of Correlation Analysis," 2d ed., Wiley, New York, 1941.

[2] E. L. Peck, Low Winter Streamflow as an Index to the Short- and Long-term Carryover from Previous Years, *Proc. Western Snow Conf.*, pp. 41–48, 1954.

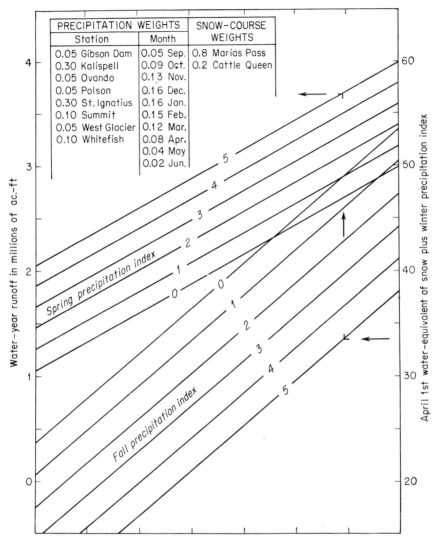

FIG. 8-15. Annual-runoff relation for South Fork, Flathead River, above Hungry Horse Reservoir, Montana. (*After U.S. Weather Bureau.*)

runoff. Because of drifting, variations in winter melt from point to point, etc., snow cover is usually more variable than precipitation within a given area. It is not economically feasible to take a sufficient number of samples to determine directly the volume of water stored in the pack, and the surveys constitute nothing more than an index. Accordingly, samples must be taken at the same points and in a consistent manner each year. Care must be taken to avoid changes in exposure brought about by forest fires, growth of timber and underbrush, etc.

Although there is good correlation between snow-survey data and seasonal runoff, it is now recognized that reliable water-supply forecasts cannot be made from snow surveys alone.[1] Runoff subsequent to the surveys is also dependent upon (1) groundwater storage, (2) antecedent soil-moisture deficiency, and (3) precipitation during the runoff period. It has been found[2] that snow-survey data can best be treated as an independent measure of winter precipitation in a multiple correlation (Fig. 8-15).

BIBLIOGRAPHY

Hydrology Handbook, *ASCE Manual* 28, pp. 33–63, 78–80, 1949.

Linsley, R. K., M. A. Kohler, and J. L. H. Paulhus: "Applied Hydrology," pp. 133–143, 309–315, 405–443, 650–655, McGraw-Hill, New York, 1949.

"Snow Hydrology, Summary Report of Snow Investigations," North Pacific Division, U.S. Corps of Engineers, Portland, Ore., June, 1956.

Strauss, F. A.: Forecasting Water Supply through Snow Surveys, *J. Am. Water Works Assoc.*, Vol. 46, pp. 853–863, 1954.

PROBLEMS

8-1. Derive a mean rainfall vs. runoff curve (Fig. 8-4) from the data shown in the table on page 191, for the Ramapo River at Pompton Lakes, New Jersey (drainage area = 160 sq mi). Compute the average error of the relation and the bias for the tabulated summer (May–October) and winter (November–April) storms.

8-2. Derive a mean rainfall vs. recharge curve from the data provided in Prob. 8-1. Compute the average error of the relation for the tabulated storms.

8-3. Using the data provided in Prob. 8-1, derive a relation similar to that shown in Fig. 8-7 for estimating basin recharge. Compute the average error of the relation for the tabulated storms. Convert the derived relation to one for computing storm runoff (like Fig. 8-8).

8-4. Compare the runoff for several assumed storms as computed from Figs. 8-8 and 8-9. Under what circumstances does Fig. 8-9 yield appreciably more runoff?

8-5. Compute the Φ and W indices for the storm depicted in Fig. 8-1.

8-6. Find the contribution to recharge and runoff (combined) for a day on which net radiation = 150 cal/sq cm; convective transfer to the snow pack = 75 cal/sq cm;

---

[1] J. C. Marr, Effect of Soil-priming by Fall Precipitation on Spring Runoff—Upper Snake Basin, *Trans. Am. Geophys. Union*, Vol. 20, Part 1, pp. 106–109, 1939.

A. R. Croft, Some Factors That Influence the Accuracy of Water-supply Forecasting in the Intermountain Region, *Trans. Am. Geophys. Union*, Vol. 27, pp. 375–388, June, 1946.

"Review of Procedures for Forecasting Inflow to Hungry Horse Reservoir, Montana," Water Management Subcommittee, Columbia Basin Interagency Committee, June, 1953.

[2] J. Hannaford, Multiple-graphical Correlation for Water Supply Forecasting, *Proc. Western Snow Conf.*, pp. 26–32, 1956.

M. A. Kohler, Water-supply Forecasting Developments, *Proc. Western Snow Conf.*, pp. 62–68, 1957.

Storm No.	Date	Antecedent-precipitation index	Week of year	Storm duration, hr	Storm precipitation, in.	Storm runoff, in.	Basin recharge, in.
1	3/15/40	0.90	11	12	2.03	1.23	0.80
2	4/22/40	2.20	16	18	1.95	1.05	0.90
3	5/17/40	0.58	20	9	1.50	0.46	1.04
4	9/ 2/40	2.70	35	12	1.81	0.33	1.48
5	10/ 3/40	1.00	40	12	1.07	0.10	0.97
6	12/17/40	0.75	51	12	1.13	0.33	0.80
7	2/ 8/41	0.50	6	15	1.95	0.99	0.96
8	4/ 7/41	0.29	14	20	1.30	0.53	0.77
9	12/25/41	1.20	52	15	1.60	0.53	1.07
10	2/ 1/42	0.65	5	9	1.06	0.30	0.76
11	2/18/42	1.03	7	12	0.79	0.22	0.57
12	3/ 4/42	0.45	9	9	1.83	0.89	0.94
13	8/10/42	1.26	32	15	2.87	0.49	2.38
14	8/18/42	3.29	33	6	2.81	1.06	1.75
15	9/28/42	1.00	39	18	3.58	1.01	2.57
16	2/ 7/43	1.06	6	18	0.67	0.17	0.50
17	6/ 2/43	1.07	22	9	1.47	0.30	1.17
18	11/10/43	2.05	45	21	2.33	0.92	1.41
19	3/ 8/44	0.45	10	12	0.95	0.50	0.45
20	4/25/44	1.57	17	21	1.94	1.10	0.84
21	1/ 2/45	1.25	1	6	1.30	0.74	0.56
22	7/23/45	5.45	30	12	3.55	2.39	1.16
23	8/ 7/45	2.56	32	9	1.61	0.42	1.19
24	11/30/45	1.42	48	24	2.25	0.92	1.33
25	5/28/46	1.44	22	15	2.90	1.44	1.46
26	9/25/46	1.03	39	12	2.27	0.43	1.84
27	6/ 9/47	1.27	23	10	1.54	0.31	1.23
28	5/14/48	1.11	20	27	2.27	0.71	1.56
29	5/30/48	1.56	22	6	1.18	0.34	0.84
30	7/14/48	1.00	28	9	1.83	0.22	1.61
31	12/31/48	0.70	52	36	4.67	2.77	1.90
32	11/26/50	1.12	48	15	3.30	1.12	2.18
33	3/31/51	1.00	13	36	5.25	3.51	1.74
34	10/ 8/51	0.40	41	18	1.85	0.11	1.74
35	3/12/52	0.81	11	12	2.83	2.09	0.74
36	4/ 6/52	0.89	14	18	3.10	1.55	1.55
37	6/ 2/52	2.17	22	15	4.10	2.07	2.03
38	8/17/52	2.66	33	15	3.08	0.83	2.25
39	9/ 2/52	1.20	35	6	3.94	1.11	2.83
40	12/ 4/52	2.11	49	12	1.50	0.71	0.79
41	3/12/53	1.01	11	36	3.50	2.15	1.35
42	3/23/53	2.33	12	12	2.00	1.08	0.92

condensation = 0.02 in. depth; rainfall (at 45°F) = 1.00 in.; and water equivalent of the snow pack = 1.35 in.

8-7. Given maximum and minimum daily temperatures of 55°F and 35°F, respectively, and assuming temperature to follow a sine curve, compute the degree days and degree hours for a 24-hr period using a base of 32°F. Repeat the computations with temperatures of 45°F and 25°F. Comment on the results.

8-8. Assuming the temperature-index station to be at an elevation of 1000 ft and the variation of temperature with elevation to be 4 F° per 1000 ft, derive a relation similar to Fig. 8-12 for a basin with the following area-elevation characteristics.

Elevation, ft	Per cent of area	Elevation, ft	Per cent of area
1000	0	5000	80
2000	5	6000	90
3000	30	7000	96
4000	60	8000	100

Compute weighted degree days for index-station temperatures of 60 and 80°F with snow-line elevations of 3000 and 5000 ft, respectively.

8-9. For a basin selected by the instructor, compile the necessary data and derive a precipitation-runoff relation of the type shown in Fig. 8-14.

9

HYDROGRAPHS OF RUNOFF

In the design of spillways, storm-drainage works, and flood-control projects an estimate of probable peak flows is necessary. Where adequate streamflow records are available, the answer may be found by use of frequency analysis (Chap. 11). More commonly, however, it is necessary to synthesize the design-flood hydrograph by other means.

The earliest method for estimating peak flows was the use of empirical formulas involving various physical characteristics of the basin. Some of these formulas are discussed in Sec. 9-10, mainly to point out their inadequacy as engineering tools. In 1932, Sherman introduced the unit hydrograph (Sec. 9-2) as the first basic tool for estimating hydrograph shape. Today the unit hydrograph is the mainstay of the flood hydrologist, but attention is also being directed toward flood-routing methods (Sec. 10-13) which offer prospect of greater flexibility and accuracy than the unit hydrograph in synthesizing the outflow hydrograph from a basin.

Chapter 8 presents methods of estimating the volume of water that would be delivered to a stream as the result of rain or melting snow. It is the purpose of this chapter to explain how this runoff volume is transformed into a hydrograph of flow at a point in the stream system. For reasons that will be developed, the methods which follow are generally applicable only to relatively small drainage basins, usually under 5000 sq mi and preferably much smaller.

9-1. The elemental hydrograph. If a small, impervious area is subjected to rainfall at a constant rate, the resulting runoff hydrograph will appear much as in Fig. 9-1. Since sheet flow over the surface cannot occur without a finite depth of water on the surface, some of the rainfall goes into temporary storage, or *surface detention*. At any instant the quantity of water in such storage is equal to the difference between total inflow to the area (rain) and total outflow from the area. When equilibrium has been reached the rate of outflow equals the rate of inflow (point C) and the volume in detention is ABC. The water is in constant motion, and any given element of rainfall may pass through the system in a fairly short time, but the volume difference between inflow and out-flow remains constant.

When rainfall ends (point D) there is no further inflow to sustain the the detention, and rate of outflow and detention volume decrease. The outflow follows a typical recession with flow decreasing at a decreasing rate; that is, d^2q/dt^2 is negative. This is usually accentuated by an exponential relation between storage and discharge.

Theoretically, an infinite time is required for both the rising portion of the hydrograph to reach equilibrium and for the recession to return to zero. Practically, both the rising and falling curves approach their

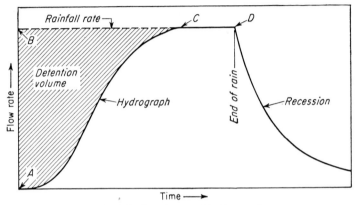

FIG. 9-1. The elemental hydrograph.

limits rapidly. The results of experimental study of the hydrographs from small areas are discussed in Sec. 9-9.

9-2. The unit-hydrograph concept. The hydrograph of outflow from a small basin is the sum of the elemental hydrographs from all the subareas of the basin, modified by the effect of transit time through the basin and storage in the stream channels. Since the physical character-istics of the basin—shape, size, slope, etc.—are constant, one might expect considerable similarity in the shape of hydrographs from storms of similar rainfall characteristics. This is the essence of the unit hydrograph as proposed by Sherman.[1] The unit hydrograph is a typical hydrograph for the basin. It is called a "unit hydrograph" because, for convenience, the runoff volume under the hydrograph is commonly adjusted to 1.00 in.

It would be wrong to imply that one typical hydrograph would suffice for any basin. Although the physical characteristics of the basin remain relatively constant, the variable characteristics of storms cause variations in the shape of the resulting hydrographs. The storm characteristics

[1] L. K. Sherman, Streamflow from Rainfall by the Unit-graph Method, *Eng. News-Record*, Vol. 108, pp. 501–505, 1932.

are rainfall duration, time-intensity pattern, areal distribution of rainfall, and amount of runoff. Their effects are discussed below.

Duration of rain. Since the unit hydrograph always contains 1 in. of runoff, increasing the duration of the rainfall lengthens the time base and lowers the unit-hydrograph peak. A separate unit hydrograph is theoretically necessary for each possible duration of rain. Actually, the effect of small differences in duration is not large, and a tolerance of ± 25 per cent from the established duration is ordinarily acceptable. Further, a unit hydrograph for a short duration of rainfall can be used to develop hydrographs for storms of longer duration (Sec. 9-5). Thus a few unit hydrographs for short durations will serve all requirements.

Time-intensity pattern. If one attempted to derive a separate unit hydrograph for each possible time-intensity pattern, an infinite number of unit hydrographs would be required. Practically, unit hydrographs can be based only on an assumption of uniform intensity of runoff. However, large variations in rain intensity (and hence runoff rate) during a storm are reflected in the shape of the resulting hydrograph. The time scale of intensity variations that are critical depends mainly on basin size. Bursts of rainfall lasting only a few minutes may cause clearly defined peaks in the hydrograph from a basin of a few acres, while on basins of several hundred square miles only changes in storm intensity lasting for hours will cause distinguishable effects on the hydrograph. If the unit hydrographs for a basin are applicable to storms of shorter duration than the critical time for the basin, hydrographs of longer storms can be synthesized quite easily (Sec. 9-8). A basic duration of about one-fourth of the basin lag (Sec. 9-6) is generally satisfactory.

Areal distribution of runoff. The areal pattern of runoff can cause variations in hydrograph shape. If the area of high runoff is near the basin outlet, a rapid rise, sharp peak, and rapid recession usually result. Higher runoff in the upstream portion of the basin produces a slow rise and recession and a lower, broader peak. Unit hydrographs have been developed for specific runoff patterns, e.g., heavy upstream, uniform, or heavy downstream. This is not wholly satisfactory because of the sub-jectivity of classification. A better solution is to apply the unit-hydrograph method only to basins small enough so that the usual areal variations will not be great enough to cause major changes in hydrograph shape. The limiting basin size is fixed by the accuracy desired and regional climatic characteristics. Generally, however, unit hydrographs should not be used for basins much over 2000 sq mi unless reduced accuracy is acceptable. What has been said does not apply to rainfall variations caused by topographic controls. Such rainfall patterns are relatively fixed characteristics of the basin. It is departures from the normal pattern that cause trouble.

Amount of runoff. A basic part of the unit-hydrograph idea is that the ordinates of flow are proportional to the volume of runoff for all storms of a given duration. This is predicated on the assumption that the time bases of all hydrographs resulting from storms of a given duration are constant. Actually, from the character of recession curves it is evident that the duration of the recession is a function of peak flow. Practically,

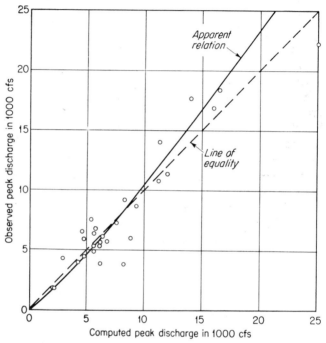

FIG. 9-2. Relation between observed and computed peak flow for Appalachee River near Buckhead, Georgia (436 sq mi).

it appears that the assumptions of a fixed time base and ordinates proportional to runoff volume are adequate for engineering purposes. There is evidence that the unit-hydrograph peak is generally somewhat higher for extreme floods than for average floods. Because of limited data on extreme floods, there is little quantitative evidence on this point. Hydrologists frequently increase peak flows from 5 to 15 per cent when making estimates of very extreme floods. Figure 9-2 shows a relation between observed flood peaks and those computed from a unit hydrograph developed from moderate floods.

In the light of the foregoing discussion, the *unit hydrograph* can be defined as *the hydrograph of one inch of direct runoff from a storm of specified duration.* For a storm of the same duration but with a different amount of runoff, the hydrograph of direct runoff can be expected to have the same time base as the unit hydrograph and ordinates of flow proportional to the runoff volume. The duration assigned to a unit hydrograph should be the duration of rainfall producing significant runoff. This should be determined by inspection of hourly-rainfall

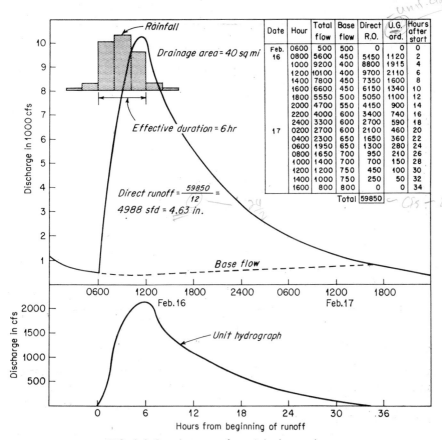

Date	Hour	Total flow	Base flow	Direct R.O.	U.G. ord.	Hours after start
Feb. 16	0600	500	500	0	0	0
	0800	5600	450	5150	1120	2
	1000	9200	400	8800	1915	4
	1200	10100	400	9700	2110	6
	1400	7800	450	7350	1600	8
	1600	6600	450	6150	1340	10
	1800	5550	500	5050	1100	12
	2000	4700	550	4150	900	14
	2200	4000	600	3400	740	16
	2400	3300	600	2700	590	18
17	0200	2700	600	2100	460	20
	0400	2300	650	1650	360	22
	0600	1950	650	1300	280	24
	0800	1650	700	950	210	26
	1000	1400	700	700	150	28
	1200	1200	750	450	100	30
	1400	1000	750	250	50	32
	1600	800	800	0	0	34
			Total	59850		

FIG. 9-3. Development of a unit hydrograph.

data. The characteristic hydrograph may be given as the percentages of the total runoff occurring in successive short increments of time. In this form it is known as a *distribution graph*.[1] Because the period averages define the hydrograph less explicitly than instantaneous flows, one need not be quite so careful in the use of the distribution graph as for the unit hydrograph. Distribution graphs are useful where estimates of

[1] M. Bernard, An Approach to Determinate Stream Flow, *Trans. ASCE*, Vol. 100, p. 347, 1935.

flow volume are more important than detailed rates of flow, as, for example, in analyzing the inflow to a reservoir.

9-3. Derivation of the unit hydrograph. The unit hydrograph is best derived from the hydrograph of a storm of reasonably uniform intensity, duration of desired length, and a runoff volume near or greater than 1.0 in. The first step (Fig. 9-3) is to separate the base flow from

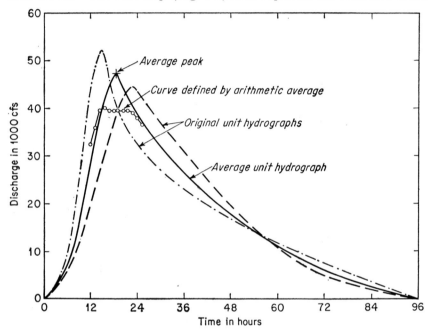

FIG. 9-4. Construction of an average unit hydrograph.

the direct runoff (Chap. 7). The volume of direct runoff is then determined, and the ordinates of the direct-runoff hydrograph are divided by the observed runoff in inches. The adjusted ordinates form a unit hydrograph for the specified storm duration.

A unit hydrograph derived from a single storm may be in error, and it is desirable to average the unit hydrographs from several storms of the same duration. This should not be an arithmetic average of concurrent coordinates, since if peaks do not occur at the same time, the average peak will be lower than many of the individual peaks. The proper procedure is to compute the average of the peak flows and times to peak. The average unit hydrograph is then sketched to conform to the shape of the other graphs, passing through the computed average peak, and having a volume of 1.00 in. (Fig. 9-4).

9-4. Derivation of unit hydrograph from complex storms. The simple approach outlined in Sec. 9-3 often proves inadequate because no such ideal storm is available in the record.   It is then necessary to develop the unit hydrograph from a complex storm.   If the individual bursts of rain in the storm result in well-defined peaks, it is possible to separate the hydrographs of the several bursts (Sec. 7-4) and use these hydrographs as independent storms.   If the resulting unit hydrographs are averaged, errors in the separation are minimized.

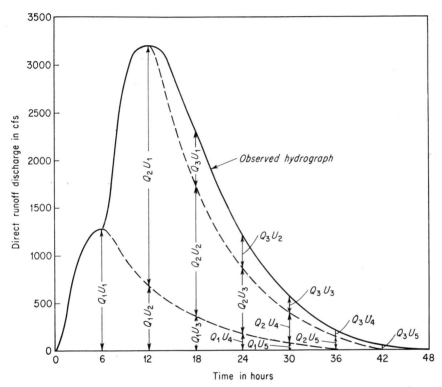

FIG. 9-5. Unit hydrographs from a complex storm.

If the hydrograph does not lend itself to separation (Fig. 9-5), the analysis begins with estimates of the direct-runoff volumes Q_1, Q_2, . . . , Q_n in successive periods during the storm.   The equation for any ordinate of the total hydrograph q_n in terms of runoff Q and unit-hydrograph ordinates U is

$$q_n = Q_n U_1 + Q_{n-1} U_2 + Q_{n-2} U_3 + \cdots + Q_1 U_n \qquad (9\text{-}1)$$

The first ordinate $q_1 = Q_1 U_1$, and since Q_1 is known (or estimated) U_1 can be computed.   The second ordinate is then

$$q_2 = Q_1 U_2 + Q_2 U_1 \qquad (9\text{-}2)$$

The only unknown in this equation is U_2 which can be computed. All the ordinates can be determined in a similar way.

Although the procedure just outlined may seem simple, there are numerous difficulties. Each computation depends on all preceding computations for values of U. Errors in estimating the runoff increments, errors in the observed streamflow, and variations in intensity and areal distribution of rainfall during the several storm periods can lead to cumulative errors which may become large in the latter portion of the unit hydrograph. Large negative ordinates sometimes develop.

A unit hydrograph can also be developed by successive approximations. A unit hydrograph is assumed and used to reconstruct the storm hydrograph (Sec. 9-8). If the reconstructed hydrograph does not agree with the observed hydrograph, the assumed unit hydrograph is modified and the process repeated until a unit hydrograph which seems to give the best fit is determined.

A more elegant but laborious method is the use of least squares, a statistical technique to find the constants a and b in an equation of the form

$$q = a + b_1Q_1 + b_2Q_2 + b_3Q_3 + \cdots + b_iQ_i \qquad (9\text{-}3)$$

Equations (9-1) and (9-3) are similar. Theoretically, for the unit hydrograph, a should be zero and the b's equivalent to the unit-hydrograph ordinates U. The least-squares technique would use data from a number of flood events for which values of q and Q are established to develop a set of average values of U. More detailed explanations can be found elsewhere.[1]

9-5. Unit hydrographs for various durations. If a unit hydrograph for duration t hr is added to itself lagged by t hr (Fig. 9-6), the resulting hydrograph represents the hydrograph for 2 in. of runoff in $2t$ hr. If the ordinates of this graph are divided by 2, the result is a unit hydrograph for duration $2t$ hr. The final graph represents the flow from 1 in. of runoff generated at uniform intensity of $1/2t$ in./hr in $2t$ hr. This simple example illustrates the ease with which a unit hydrograph for a short duration can be converted to a unit hydrograph for any multiple of the original duration.

Construction of a short-duration unit hydrograph from a longer duration can be accomplished by the methods described in Sec. 9-4. A more convenient technique for conversion to either a shorter or longer duration is the S-curve, or summation-curve, method. The S curve is the hydrograph that would result from an infinite series of runoff incre-

[1] R. K. Linsley, M. A. Kohler, and J. L. H. Paulhus, "Applied Hydrology," pp. 448–449, McGraw-Hill, New York, 1949.

W. M. Snyder, Hydrograph Analysis by Method of Least Squares, *Proc. ASCE*, Vol. 81, Separate 793, September, 1955.

ments of 1 in. in t hr.   Thus, each S curve applies to a specific duration within which each inch of runoff is generated.   The S curve is constructed by adding together a series of unit hydrographs, each lagged t hr with respect to the preceding one (Fig. 9-7).   If the time base of the unit hydrograph is T hr, then a continuous rainfall producing 1 in. of runoff

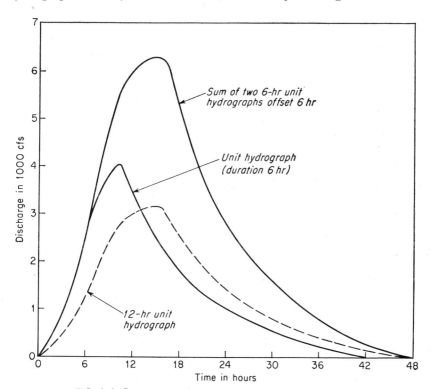

FIG. 9-6. Construction of a unit hydrograph for duration 2t.

every t hr would develop a constant outflow at the end of T hr.   Thus only T/t unit hydrographs need be combined to produce an S curve which should reach equilibrium at flow q_e:

$$q_e = \frac{24 \times 26.9 \times A}{t} = \frac{645.6A}{t} \qquad (9\text{-}4)$$

where A is drainage area in square miles, t is duration in hours, 24 is the number of hours in a day, and 26.9 is the number of second-foot-days in 1 in. of runoff from 1 sq mi.

Commonly, the S curve tends to fluctuate about the equilibrium flow. This means that the initial unit hydrograph does not actually represent runoff at a uniform rate for t hr.   If a uniform rate of runoff is applied to a basin, equilibrium flow at the rate given by Eq. (9-4) must eventually develop.   If the actual effective duration of runoff associated with the original unit hydrograph is not t hr, the summation process results in a runoff diagram with either periodic gaps or periodic increases to a rate of 2 in. in t hr (Fig. 9-8).   Thus the S curve serves as an approximate

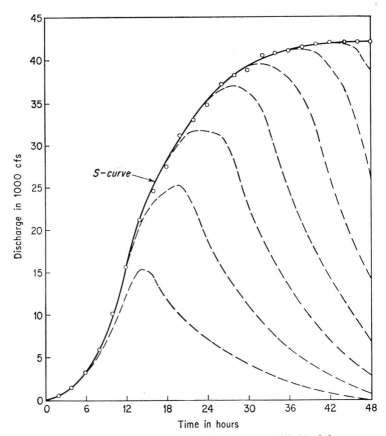

FIG. 9-7. Graphical illustration of the S curve of Table 9-1.

check on the assumed duration of effective rainfall for the unit hydrograph.   A duration which results in minimum fluctuation of the S curve can be found by trial.   Note, however, that fluctuation of the S curve can also result from nonuniform runoff generation during the t hr, unusual areal distribution of rain, or errors in the basic data.   For this reason, the S curve can indicate only an approximate duration.

Construction of an S curve does not require tabulating and adding T/t unit hydrographs with successive lags of t hr.   Table 9-1 illustrates the computation of an S curve, starting with an initial unit hydrograph for which $t = 6$ hr. For the first 6 hr the unit hydrograph and S curve are identical (Cols. 2 and 4). The S-curve additions (Col. 3) are the ordinates of the S curve set ahead 6 hr. Since an S-curve ordinate is the sum of all the unit-hydrograph ordinates falling at that time, combining the S-curve additions with the initial unit hydrograph is the same as adding all previous unit hydrographs.

The difference between two S curves with their initial points displaced by t' hr gives a hydrograph for the new duration t' hr. Since the S curve

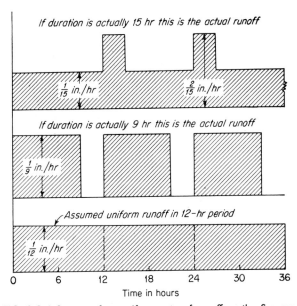

FIG. 9-8. Influence of nonuniform rate of runoff on the S curve.

represents runoff production at a rate of 1 in. in t hr, the runoff volume represented by this new hydrograph will be t'/t in. Thus the ordinates of the unit hydrograph for t' hr are computed by multiplying the S-curve differences by the ratio t/t'. The computations for a 2-hr unit hydrograph are illustrated in Table 9-1.

9-6. Synthetic unit hydrographs. Only a relatively small number of the streams in the United States are gaged. Unit hydrographs can be derived as described in the previous sections only if records are available. Hence some means of deriving unit hydrographs for ungaged basins is necessary. This requires a relation between the physical geometry of the basin and the resulting hydrographs. Three approaches have been used: formulas relating hydrographs to basin characteristics, transposition of unit hydrographs from one basin to another (Sec. 9-7), and storage routing (Sec. 10-13).

Most attempts to derive formulas for the unit hydrograph have been
aimed at determining time of peak, peak flow, and time base. These
items plus the fact that the volume must equal 1.00 in. permit sketching
of the complete hydrograph. The key item in most studies has been the

TABLE 9-1. Application of S-curve Method

Time, hr	6-hr unit graph	S-curve additions	S-curve Col. (2) + (3)	Lagged S-curve	Col. (4) − (5)	2-hr unit graph
(1)	(2)	(3)	(4)	(5)	(6)	(7)
0	0	......	0	.....	0	0
2	400	......	400	0	400	1,200
4	1,400	......	1,400	400	1,000	3,000
6	3,100	0	3,100	1,400	1,700	5,100
8	5,400	400	5,800	3,100	2,700	8,100
10	8,600	1,400	10,000	5,800	4,200	12,600
12	12,600	3,100	15,700	10,000	5,700	17,100
14	15,400	5,800	21,200	15,700	5,500	16,500
16	14,600	10,000	24,600	21,200	3,400	10,200
18	11,800	15,700	27,500	24,600	2,900	8,700
20	9,900	21,200	31,100	27,500	2,400*	7,200
22	8,400	24,600	33,000	31,100	2,000*	6,000
24	7,200	27,500	34,700	33,000	1,800*	5,400
26	6,000	31,100	37,100	34,700	1,600*	4,800
28	5,100	33,000	38,100	37,100	1,400*	4,200
30	4,200	34,700	38,900	38,100	1,200*	3,600
32	3,400	37,100	40,500	38,900	1,000*	3,000
34	2,700	38,100	40,800	40,500	800*	2,400
36	2,100	38,900	41,000	40,800	600*	1,800
38	1,600	40,500	41,500*	41,000	400*	1,200
40	1,100	40,800	41,900	41,500	200*	600
42	700	41,000	42,000*	41,900	100	300
44	400	41,500*	42,000*	42,000	0	0
46	200	41,900	42,100	42,000	0*	
48	0	42,000	42,100*	42,100	0	

* Adjusted value.

basin lag, most frequently defined as the time from the centroid of rainfall to the hydrograph peak.[1] The first synthetic-unit-hydrograph procedure was presented by Snyder.[2] In a study of basins in the Appalachian Mountains region, he found that the basin lag t_p (in hr) could be
expressed by

$$t_p = C_t(LL_c)^{0.3} \qquad (9\text{-}5)$$

[1] Lag is also defined as the time difference between the centroid of rainfall and the
centroid of runoff. This definition is more rigorous, but the one in the text is simpler
to apply.

[2] F. F. Snyder, Synthetic Unit Hydrographs, *Trans. Am. Geophys. Union*, Vol. 19,
Part 1, pp. 447–454, 1938.

where L is the length of the main stream from outlet to divide in miles and L_c is the distance from the outlet to a point on the stream nearest the centroid of the basin. The product LL_c is a measure of the size and shape of the basin. The coefficient C_t varied from 1.8 to 2.2, with some indication of lower values for basins with steeper slopes.

Before an equation for peak flow can be written, a standard duration of rain t_r must be adopted, and Snyder took $t_r = t_p/5.5$. For rains of this duration he found that the unit-hydrograph peak q_p was given by

$$q_p = \frac{640 C_p A}{t_p} \tag{9-6}$$

where A is the drainage area in square miles, C_p is a coefficient ranging from 0.56 to 0.69, and 640 is a conversion factor to give q_p in cubic feet per second.

Snyder adopted the time base T (in days) of the hydrograph as

$$T = 3 + 3\frac{t_p}{24} \tag{9-7}$$

The constants of Eq. (9-7) are fixed by the procedure used to separate base flow from direct runoff. Equations (9-5) to (9-7) define the three factors necessary to construct the unit hydrograph for duration t_r. For any other duration t_R the lag is

$$t_{p_R} = t_p + \frac{t_R - t_r}{4} \tag{9-8}$$

and this modified lag t_{p_R} is used in Eqs. (9-6) and (9-7).

Taylor and Schwarz,[1] using 20 basins in the North and Middle Atlantic States, found an expression for lag as

$$t_p = C_t e^{m t_R} \tag{9-9}$$

where the exponent m is given by

$$m = \frac{0.212}{(LL_c)^{0.36}} \tag{9-10}$$

and the coefficient C_t is

$$C_t = \frac{0.6}{\sqrt{s}} \tag{9-11}$$

where s is the weighted slope of the channel. Several measures of basin size and shape were tested, but the term LL_c with an exponent very nearly equal to Snyder's value was found best. The place of slope in the coefficient C_t was also qualitatively indicated by Snyder.

[1] A. B. Taylor and H. E. Schwarz, Unit-hydrograph Lag and Peak Flow Related to Basin Characteristics, *Trans. Am. Geophys. Union*, Vol. 33, pp. 235–246, April, 1952.

Taylor and Schwarz also derived an expression for the unit-hydrograph peak in the same form as Eq. (9-9) but with more complex expressions for the coefficient and exponent.   They give a nomogram for solving the relationship.

Snyder's synthetic-unit-hydrograph formulas have been tried elsewhere in the country with varying success.   The coefficients C_t and C_p

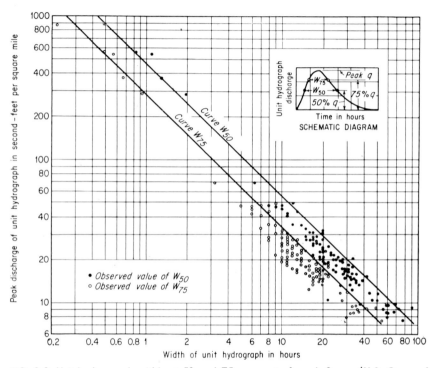

FIG. 9-9. Unit-hydrograph width at 50 and 75 per cent of peak flow.   (U.S. Corps of Engineers.)

are found to vary considerably.[1]   The best way to use his equations is to derive values of C_t and C_p from unit hydrographs for gaged basins of similar characteristics as the problem area and apply these coefficients to the ungaged stream.   The procedure thus becomes a means of transposing unit-hydrograph characteristics from one basin to another.

Figure 9-9 presents the results of an analysis by the Corps of Engineers[2] of the width of unit hydrographs (in hr) at 50 and 75 per cent of the peak

[1] R. K. Linsley, Application of Synthetic Unit-graphs in the Western Mountains States, *Trans. Am. Geophys. Union*, Vol. 24, Part 2, pp. 580–587, 1943.

[2] "Engineering Manual for Civil Works," Part II, Chap. 5, Office of Chief of Engineers, Department of Army, April, 1946.

flow. This provides a supplementary guide for sketching the unit hydrograph.

9-7. Transposing unit hydrographs. From Sec. 9-6 a general expression for basin lag might be expected to take the form

$$t_p = C_t \left(\frac{LL_c}{\sqrt{s}}\right)^n \qquad (9\text{-}12)$$

If known values of lag are plotted against $LL_c/\sqrt{s}$ on logarithmic paper

		Drainage area, sq mi			Drainage area, sq mi
1.	San Gabriel River at San Gabriel dam	162.0	10. Live Oak Creek at Live Oak dam		2.3
2.	West Fork San Gabriel River at Cogswell dam	40.4	11. Tujunga Creek at Big Tujunga dam No. 1		81.4
3.	Santa Anita Creek at Santa Anita dam	10.8	12. East Fullerton Creek at Fullerton dam		3.1
4.	San Dimas Creek at San Dimas dam	16.2	13. Los Angeles River at Sepulveda dam		152.0
5.	Eaton Wash at Eaton Wash dam	9.5	14. Pacoima Wash at Pacoima dam		27.8
6.	San Antonio Creek near Claremont	16.9	15. Alhambra Wash above Short Street		14.0
7.	Santa Clara River near Saugus	355.0	16. Broadway drain above Raymond dike		2.5
8.	Temecula Creek at Pauba Canyon	168.0	17. Ballona Creek at Sawtelle Blvd.		88.6
9.	Santa Margarita River near Fallbrook	645.0	18. San Jose Creek at Workman Mill Road bridge		81.3

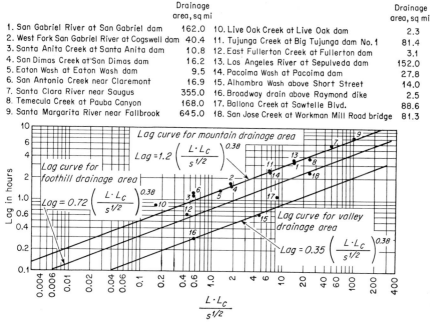

FIG. 9-10. Relationship between basin lag (beginning of rain to $\int q\, dt = Q/2$) and basin characteristics. (*U.S. Corps of Engineers.*)

(Fig. 9-10) the resulting plot should define a straight line, provided that the values are taken from basins of similar hydrologic characteristics, that is, $C_t = \text{const.}$ A relation such as Fig. 9-10 offers a means of estimating basin lag. The peak flow and shape of the unit hydrograph may be estimated by use of a plot relating q_p to t_p or by use of dimensionless hydrographs[1] such as Fig. 9-11. The dimensionless form eliminates the effect of basin size and much of the effect of basin shape. The similarity of the several graphs of Fig. 9-11 reflects a considerable similarity in flood

[1] G. G. Commons, Flood Hydrographs, *Civil Eng.*, Vol. 12, p. 571, 1942.
H. M. Williams, Discussion of "Military Airfields," *Trans. ASCE*, Vol. 110, p. 820, 1945.

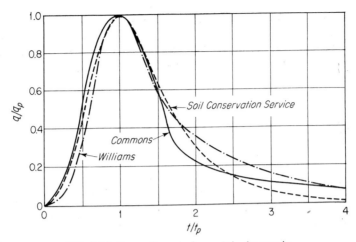

FIG. 9-11. Some dimensionless unit hydrographs.

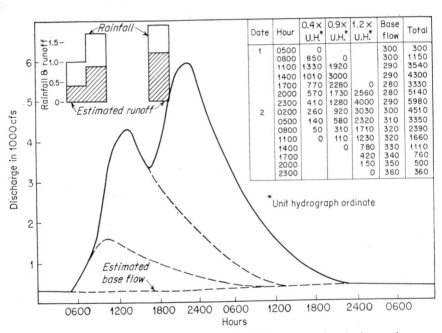

Date	Hour	0.4× U.H.*	0.9× U.H.*	1.2× U.H.*	Base flow	Total
1	0500	0			300	300
	0800	850	0		300	1150
	1100	1330	1920		290	3540
	1400	1010	3000		290	4300
	1700	770	2280	0	280	3330
	2000	570	1730	2560	280	5140
	2300	410	1280	4000	290	5980
2	0200	260	920	3030	300	4510
	0500	140	580	2320	310	3350
	0800	50	310	1710	320	2390
	1100	0	110	1230	320	1660
	1400		0	780	330	1110
	1700			420	340	760
	2000			150	350	500
	2300			0	360	360

*Unit hydrograph ordinate

FIG. 9-12. Use of a unit hydrograph to synthesize a streamflow hydrograph.

hydrographs from various regions. Unfortunately, the relationships between the hydrograph shape and the characteristics of the basin are so complex that no completely successful relationships have been derived.[1]

[1] C. G. Edson, Parameters for Relating Unit Hydrographs to Watershed Characteristics, *Trans. Am. Geophys. Union*, Vol. 32, pp. 591–596, August, 1951.

9-8. Application of the unit hydrograph. The application of a unit hydrograph has been demonstrated in Sec. 9-5 on the basis of uniform production of runoff. Figure 9-12 illustrates the use of a 3-hr unit hydrograph to synthesize the storm hydrograph from a series of rainfall periods, with varying intensity. The increments of runoff for successive 3-hr periods are computed using runoff relations (Chap. 8). The hydrograph of direct runoff resulting from each 3-hr increment is given by multiplying the unit hydrograph by the period runoff. The total hydrograph is the sum of all the incremental hydrographs and estimated base flow.

FIG. 9-13. Definition sketch for laminar sheet flow.

9-9. The hydrograph of overland flow. Although the depth of flow in the overland sheet is quite small, the quantity of water temporarily detained in this sheet (*surface detention*) is relatively great. It is generally assumed that overland flow is laminar (Fig. 9-13). Hence,

$$\rho g (D - y) s = \mu \frac{dv}{dy} \tag{9-13}$$

where ρ is density, g is gravity, and μ is absolute viscosity. The assumption is made that the slope is so small that the sine and tangent are equal. Since μ/ρ is equal to kinematic viscosity ν,

$$dv = \frac{gs}{\nu} (D - y) \, dy \tag{9-14}$$

Integrating and noting that $v = 0$ when $y = 0$,

$$v = \frac{gs}{\nu} \left(yD - \frac{y^2}{2} \right) \tag{9-15}$$

Integrating from $y = 0$ to $y = D$ and dividing by D, the mean velocity is

$$v_m = \frac{gsD^2}{3\nu} \tag{9-16}$$

and the discharge per unit width is $v_m D$ or

$$q = bD^3 \tag{9-17}$$

where b is a coefficient involving slope and viscosity.

The most extensive experiments on overland flow are those of Izzard.[1]

[1] C. F. Izzard, Hydraulics of Runoff from Developed Surfaces, *Proc. Highway Research Board*, Vol. 26, pp. 129–150, 1946.

R. K. Linsley, M. A. Kohler, and J. L. H. Paulhus, "Applied Hydrology," pp. 275–282, McGraw-Hill, New York, 1949.

He made tests on long flumes at various slopes and with various surfaces. His tests showed that the time to equilibrium is

$$t_e = \frac{2V_e}{60q_e} \qquad (9\text{-}18)$$

where t_e is defined as the time in minutes when flow is 97 per cent of the supply rate and V_e is the volume of water in surface detention at equilibrium. From a strip of unit width the equilibrium flow q_e is

$$q_e = \frac{iL}{43,200} \qquad (9\text{-}19)$$

where i is the rainfall rate (or the rate of rainfall excess if the surface is pervious) and L is the distance of overland flow. The constant 43,200 gives q_e in cubic feet per second when i is in inches per hour. Substituting average depth on the strip V_e/L for outflow depth, Eq. (9-17) becomes

$$\frac{V_e}{L} = kq_e^{\frac{1}{3}} \qquad (9\text{-}20)$$

Substituting Eq. (9-19) for q_e gives

$$V_e = \frac{kL^{\frac{4}{3}}i^{\frac{1}{3}}}{35.1} \qquad (9\text{-}21)$$

where V_e is the volume of detention (cu ft) on the strip at equilibrium. Experimentally k was found to be given by

$$k = \frac{0.0007i + c}{s^{\frac{1}{3}}} \qquad (9\text{-}22)$$

where s is the surface slope and the retardance coefficient c is as given in Table 9-2.

TABLE 9-2. Retardance Coefficient c in Eq. (9-22)

Very smooth asphalt pavement	0.007
Tar and sand pavement	0.0075
Crushed-slate roofing paper	0.0082
Concrete	0.012
Tar and gravel pavement	0.017
Closely clipped sod	0.046
Dense bluegrass turf	0.060

Izzard found that the form of the overland-flow hydrograph could be presented as a dimensionless graph (Fig. 9-14). With t_e and q_e known, the q/q_e curve permits plotting of the rising limb of the overland-flow hydrograph. The dimensionless recession curve of Fig. 9-14b defines the shape of the receding limb. At any time t_a after the end of rain, the factor β is

$$\beta = \frac{60q_e t_a}{V_0} \tag{9-23}$$

where V_0 is the detention given by Eqs. (9-20) and (9-22), taking $i = 0$.

9-10. Flood formulas. Many empirical formulas have been presented for estimating flood peaks from small basins. For the most part these formulas are misleading and unsound, and they are discussed here

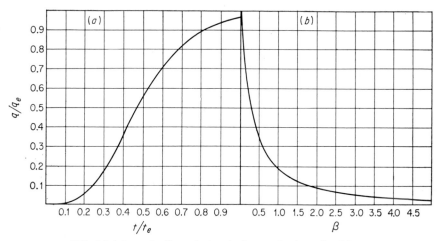

FIG. 9-14. Izzard's dimensionless hydrograph of overland flow.

only in a general way. One type of formula makes the peak flow a function of basin area:

$$q_p = bA^m \tag{9-24}$$

Fuller[1] suggested $m = 0.8$, Myers[2] proposed $m = 0.5$, and Fanning used $m = 5/6$. The Talbot formula, which gives cross-sectional area of the waterway rather than peak flow, uses the exponent 0.75. The differences in these exponents is sufficient evidence that the formula is inadequate. The coefficient b must incorporate the parameters of a rainfall-runoff relation, frequency curve, and the factors which control hydrograph shape. Only luck will permit the selection of the correct value of b for a basin. Formulas of this type should never be used for engineering design.

Another group of formulas is typified by that of Burkli-Ziegler,[3]

$$q_p = Aci \sqrt{\frac{s}{A}} \tag{9-25}$$

[1] W. E. Fuller, Flood Flows, *Trans. ASCE*, Vol. 77, pp. 564–694, 1914.
[2] C. S. Jarvis, Flood-flow Characteristics, *Trans. ASCE*, Vol. 89, pp. 985–1032, 1926.
[3] "The Greatest Discharge of Municipal Sewers," Zurich, 1880.

where i is the expected average rainfall in inches per hour, s is the average slope of the watershed in feet per 1000 ft, A is the area in acres, and q_p is in cubic feet per second. The McMath[1] formula is of the same form except that the fifth root is used. The coefficient c in these formulas is almost as inclusive as b in Eq. (9-24). Land slope is recognized as a factor in basin storage, and the rainfall factor is introduced. Equations of this type have no place in modern engineering design.

The most widely used design equation for small basins is given the misleading name "rational formula,"

$$q_p = CiA \qquad (9\text{-}26)$$

where q_p is in acre-inches per hour, i is average rainfall intensity in inches per hour for a duration equal to the time of concentration of the basin, and A is area in acres. With an error of less than 1 per cent, flow rate in inches per hour per acre is equal to flow rate in cubic feet per second. The equation states that the rate of runoff equals the rate of supply (rainfall excess) if the rain lasts long enough to permit the entire area to contribute. This assumption is literally true for an area of a few square feet and may not involve serious error for basins up to a few acres in area if the time of concentration is correct. For larger areas, the coefficient C not only expresses the proportion of the total rainfall which runs off but also the effect of overland flow and channel storage on the peak. The coefficient is the ratio of the theoretical absolute peak (100 per cent runoff and no storage) to the actual peak. The problem of estimating C is no less than for any other formula. Whether C is defined as q_p/iA or as total runoff divided by total rainfall, experience shows that its value varies widely from storm to storm. Frequency is presumably accounted for by choosing i of known return period. If C and i are statistically independent, C should have a return period of unity (1 yr) if the return period of the computed q_p is to be the

TABLE 9-3. Values of Coefficient C in Eq. (9-26)

Type of Area	Value of C
Flat residential, 30% impervious area	0.40*
Moderately steep residential, 50% impervious	0.65*
Built-up area, 70% impervious	0.80*
Flat cultivated land, open sandy soil	0.20†
Rolling cultivated land, clay-loam soil	0.50†
Hill land, forested, clay-loam soil	0.50†

* W. W. Horner and F. L. Flynt, Relation between Rainfall and Runoff from Small Urban Areas, *Trans. ASCE*, Vol. 101, p. 140, 1936.

† M. Bernard, Discussion of Run-off—Rational Runoff Formulas, by R. L. Gregory and C. E. Arnold, *Trans. ASCE*, Vol. 96, p. 1038, 1932.

[1] R. E. McMath, Determination of the Size of Sewers, *Trans. ASCE*, Vol. 16, pp. 183–190, 1887.

same as that for i.   In practice, C is related only to type of terrain without regard to frequency (Table 9-3).   Of all the flood formulas, the rational formula has the advantage that its physical meaning is reasonably clear.   However, it should be used with extreme caution since it does not adequately recognize all the complications of the runoff process.

BIBLIOGRAPHY

Hoyt, W. G., and others: Studies of Relations of Rainfall and Runoff in the United States, *U.S. Geol. Survey Water-supply Paper* 772, 1936.
Hydrology Handbook, *ASCE Manual* 22, 1949.
Jarvis, Clarence S.: Floods, Chap. XI G, in O. E. Meinzer (ed.), "Hydrology," McGraw-Hill, New York, 1942.
Jarvis, C. S., and others: Floods in the United States, Magnitude and Frequency, *U.S. Geol. Survey Water-supply Paper* 771, 1936.
Langbein, W. B., et al.: Topographic Characteristics of Drainage Basins, *U.S. Geol. Survey Water-supply Paper* 968-C, 1947.
Linsley, R. K., M. A. Kohler, and J. L. H. Paulhus: "Applied Hydrology," Chap. 11, McGraw-Hill, New York, 1949.
Sherman, L. K.: The Unit Hydrograph, Chap. XI E, in O. E. Meinzer (ed.), "Hydrology," McGraw-Hill, New York, 1942.
Williams, G. R.: Hydrology, Chap. IV, in Hunter Rouse (ed.), "Engineering Hydraulics," Wiley, New York, 1950.

PROBLEMS

9-1. Neglecting storage and assuming a linear rise and recession of the elemental hydrograph, sketch the outflow hydrograph from a basin in the shape of a 60° sector of a circle with outflow at the apex.   Assume travel time proportional to distance and rainfall duration equal to time of concentration.

9-2. Repeat Prob. 9-1 for a semicircle with outflow at the mid-point of the boundary diameter.   What change in shape would result if the rainfall (runoff) were to occur at unit rate for half the duration and three times that rate for the remainder?

9-3. How would the hydrograph of Prob. 9-2 be affected if runoff were to occur only from the outer half of the area?

9-4. Given below are the observed flows from a storm of 3-hr duration on a stream with a drainage area of 122 sq mi.   Derive the unit hydrograph.   Assume constant base flow = 600 cfs.

Hour	Day 1	Day 2	Day 3
3 A.M.	600	4600	1700
6 A.M.	550	4000	1500
9 A.M.	6000	3500	1300
Noon	9500	3100	1100
3 P.M.	8000	2700	900
6 P.M.	7000	2400	800
9 P.M.	6100	2100	700
Midnight	5300	1900	600

9-5. Given below are three unit hydrographs derived from separate storms on a small basin. All are believed to have resulted from 4-hr rains. Find the average unit hydrograph. Drainage area = 3.5 sq mi.

Hours	Storm 1	Storm 2	Storm 3
0	0	0	0
1	110	25	16
2	365	125	58
3	500	358	173
4	390	465	337
5	310	405	440
6	235	305	400
7	175	220	285
8	130	170	215
9	95	130	165
10	65	90	122
11	40	60	90
12	22	35	60
13	10	20	35
14	5	8	16
15	0	0	0

9-6. The hydrograph tabulated below resulted from three successive 6-hr periods of rainfall having runoffs estimated as 0.6, 1.2, and 0.9 in., respectively. Using the method illustrated by Eq. (9-1), find the 6-hr unit hydrograph for this basin. Drainage area = 58 sq mi. Base flow has been subtracted.

Time, hr	Flow, cfs
0	0
3	750
6	2800
9	2830
12	6620
15	4320
18	6450
21	3140
24	1950
27	930
30	310
33	90
36	0

9-7. As an illustration of the effect of minor errors on the computation of Prob. 9-6, repeat, using the same figures except for the ordinate at 6 hr which is changed to 2600 cfs.

9-8. Using storm 2 of Prob. 9-5, construct the S curve and find the 2- and 6-hr unit hydrographs. Smooth the S curve as required.

9-9. Given below is the 4-hr unit hydrograph for a basin of 84 sq mi.   Construct the S curve and find the 2- and 6-hr unit hydrographs.

Time, hr	Flow, cfs	Time, hr	Flow, cfs
0	0	11	2700
1	400	12	2200
2	2500	13	1800
3	4400	14	1400
4	6000	15	1100
5	7000	16	800
6	6100	17	600
7	5200	18	400
8	4500	19	200
9	3800	20	100
10	3200	21	0

9-10. Using the unit hydrograph of storm 3, Prob. 9-5, find the peak flow resulting from four successive 4-hr periods of rainfall producing 0.35, 0.87, 1.39, and 0.77 in. of runoff, respectively.   Ignore base flow.

9-11. For a drainage basin selected by your instructor, derive a synthetic unit hydrograph using Snyder's method with $C_t = 2.0$ and $C_p = 0.62$.

9-12. A basin of 139 sq mi has $L = 16$ mi, $L_c = 6$ mi.   Using Snyder's method, coefficients as in Prob. 9-11, and $t_R = 3$ hr, find the unit hydrograph.

9-13. Using actual streamflow data for a basin assigned by your instructor, find the unit hydrograph for a storm.   What values of C_t and C_p for Snyder's method are indicated by the data?

9-14. A parking lot 150 ft long in the direction of the slope and 80 ft wide has a tar and gravel pavement on a slope of 0.0025.   Assuming a rainfall intensity of 2.75 in./hr, construct the outflow hydrograph, using Izzard's method.

9-15. A city lot 200 ft deep and 100 ft wide has a slope of 0.005 toward the street. The street is 60 ft wide and has a 6-in. crown.   Assuming a rainfall intensity of 1.8 in./hr, $c = 0.040$ for the lot and 0.007 for the street, and a rainfall duration of 60 min, find the peak flow into the gutter.   What will be the peak flow if the rainfall duration is 10 min?

10

STREAMFLOW ROUTING

As the discharge in a channel increases, stage also increases and with it the volume of water in temporary storage in the channel. During the falling portion of a flood an equal volume of water must be released from storage. As a result, a flood wave moving down a channel appears to have its time base lengthened and (if volume remains constant) its crest lowered. The flood wave is said to be *attenuated*. *Streamflow routing* is the technique used in hydrology to compute the effect of channel storage on the shape and movement of a flood wave.

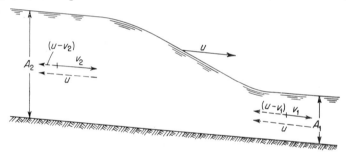

FIG. 10-1. Definition sketch for analysis of a monoclinal rising wave.

Given the flow at an upstream point, routing may be used to compute the flow at a downstream point. The principles of routing apply also to computation of the effect of a reservoir on the shape of a flood wave. Hydraulic storage occurs not only in channels and reservoirs but also as water flowing over the ground surface. Hence, storage is effective at the very inception of the flood wave, and routing techniques may be used to compute the hydrograph which will result from a specified pattern of rainfall excess.

10-1. Wave movement. One of the simplest wave forms is the *monoclinal rising wave* in a uniform channel. Such a wave (Fig. 10-1) consists of an initial steady flow, a period of uniformly increasing flow, and a continuing steady flow at the higher rate. Superimposing on this wave system a velocity equal and opposite to the wave celerity u causes

216

the wave configuration to become stationary, and a steady flow q' takes place from right to left, with the velocities shown. This flow, known as the *overrun*, is

$$q' = (u - v_1)A_1 = (u - v_2)A_2 \tag{10-1}$$

where A is the cross-sectional area of the channel. Solving Eq. (10-1) for the wave celerity gives

$$u = \frac{A_1v_1 - A_2v_2}{A_1 - A_2} = \frac{q_1 - q_2}{A_1 - A_2} \tag{10-2}$$

The celerity of a monoclinal wave is thus a function of the area-discharge relation for the stream (Fig. 10-2).

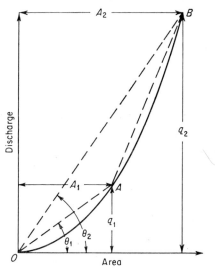

Since velocity usually increases with stage, area-discharge curves are usually concave upward. The slopes of the secants OA and OB represent the water velocities at sections 1 and 2, respectively ($v_1 = q_1/A_1 = \tan \theta_1$), while the slope of the secant AB represents the wave celerity [Eq. (10-2)]. It may be concluded that (1) wave celerity is greater than the water velocity in most channels; (2) for a given peak flow, the wave having the highest initial flow will travel fastest; and (3) for a wave of very small height

$$u = \frac{dq}{dA} = \frac{1}{B}\frac{dq}{dy} \tag{10-3}$$

FIG. 10-2. Typical area-discharge relation for a stream and its influence on wave celerity.

where B is the channel width. Equation (10-3) is known as *Seddon's law* after the man[1] who first demonstrated its validity on the Mississippi River.

From the Chézy formula for flow in a wide, open channel (assuming depth equal to hydraulic radius),

$$v = Cy^{1/2}s^{1/2} \tag{10-4}$$

and

$$q = Av = vBy = CBy^{3/2}s^{1/2} \tag{10-5}$$

Differentiating,

$$\frac{dq}{dy} = \frac{3}{2} CBy^{1/2}s^{1/2} = \frac{3}{2} Bv \tag{10-6}$$

[1] J. Seddon, River Hydraulics, *Trans. ASCE*, Vol. 43, pp. 217–229, 1900.

Substituting Eq. (10-6) in Eq. (10-3),

$$u = \frac{3}{2} v \qquad (10\text{-}7)$$

The derived ratio between water velocity and wave celerity depends on channel shape and the flow formula used. Values shown in Table 10-1 may be used as rough guides for estimates of wave celerity.

TABLE 10-1. Theoretical Ratio between Wave Celerity and Water Velocity for Typical Sections

Shape	Manning	Chézy
Triangle....................	1.33	1.25
Wide rectangle.............	1.67	1.50
Wide parabola.............	1.44	1.33

A second type of wave is shown in Fig. 10-3. This is an abrupt wave, and the figure illustrates conditions 1 sec after the instantaneous opening

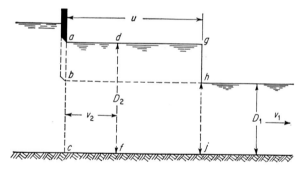

FIG. 10-3. Definition sketch for the analysis of an abrupt translatory wave.

of the gate. The volume of water entering the channel in this time is $q_2 = A_2 v_2$ (area *acfd*). The increased volume *abhg* is

$$q_2 - q_1 = u(A_2 - A_1) \qquad (10\text{-}8)$$

Substituting $Av = q$,

$$v_2 = (A_1 v_1 + A_2 u - A_1 u)\frac{1}{A_2} \qquad (10\text{-}9)$$

The volume *dfjg* has been accelerated from v_1 to v_2 by the force F:

$$F = \frac{w}{g}(v_2 - v_1) = \frac{(u - v_2)(v_2 - v_1)A_2 w}{g} \qquad (10\text{-}10)$$

where w is the specific weight of water. Since F also equals the difference in pressure on A_1 and A_2,

$$F = wA_2\bar{y}_2 - wA_1\bar{y}_1 \qquad (10\text{-}11)$$

where $\bar{y}$ is the depth to center of gravity of the section. Equating Eqs. (10-10) and (10-11), inserting v_2 from Eq. (10-9), and solving for u give

$$u = v_1 \pm \sqrt{g\,\frac{A_2\bar{y}_2 - A_1\bar{y}_1}{A_1(1 - A_1/A_2)}} \qquad (10\text{-}12)$$

In unit width of rectangular channel we may substitute $D = A$ and $D/2 = \bar{y}$. Hence

$$u = v_1 \pm \sqrt{\frac{gD_2}{2D_1}(D_2 + D_1)} \qquad (10\text{-}13)$$

For very small wave height, $D_1 \approx D_2$ and

$$u = v_1 \pm \sqrt{gD} \qquad (10\text{-}14)$$

Equation (10-12) is a general equation applying to any channel. Equation (10-13) applies only to rectangular channels, and Eq. (10-14) only to waves of very small height in rectangular channels. Abrupt translatory waves occur as tidal bores in many estuaries, as surges in power canals and tailraces, as seiches in lakes, and occasionally as flood waves caused by intense, small-area storms.

10-2. Waves in natural channels. Controlled experiments[1] in flumes of regular cross section have confirmed the equations developed in Sec. 10-1. Reasonable checks have also been obtained in natural streams where the effect of local inflow is negligible, as in Seddon's work on the Lower Mississippi and Wilkinson's[2] study of waves downstream from TVA dams. Equation (10-14) gives very good estimates of the celerity of impulse waves in still water.

Simple mathematical treatment of flood waves is necessarily limited to uniform channels with fairly regular cross section. The hydrologist must deal with nonuniform channels of complex section with nonuniform slope and varying roughness. The formulas of Sec. 10-1 apply to waves generated at a point on a channel, but most flood waves are generated by nonuniform lateral inflow along all the channels of the stream system. Thus natural flood waves are considerably more complex than the

---

[1] R. E. Horton, Channel Waves Subject Chiefly to Momentum Control, *Permanent Intern. Assoc. Navigation Congr. Bull.* 27, 1939.

E. E. Moots, A Study in Flood Waves, *Univ. Iowa Studies Eng. Bull.* 14, 1938.

A. Schoklitsch, Dam Break Waves, *Math. naturw. Klasse*, Vol. 126, pp. 1489–1514, 1917.

[2] J. H. Wilkinson, Translatory Waves in Natural Channels, *Trans. ASCE*, Vol. 72, pp. 1203–1236, 1945.

simplified cases which yield to mathematical analysis and experimental verification.

Theoretical treatment is useful in studies of surges in canals, impulse waves in still water (including seiches and tides), and waves released from dams. Waves in natural channels are usually analyzed by use of the continuity equation. Natural flood waves are generally intermediate between pure translation as described in Sec. 10-1 and pondage which would occur in a reservoir or lake. Figure 10-4 shows an example

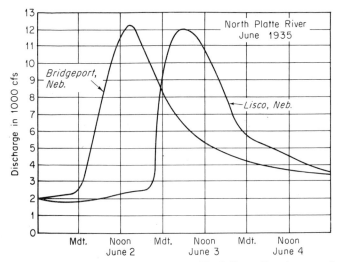

FIG. 10-4. Example of translatory wave movement, North Platte River between Bridgeport and Lisco, Nebraska.

of a flood wave moving with nearly pure translation, i.e., little change in shape. Figure 10-5 illustrates the great modifications which can occur when a flood wave moves through a reservoir in which discharge is a function of the quantity of water in storage. Momentum forces predominate in pure translatory waves, and such waves have relatively short time bases compared with the dimensions of the system in which they move. Most natural waves move under friction control and have time bases considerably exceeding the dimensions of the stream system.

10-3. The storage equation. *Routing* is the solution of the storage equation which is an expression of continuity:

$$I - O = \frac{dS}{dt} \tag{10-15}$$

or, more commonly,

$$\bar{I} - \bar{O} = \frac{\Delta S}{t} \tag{10-16}$$

where I is inflow rate, O is outflow rate, and S is storage, all for a specific reach of a stream. Equation (10-16) is exact, but its application to practical problems involves approximations. To provide a form more convenient for use, it is commonly assumed that the average of the flows at the beginning and ending of a short time period t (*routing period*) equals

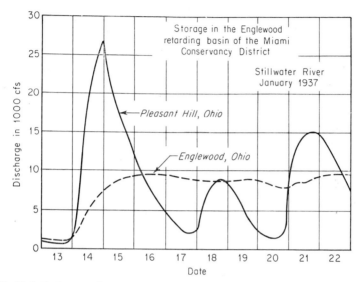

FIG. 10-5. Reduction of discharge through reservoir action, Stillwater River, Ohio.

the average flow during the period. Using subscripts 1 and 2 to represent the beginning and end of the period, respectively,

$$\frac{I_1 + I_2}{2} t - \frac{O_1 + O_2}{2} t = S_2 - S_1 \qquad (10\text{-}17)$$

Most storage-routing methods are based on Eq. (10-17). It is assumed that I_1, I_2, O_1, and S_1 are known and O_2 and S_2 must be determined. Since there are two unknowns, a second relation between storage and flow is needed to complete a solution. The major difficulties in storage routing are involved in this latter relation.

The assumption that $(I_1 + I_2)/2 = \bar{I}$ implies that the hydrograph is a straight line during the routing period t. Thus the controlling factor in selecting the routing period is that it be sufficiently short so that this assumption is not seriously violated. The routing period should never be greater than the time of travel through the reach, for, if it were, it would be possible for the wave crest to pass completely through the reach during a routing period. If the routing period is shorter than is really necessary, the work of routing is increased since the same computations are required for each routing period.   Generally a routing period between one-half and one-third of the time of travel will work quite well.

10-4. Determination of storage.   Before a relation between storage and flow can be established it is necessary to determine the volume of water in the stream at various times.   The obvious method for finding storage is to compute volumes in the channel from cross sections by use of the prismoidal formula.   The water surface is usually assumed to be level between cross sections.   Total storage in the reach for any given flow conditions is the sum of the storage increments between successive cross sections.   For the summation, the elevation in any subreach is

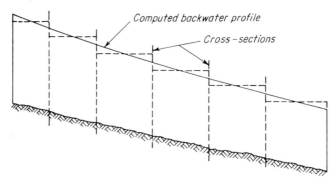

FIG. 10-6. Computation of reach storage from channel cross sections.

the elevation indicated by a backwater curve for the mid-point of the subreach (Fig. 10-6).   This method requires extensive surveys to provide adequate cross sections and computation of water-surface profiles for many unsteady, nonuniform flow situations in order to represent the range of conditions expected.   The method is difficult and relatively costly and is used where no alternative is possible.   It would be used, for example, to compute storage in a reach in which channel alteration or levee construction is planned, since conditions after construction would be quite unlike those existing before construction.

Storage-elevation curves for reservoirs are usually computed by planimetering the area enclosed within successive contours on a topographic map.   The measured area multiplied by the contour interval gives the increment of volume from the mid-point of one contour interval to the mid-point of the next highest interval.   A level water surface is usually assumed, a condition which is satisfied in most reservoirs.   In reservoirs with relatively small cross-sectional area, the water surface may be far from level when large flows occur (Fig. 10-7).   Under such conditions a computation similar to that described above for natural channels must be used.

The common method of determining storage in a reach of natural channel is to use Eq. (10-16) or (10-17) with observed flows. Figure 10-8 shows the inflow and outflow hydrographs for a reach of river. When inflow exceeds outflow, ΔS is positive, and when outflow exceeds inflow, ΔS is negative. Since routing involves only ΔS, absolute storage volumes are not necessary and the point of zero storage can be taken arbitrarily. Thus, the storage at any time is the sum of the positive and negative storage increments since the selected zero point. The computation is illustrated in the figure.

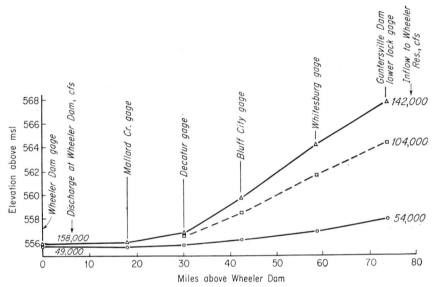

FIG. 10-7. Profiles of the water surface in Wheeler Reservoir on the Tennessee River. (*Data from TVA.*)

One of the most annoying problems in flood routing is the treatment of the *local inflow* which enters the reach between the inflow and outflow stations. If the local inflow enters mainly near the upstream end of the reach, it is usually added to the main-stream inflow to obtain total inflow. If local inflow occurs primarily near the downstream end of the reach, it may be *subtracted* from the outflow before storage is computed. In this case, the main-stream flow is routed through the reach and the local inflow added after routing is complete. Between these two extremes lie many possibilities of combining various percentages of the local with the main-stream inflow before routing and adding the remainder to the outflow after routing. If the local inflow is relatively small compared with the main-stream inflow, any reasonable treatment consistently applied should give satisfactory results. If local inflow is large, consideration should be given to reducing the length of the reach.

The total volume of ungaged local inflow can be found by subtracting measured outflow from measured inflow for a period beginning and ending at about the same low flow, that is, $\Delta S = 0$. The time distribution of the ungaged local inflow is usually assumed to agree with the observed flows in a small tributary similar in size and character to the typical streams of the ungaged area. This procedure throws all errors of flow measurement into the ungaged local inflow, and the resulting flows may

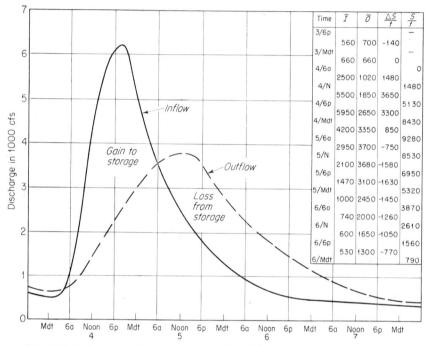

Time	$\bar{I}$	$\bar{O}$	$\frac{\Delta S}{t}$	$\frac{S}{t}$
3/6p				—
	560	700	-140	
3/Mdt				—
	660	660	0	
4/6a				0
	2500	1020	1480	
4/N				1480
	5500	1850	3650	
4/6p				5130
	5950	2650	3300	
4/Mdt				8430
	4200	3350	850	
5/6a				9280
	2950	3700	-750	
5/N				8530
	2100	3680	-1580	
5/6p				6950
	1470	3100	-1630	
5/Mdt				5320
	1000	2450	-1450	
6/6a				3870
	740	2000	-1260	
6/N				2610
	600	1650	-1050	
6/6p				1560
	530	1300	-770	
6/Mdt				790

FIG. 10-8. Calculations of channel storage from inflow and outflow hydrographs.

not appear altogether reasonable. If influent seepage is large, the computed ungaged inflow may be negative.

10-5. Routing in a simple reservoir. A reservoir in which the discharge is a function of water-surface elevation offers the simplest of all routing situations. Such a reservoir may have ungated sluiceways and/or an uncontrolled spillway. Reservoirs having sluiceway or spillway gates may be treated as simple reservoirs if the gates remain at fixed openings. The known data on the reservoir are the elevation-storage curve and the elevation-discharge curve (Fig. 10-9). Equation (10-17) may be transformed[1] to

[1] R. D. Goodrich, Rapid Calculation of Reservoir Discharge, *Civil Eng.*, Vol. 1, pp. 417–418, 1931.

$$I_1 + I_2 + \left(\frac{2S_1}{t} - O_1\right) = \frac{2S_2}{t} + O_2 \qquad (10\text{-}18)$$

Solution of Eq. (10-18) requires a routing curve showing $2S/t + O$ vs. O (Fig. 10-9). All terms on the left-hand side of the equation are known, and a value of $2S_2/t + O_2$ can be computed. The corresponding value

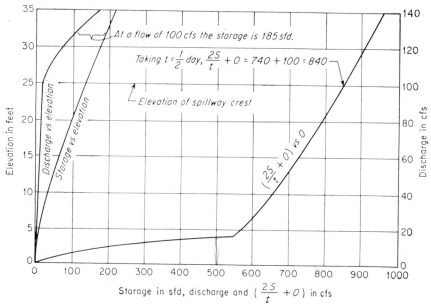

FIG. 10-9. Routing curves for a typical reservoir.

of O_2 can be determined from the routing curve. The computation is then repeated for succeeding routing periods. Table 10-2 illustrates a typical solution. It should be noted that $2S/t - O$ is easily computed as $(2S/t + O) - 2O$.

TABLE 10-2. Routing with the $2S/t + O$ Curve of Fig. 10-9

Date	Hour	I, cfs	$\dfrac{2S_1}{t} - O$, cfs	$\dfrac{2S_2}{t} + O$, cfs	O, cfs
1	Noon	**20**	470	500	**15**
	Midnight	**50**	508	540	16
2	Noon	**100**	578	658	40
	Midnight	**120**	632	798	83
3	Noon	**80**	642	832	95
	Midnight	**40**	620	762	71

NOTE. Data available at start of routing shown in boldface.

10-6. Routing in a gated reservoir. Routing in a reservoir with gated outlets depends on the method of operation. A general equation is obtained by modifying Eq. (10-17) to

$$\frac{I_1 + I_2}{2} t - \frac{O_1 + O_2}{2} t - \bar{O}_R t = S_2 - S_1 \qquad (10\text{-}19)$$

where O is uncontrolled outflow and O_R is regulated outflow. If O is

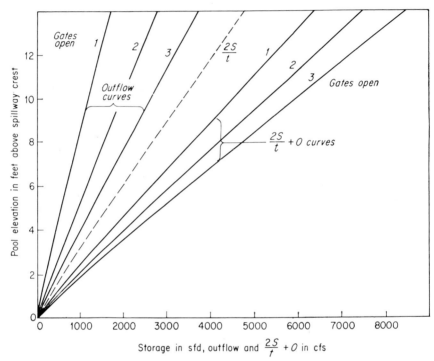

FIG. 10-10. Routing curves for a gated reservoir.

zero, Eq. (10-19) becomes

$$\bar{I} t - \bar{O}_R t + S_1 = S_2 \qquad (10\text{-}20)$$

which can be readily solved for S_2 and reservoir elevation. If O is not zero, the routing equation becomes

$$I_1 + I_2 - 2\bar{O}_R + \left(\frac{2S_1}{t} - O_1\right) = \left(\frac{2S_2}{t} + O_2\right) \qquad (10\text{-}21)$$

The solution of Eq. (10-21) is identical with that outlined in Sec. 10-5 except for the inclusion of O_R.

If the gates are set at fixed openings so that the discharge is a function of head, the solution requires a family of $2S/t + O$ curves for various gate openings (Fig. 10-10). The routing method is the same as that illustrated in Sec. 10-5 except that the curve appropriate to the existing gate opening is used each time.

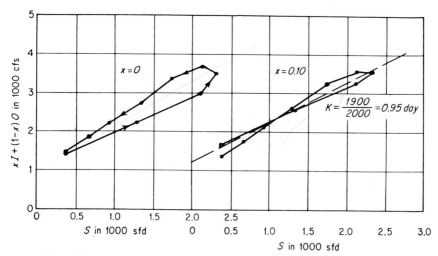

FIG. 10-11. Determination of the Muskingum storage constants [Eq. (10-23)].

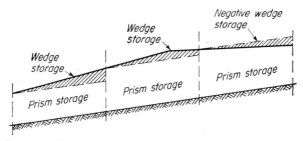

FIG. 10-12. Some possible water-surface profiles during the passage of a flood wave.

10-7. Routing in river channels. Routing in natural river channels is complicated by the fact that storage is not a function of outflow alone. This is illustrated when the storage computed in Fig. 10-8 is plotted against simultaneous outflow. The resulting curve is usually a wide loop indicating greater storage for a given outflow during rising stages than during falling (Fig. 10-11). The cause is obvious if one considers the backwater profiles existing at various times during the passage of the flood wave (Fig. 10-12). The storage beneath a line parallel to the stream bed is called *prism storage;* between this line and the actual profile, *wedge storage.* During rising stages a considerable volume of wedge storage may exist before any large increase in outflow occurs. During falling stages, inflow drops more rapidly than outflow and the wedge-storage volume becomes negative. Routing in streams requires a storage relationship which adequately represents the wedge storage. This is usually done by including inflow as a parameter in the storage equation.

10-8. Streamflow routing: analytical method. One expression for storage in a reach of a stream is

$$S = \frac{b}{a} [xI^{m/n} + (1 - x)O^{m/n}] \tag{10-22}$$

where a and n are constants from the mean stage-discharge relation for the reach, $q = ag^n$, and b and m are constants in the mean stage-storage relation for the reach, $S = bg^m$. In a uniform rectangular channel, storage would vary with the first power of stage ($m = 1$) and discharge would vary as the $\frac{5}{3}$ power (Manning formula). In a natural channel with overbank flood plains the exponent n may approach or become less than unity. The constant x expresses the relative importance of inflow and outflow in determining storage. For a simple reservoir, $x = 0$ (inflow has no effect), while if inflow and outflow were equally effective, x would be 0.5. For most streams, x is between 0 and 0.3 with a mean value near 0.2.

The Muskingum method[1] assumes that $m/n = 1$ and lets $b/a = K$. Equation (10-22) then becomes

$$S = K[xI + (1 - x)O] \tag{10-23}$$

The constant K, known as the *storage constant*, is the ratio of storage to discharge and has the dimension of time. It is approximately equal to the travel time through the reach and, in the absence of better data, is sometimes estimated in this way. If flow data on previous floods are available, K and x are determined by plotting S vs. $xI + (1 - x)O$ for various values of x (Fig. 10-11). The best value of x is that which causes the data to plot most nearly as a single-valued curve. The Muskingum method assumes that this curve is a straight line with slope K. The units of K depend on the units of flow and storage. If storage is in second-foot-days and flow in cubic feet per second, K is in days.

If Eq. (10-23) is substituted for S in Eq. (10-17) and like terms are collected, the resulting equation reduces to

$$O_2 = c_0 I_2 + c_1 I_1 + c_2 O_1 \tag{10-24}$$

---

[1] G. T. McCarthy, The Unit Hydrograph and Flood Routing, presented at conference of North Atlantic Division, U.S. Corps of Engineers, June, 1938 (see also "Engineering Construction—Flood Control," pp. 147–156, The Engineer School, Ft. Belvoir, Va., 1940).

where

$$c_0 = -\frac{Kx - 0.5t}{K - Kx + 0.5t} \qquad (10\text{-}24a)$$

$$c_1 = \frac{Kx + 0.5t}{K - Kx + 0.5t} \qquad (10\text{-}24b)$$

$$c_2 = \frac{K - Kx - 0.5t}{K - Kx + 0.5t} \qquad (10\text{-}24c)$$

Combining Eqs. (10-24, a, b, and c)

$$c_0 + c_1 + c_2 = 1 \qquad (10\text{-}24d)$$

In these equations t is the routing period in the same time units as K. With K, x, and t established, values c_0, c_1, and c_2 can be computed. The routing operation is simply a solution of Eq. (10-24) with the O_2 of one routing period becoming the O_1 of the succeeding period. Table 10-3 illustrates a typical computation.

TABLE 10-3. Application of the Muskingum Method

Date	Hour	I, cfs	$c_0 I_2$	$c_1 I_1$	$c_2 O_1$	O, cfs
1	6 A.M.	10	...	....	....	10
	Noon	30	3.7	3.5	5.2	12.4
	6 P.M.	68	8.4	10.6	6.5	25.5
	Midnight	50	6.2	24.0	13.3	43.5
2	6 A.M.	40	5.0	17.7	22.7	45.4
	Noon	31	3.8	14.1	23.7	41.6
	6 P.M.	23	2.9	10.9	21.8	35.6

NOTE. Based on $K = 11$ hr, $t = 6$ hr, $x = 0.13$; hence, $c_0 = 0.124$, $c_1 = 0.353$, and $c_2 = 0.523$. Values known at the beginning of routing are shown in boldface.

Since most routing procedures involve computation of cumulative storage, the outflow at any time can be determined only by routing from the last known value of outflow. An expression for O_4 can be written from Eq. (10-24) as

$$O_4 = c_0 I_4 + c_1 I_3 + c_2 c_0 I_3 + c_1 c_2 I_2 + c_2{}^2 c_0 I_2 + c_2{}^2 c_1 I_1 + c_2{}^3 O_1 \qquad (10\text{-}25)$$

Since c_2 is less than unity, $c_2{}^3$ will usually be negligible, and combining coefficients gives

$$O_4 = aI_4 + bI_3 + cI_2 + dI_1 \qquad (10\text{-}26)$$

Equation (10-26) provides a means of computing outflow at any time if the preceding inflows are known.

10-9. Streamflow routing: semigraphical methods. The Muskingum method assumes that K is constant at all flows. While this assumption is generally adequate, in some cases the storage-flow relation is so curved that an alternative method must be found.   If storage is expressed as a function of $aI + O$, Eq. (10-18) can be written

$$I_1 + (1 + a)I_2 + \left(\frac{2S_1}{t} - O_1\right) = \frac{2S_2}{t} + aI_2 + O_2 \qquad (10\text{-}27)$$

A curve relating $2S/t + aI + O$ and $aI + O$ is required.   All terms on the left are known, and a value of $2S_2/t + aI_2 + O_2$ can be computed and

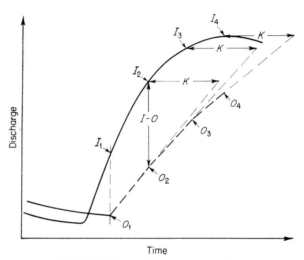

FIG. 10-13. A graphical routing method.

the corresponding value of $aI_2 + O_2$ read from the curve.   Since I_2 is known, O_2 can be computed.

Many solutions of the semigraphical type are possible using any storage function which reduces the data to a single-valued curve.   All solutions are based on a transformation of Eq. (10-18) to fit the selected storage function.   Equation (10-27) should be considered as a typical example rather than as a specific method.

10-10. Streamflow routing: graphical methods.   A variety of graphical methods for solving the routing equation have been suggested. Often graphical methods are less convenient than other methods unless many repetitions of the operation are expected.   Graphical methods are the basis for a number of mechanical routing devices.

The Muskingum storage equation with $x = 0$ may be expressed as

$$\frac{dS}{dt} = K \frac{dO}{dt} \qquad (10\text{-}28)$$

From Eq. (10-15), $I - O = dS/dt$. Combining this with Eq. (10-28) gives

$$\frac{I - O}{K} = \frac{dO}{dt} \tag{10-29}$$

Equation (10-29) can be used as the basis for a very simple graphical routing method.[1] Given an inflow hydrograph (Fig. 10-13), a straight

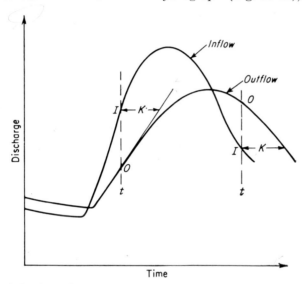

FIG. 10-14. Graphical determination of the storage factor K.

line connecting O_2 with a point K time units to the right of I_2 indicates the slope of the outflow hydrograph at O_2. No routing period is involved, and the slope of the outflow hydrograph can be defined at any desired point. Note that K need not be constant but can be expressed as a function of O. The procedure is therefore suitable for routing through an ungated reservoir for which a K curve (dS/dO vs. O) can be constructed.

It is not necessary to determine K by the procedure described in Sec. 10-8. Instead, K may be found by reversing the routing procedure described above. A straight line conforming to the slope of the outflow hydrograph at any time t is projected to a discharge value equal to the inflow at that time. The time difference between the inflow and this projection is K (Fig. 10-14).

The graphical procedure described above assumes pure reservoir action ($x = 0$), and the peak of the outflow hydrograph must fall on the receding limb of the inflow hydrograph. A graphical construction introducing the equivalent of the Muskingum x could be derived, but a simpler

[1] W. T. Wilson, A Graphical Flood-routing Method, *Trans. Am. Geophys. Union,* Vol. 21, Part 3, pp. 893–898, 1941.

solution is available. The factor x may be viewed as a measure of the translatory component of the wave motion. Figure 10-15 shows that,

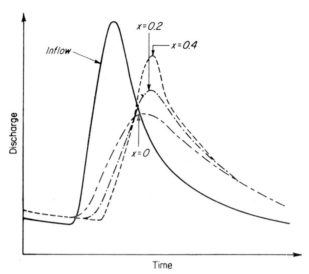

FIG. 10-15. Effect of changes in the Muskingum x on the outflow hydrograph.

with a constant K, the translation of the hydrograph increases as x increases. Thus the effect of increasing x can be introduced by lagging the inflow hydrograph. If the lag T_L is constant, it is immaterial whether the inflow is lagged and then routed or the routed flow is lagged. A completely flexible procedure would utilize both variable K and T_L as functions of flow. Since, with no translation, the outflow peak would fall on the inflow recession, a measure of T_L is the time difference between the outflow peak and the occurrence of an equal flow during the recession of inflow (Fig. 10-16). Values of T_L can be determined from the hydrographs of several historic floods and plotted as a T_L vs. I curve (Fig. 10-17). Using the historic data, inflow is lagged according to the T_L vs. I curve, and a K vs. O curve is constructed from the lagged inflow and observed outflow as described earlier.[1]

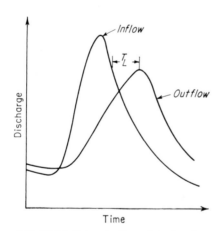

FIG. 10-16. Determination of the lag T_L.

[1] M. A. Kohler, Mechanical Analogs Aid Graphical Flood Routing, *J. Hydraulics Div. ASCE*, Vol. 84, April, 1958.

10-11. Streamflow routing: statistical methods. Equations (10-24) and (10-26) are linear, multivariable equations. The constants in the equations could be established by conventional least-squares analysis using data from historic floods. Another approach is the use of the coaxial graphical-correlation technique. Figure 10-18 illustrates such a graphical correlation using an equation such as Eq. (10-26) involving only inflow values. A similar relationship might have been developed using the conventional parameters (I_1, I_2, O_1, O_2).

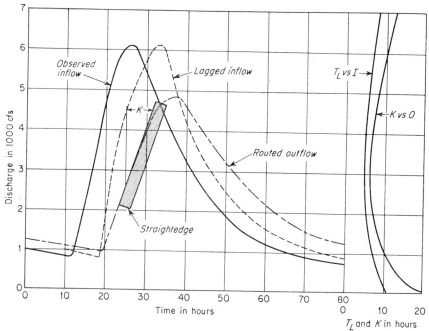

FIG. 10-17. Graphical flood routing with a variable lag and storage factor.

10-12. Routing aids. Routing is one of the few operations in hydrology which lends itself to computational aids, and numerous such devices have been developed. These aids can be classified as slide rules or nomograms for solving the routing equations, mechanical devices which perform the routing operation graphically, and analogs which simulate hydraulic wave travel with some other medium.

Since Eq. (10-18) involves only addition of terms, this can be easily accomplished with a slide rule (Fig. 10-19). Scales are laid off in terms of the factors in the equation but marked in terms of inflow and outflow by use of the relation between outflow and storage. Nomograms may be developed to serve the same purpose. More complicated scale arrangements are possible to handle special situations.

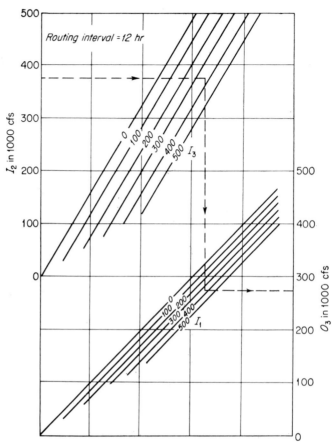

FIG. 10-18. Coaxial graphical-routing relation.   With $t = 12$ hr, the curves correspond
closely to $K = 12$ hr, $x = 0.2$.

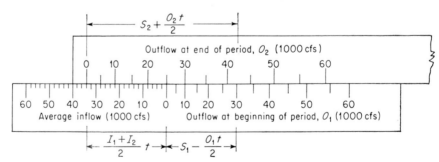

FIG. 10-19. A simple routing slide rule using modified form of Eq. (10-18).   Outflow values
are marked at distances from origin equal to corresponding values of $S \pm Ot/2$.

Mechanical routing devices are either linkages similar to a pantograph or rolling devices which perform a graphical-routing solution mechanically. In the pantograph type the operator usually follows a storage curve and inflow hydrograph with pointers while a third pointer traces the outflow hydrograph. Such devices usually require considerable modification to adapt them from one reach to another. A rolling device, the Harkness flood router, is shown in Fig. 10-20. This device uses a

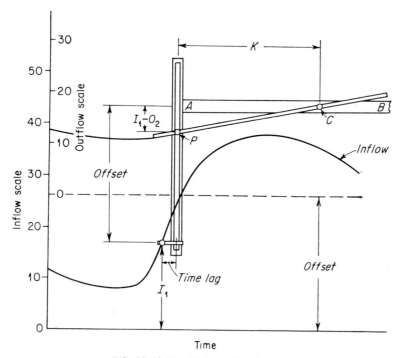

FIG. 10-20. The Harkness flood router.

solution similar to that described in Sec. 10-10. The constant K is set along bar AB and the pencil P traces the outflow graph, so that PC is equivalent to the straightedge of Fig. 10-17. Because of mechanical problems, the outflow hydrograph is offset vertically by a fixed distance so that the outflow pencil and the inflow tracer will not be at the same point when the hydrographs cross. A more flexible mechanical analog has since been developed[1] which can be used for problems involving variable K and T_L.

The most convenient analog computer is electrical. In a simple circuit having a capacitor of capacitance C, the charge stored in the

[1] M. A. Kohler, Mechanical Analogs Aid Graphical Flood Routing, *J. Hydraulics Div. ASCE*, Vol. 84, April, 1958.

capacitor is equal to CE, where E is the voltage drop across the capacitor. Since $E = Ri$, the product of resistance and current,

$$S = CRi \qquad (10\text{-}30)$$

which is equivalent to the hydrologic equation $S = Kq$. A circuit such as that given in Fig. 10-21 can be shown to have characteristics such that storage in the two capacitors conforms to Eq. (10-23), when I is the inflow current and O is the outflow current.[1] The inflow hydrograph

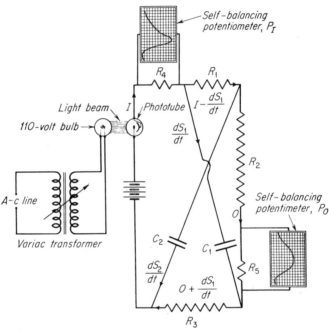

FIG. 10-21. Circuit diagram for an electronic flood-routing device. (*U.S. Weather Bureau.*)

is drawn on the chart of potentiometer P_I and the inflow current controlled so that the pen of the potentiometer follows this trace. Since the storage in the system is analogous to that of a stream, the current at potentiometer P_O represents outflow. Values of K and x for the system are adjusted by changing the resistances R_1, R_2, and R_3 or chart speed. Since the analog solves the differential form of the storage equation [Eq. (10-15)], it is free of the errors introduced by use of finite routing periods. Values of K and x for a reach may be found by trial and error rather than by the analysis presented in Sec. 10-8.

[1] R. K. Linsley, L. W. Foskett, and M. A. Kohler, Electronic Device Speeds Flood Routing, *Eng. News-Record*, Vol. 141, No. 26, pp. 64–66, Dec. 23, 1948.

10-13. Deriving basin outflow by routing. The shape of the hydrograph from a basin is dependent on the travel time through the basin and on the shape and storage characteristics of the basin. Considering excess rainfall (runoff) to be inflow and the hydrograph to be outflow, the problem is analogous to storage routing. The similarity of Eqs. (9-1) and (10-26) shows that the unit hydrograph itself is basically a set of average routing coefficients.

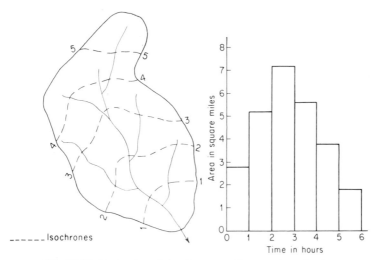

FIG. 10-22. Derivation of the time-area diagram for a basin.

The nature of the problem suggests the use of "lag and route" methods (Sec. 10-10). Inflow may be lagged by dividing the basin into zones by isochrones of travel time from the outlet. The area between isochrones is then measured and a time-area diagram (Fig. 10-22) is plotted. This diagram may be viewed as inflow to a hypothetical reservoir with storage characteristics equivalent to those of the basin and located at the basin outlet. Thus routing the time-area diagram by the Muskingum method (Sec. 10-8) with $x = 0$ yields the outflow hydrograph after adjustment for units. Because of the method of constructing the time-area diagram, such a hydrograph would be the result of an instantaneous rainfall (duration $= 0$ hr), and it is called an *instantaneous unit hydrograph*. It can be converted to a unit hydrograph for any duration t by averaging ordinates t units of time apart and plotting the average at the end of the period (Fig. 10-23).

The technique outlined above need not be limited to deriving unit hydrographs. For a storm of duration equal to the interval between isochrones, the average runoff may be estimated for each time zone and expressed in cubic feet per second.[1] The resulting time-runoff diagram is then routed through storage to give the actual outflow hydrograph. If rain lasts for several time periods, the time-runoff diagrams are lagged and superimposed (Fig. 10-24), and the summation is routed. The method accounts for time-intensity variations and areal distribution of rainfall, two factors which the unit hydrograph cannot readily consider. For this reason the routing approach can be applied to much larger basins than can the simple unit-hydrograph approach.

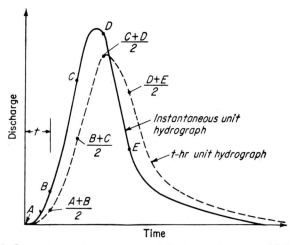

FIG. 10-23. Converting an instantaneous unit hydrograph to one of finite duration.

Horton[2] suggested that for a storm of reasonably uniform rainfall intensity the "virtual channel-inflow graph" would be approximately triangular. He assumed that the shape of this triangle (Fig. 10-25) is fixed by the following:

1. Inflow and outflow must begin at the same time.

2. The inflow hydrograph must pass through the crest of the outflow hydrograph (reservoir conditions).

3. Inflow ends at the point of contraflexure on the recession limb of the outflow hydrograph.

4. Volumes of inflow and outflow must be equal.

Using these rules, Horton demonstrated that the hydrograph could be

---

[1] q in cubic feet per second $= (24 \times 26.9AQ)/t = 646AQ/t$, where A is in square miles, Q is in inches, and t is in hours.

[2] R. E. Horton, Virtual Channel-inflow Graphs, *Trans. Am. Geophys. Union*, Vol. 22, Part 3, pp. 811–820, 1941, and Flood-crest Reduction by Channel-storage, *Trans. Am. Geophys. Union*, Vol. 22, Part 3, pp. 820–835, 1941.

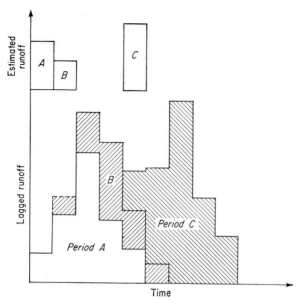

FIG. 10-24. Time-runoff diagram for a long storm.

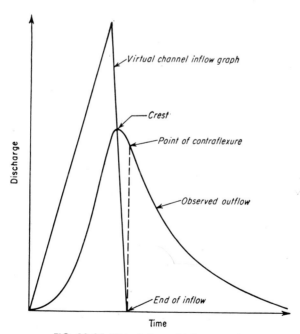

FIG. 10-25. Virtual channel-inflow graph.

accurately reproduced by routing the triangular inflow hydrograph through storage.

The difficulty with the use of the routing technique lies in determining the routing constant K and the lag through the basin T_L. Generally, a trial-and-error approach has been used in which various values are tried until a combination that gives a good fit to historical floods is found. Although laborious, this procedure is satisfactory for gaged streams but obviously unsuited to ungaged basins.

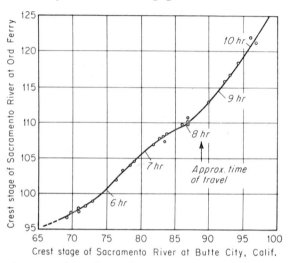

FIG. 10-26. Simple gage relation for the Sacramento River from Ord Ferry to Butte City, California. (U.S. Weather Bureau.)

An estimate of K may be obtained from data on the recession of flow for a basin. From Eqs. (7-3) and (10-23), assuming $x = 0$,

$$K = -\frac{1}{\log_e K_r} \tag{10-31}$$

where K_r is the recession constant for the stream.

Clark[1] described the derivation of a unit hydrograph by routing the time-area diagram of a basin as explained above. He suggested that K (in hr) is given by

$$K = \frac{cL}{\sqrt{s}} \tag{10-32}$$

where L is the length of the main stream in miles, s is the mean channel slope, and c varies from about 0.8 to 2.2. Linsley in a discussion of Clark's paper suggested the formula

[1] C. O. Clark, Storage and the Unit Hydrograph, *Trans. ASCE*, Vol. 110, pp. 1419–1488, 1945.

$$K = \frac{bL \sqrt{A}}{\sqrt{s}} \qquad (10\text{-}33)$$

where A is the drainage area in square miles and b varies from about 0.04 to 0.08 for the basins tested.

It is often assumed that the lag $T_L = K$, but there is evidence that this is not necessarily true.[1] One possible estimate of T_L is the basin lag

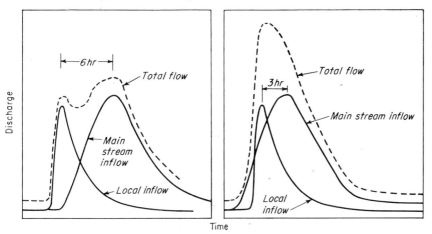

FIG. 10-27. Effect of timing of flood peaks on reach outflow.

t_p, using any of the methods of Sec. 9-6 or 9-7. It should be noted that basin lag can be observed quite readily by noting the time of peak and comparing this with the time of rain, even though the basin is ungaged.

10-14. Gage relations. A discussion of wave travel and routing would be incomplete without brief mention of a simple empirical solution which is often quite successful. *Gage relations* are graphs correlating an observed stage or discharge at an upstream station with the resulting stage or discharge at a downstream station. Gage relations are most effective when $dS/dt = 0$, i.e., at crest (Fig. 10-26). If a relation like that in Fig. 10-26 is to be reliable, the quantity of local inflow between the stations in each flood must bear a fixed relation to the reach inflow at the upstream station. Since such a proportional relation is unlikely, gage relations are most effective when the local inflow is relatively small compared with the main-stream inflow. It is also necessary that the peak of the local inflow bear a fixed time relation to the peak of the main-stream inflow. If a slight difference in time of occurrence can cause a considerable difference in the resulting outflow (Fig. 10-27), gage relations will not be successful. Thus gage relations are most useful on large streams where local inflow is small with respect to main-stream flow and rates of change of flow are relatively low.

[1] Research in progress at Stanford University.

More complex gage relations can be constructed so as to account for variable tributary inflow (Fig. 10-28). It is also possible to derive charts for routing in terms of stage.[1] Stage relations and stage routing are

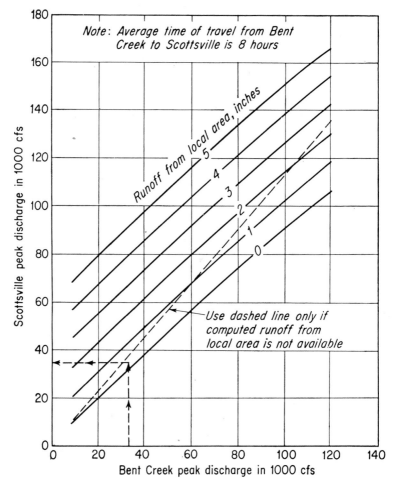

FIG. 10-28. Gage relation for the James River from Bent Creek to Scottville, Virginia, with parameter for local inflow. (*U.S. Weather Bureau.*)

useful when dealing with streams for which discharge data are not available. It should be emphasized that any change in the channel, either natural or artificial, may result in changes in the stage-discharge and stage-storage relationships for the reach. An analysis in terms of stage may be invalidated by such changes. Stage routing and gage relations are useful in the field of flood forecasting. Here speed is of paramount

[1] M. A. Kohler, A Forecasting Technique for Routing and Combining Flow in Terms of Stage, *Trans. Am. Geophys. Union*, Vol. 25, Part 6, pp. 1030–1035, 1944.

importance, and stage is the desired answer.   Thus a technique which
eliminates the conversions from stage to discharge and back to stage is
potentially valuable if it is sufficiently reliable.

BIBLIOGRAPHY

Gilcrest, B. R.: Flood Routing, Chap. X, pp. 635–709, in Hunter Rouse (ed.), "Engi-
   neering Hydraulics," Wiley, New York, 1950.
Keulegan, G. H.: Wave Motion, Chap. XI, pp. 711–768, in Hunter Rouse (ed.),
   "Engineering Hydraulics," Wiley, New York, 1950.
Linsley, R. K., M. A. Kohler, and J. L. H. Paulhus: "Applied Hydrology," Chaps. 18
   and 19, pp. 465–541, McGraw-Hill, New York, 1949.
Thomas, H. A.: The Hydraulics of Flood Movement in Rivers, *Carnegie Inst. Technol.
   Eng. Bull.*, 1935.

PROBLEMS

10-1. If the channel width for the stream whose stage-discharge relation is shown
in Fig. 4-12 is 30 ft at a stage of 4 ft, what would be the wave celerity for a translatory
monoclinal wave of small height?

10-2. Find the ratio between wave celerity and water velocity for a semicircular
channel when $y = r$.   When $y = 0.2r$.   Use the Chézy formula.

10-3. A uniform rectangular channel 10 ft wide ($n = 0.015$) on a slope of 0.0004 is
flowing at a depth of 5 ft.   A sudden gate opening increases the depth to 6 ft.   What
is the celerity of the resulting abrupt wave?

10-4. Given the hydrographs tabulated below, find the storage in the reach, and
plot a curve showing storage at any instant as a function of simultaneous outflow.
Ignore local inflow.

Date	Hour	Inflow, cfs	Outflow, cfs
1	Midnight	40	40
2	Noon	35	39
	Midnight	37	37
3	Noon	125	52
	Midnight	340	130
4	Noon	575	287
	Midnight	722	472
5	Noon	740	624
	Midnight	673	676
6	Noon	456	638
	Midnight	320	574
7	Noon	245	394
	Midnight	192	307
8	Noon	144	235
	Midnight	118	180
9	Noon	95	142
	Midnight	80	114
10	Noon	67	93
	Midnight	56	77
11	Noon	50	64
	Midnight	42	55

10-5. A small reservoir has an area of 300 acres at spillway level, and the banks are essentially vertical for several feet above spillway level. The spillway is 15 ft long and has a coefficient of 3.75. Taking the inflow hydrograph of Prob. 10-4 as the inflow to the reservoir, compute the maximum pool level and maximum discharge to be expected if the reservoir is initially at the spillway level at midnight on the first.

10-6. Tabulated below are the elevation-storage and elevation-discharge data for a small reservoir. Taking the inflow hydrograph of Prob. 10-4 as the reservoir inflow and assuming the pool elevation to be 875 at midnight on the first, find the maximum pool elevation and peak outflow rate.

Elevation	Storage, acre-ft	Discharge, cfs
862	0	0
865	40 20·16	0
870	200 100·8	0
875	500 252	0
880	1000 504	0
882	668 1220	100
884	1630 822	230
886	1144 2270	394
888	3150 1588	600

10-7. Find the Muskingum K and x for the flood of Problem 10-4.

10-8. Taking the outflow hydrograph of Prob. 10-4 as the inflow to a reach with $K = 27$ hr and $x = 0.2$, find the peak outflow, using the Muskingum method of routing.

10-9. Write the routing equation for the case when storage is a function of $aI + bO$.

10-10. Using the graphical method of Sec. 10-10, find the K curve for the flood of Prob. 10-4.

10-11. Using the outflow hydrograph of Prob. 10-4 as the inflow to a reach for which the lag $T_L = 6$ hr and $K = 18$ hr, find the peak outflow and time of peak by the graphical method of Sec. 10-10.

11

FREQUENCY AND DURATION STUDIES

One of the most common phases of hydrologic design is related to the frequency with which flows of a given magnitude will be equaled or exceeded, or "What is the average lapsed time between the occurrence of two floods equaling or exceeding a specified discharge?" Information concerning probable extremes which proposed structures may be required to withstand and many other hydrologic problems can be solved by frequency analysis, using past records of flood peaks, flood volumes, minimum flows, etc. The selection of a design frequency must rest on economic analysis and policy decisions.[1]

Flood-frequency analysis has long been a controversial topic among engineers, and general agreement as to methods is not yet in sight. Criticism has been brought about largely by abuse through misunderstanding. That design of hydraulic structures must rest on some form of frequency analysis is unquestionable. Those responsible must, through experience or otherwise, agree on basic criteria. Frequency analysis should then provide a reasonable basis for transposing experience.

In a report of the National Research Council[2] on deficiencies of hydrologic data it is stated," . . . No less than 60 important dams have failed during the past 50 years as a result of overtopping by floods . . . ." Is it then to be concluded that failure of a structure *always* constitutes underdesign? Designing for the 10-yr flood, the 100-yr flood, or in fact any flow below the maximum possible involves a calculated risk, and failures here are just as certain as death in the life insurance business.

Efficiency of projects, such as run-of-river power plants and municipal water supplies without appreciable storage, often depends on the time distribution of streamflow; i.e., the per cent of time flow can be expected to exceed specified quantities. If projects are to embody appreciable

[1] E. L. Grant, "Principles of Engineering Economy," 3d ed., Ronald, New York, 1950.

[2] "Deficiencies in Basic Hydrologic Data," p. 3, Report of the Special Advisory Committee on Standards and Specifications for Hydrologic Data, Water Resources Committee, National Resources Committee, September, 1936.

storage, the effects they would have had on past streamflow must be considered in evaluating available flow.   In designing storage facilities, the engineer must determine the quantity of storage required to assure adequate supply in low-water periods.   The analysis upon which such decisions are based is discussed in the last sections of this chapter.

FREQUENCY ANALYSIS

This section is limited to a discussion of station, or point, analysis of flood flows and rainfall intensities.   It will be noted that most of the material of a specific nature is for peak discharge, but rainfall intensities could as well be used in most cases.   Although the importance of rainfall-frequency analysis in hydrologic design is well recognized, the determination of rainfall frequencies is, hydrologically speaking, "the means to an end," the end product being the estimation of flood frequencies.

Flood frequencies in terms of stage are often required in connection with estimating frequency of inundation of buildings and other valuable property located in the flood plain.   For reasons explained below, however, it is recommended that analysis be made in terms of discharge and the results converted to stage by use of an applicable rating

11-1. Selection and compilation of data. Since theoretical aspects of frequency analysis require that all data for the period of study be comparable (all representing true, unbiased observations of the desired element) it is extremely important that the basic data be thoroughly scrutinized.   Some of the more obvious considerations are as follows:

1. Pronounced shifts in the stage-discharge relation render stage data inconsistent for frequency studies.   Although adjustments can sometimes be made, the use of discharge data in the analysis is to be preferred.   If stage frequencies are required, the results can be transformed to stage using the most recent rating.

2. Changes in the datum of a river gage directly affect the recorded values, and, if analysis is to be made in terms of stage, adjustments must be made.

3. Moving a river gage and/or discharge section even a short distance may have a significant effect on recorded stage and/or discharge values. Such changes are usually fully described in data publications so that required adjustments can be made.

4. Construction of dams, levees, etc., can cause material changes in the streamflow regime.   The effect of all such construction should be investigated and adjustments made as required.

5. Historical data, events occurring prior to the beginning of continuous record, should be included in the analysis if the evidence is sufficient to assign magnitude, order, and period.[1]   Even though only 30 yr of com-

[1] Hydrology Handbook, *ASCE Manual* 28, pp. 102–104, 1949.

plete records are available, 1926–1955 for example, it may be an established fact that the 2500-cfs flood of 1891 was the greatest since 1850 and has not since been exceeded. Under these circumstances, all required information ($m = 1$, $n = 106$, and $X = 2500$) is known, and the flood can be plotted in accordance with Eq. (11-1), page 249.

The data may be assembled in several different ways, the selection usually being based on personal preference, availability of data, and purpose of the study. If extreme floods are of primary concern, it is customary to use only the *annual floods*, i.e., the maximum flood peak of each calendar or water year. Such a series ignores the second- and lower-order events of each year which may be even greater than annual floods of other years. This objection is met by an alternative approach using all floods above a selected base, without regard to time of occurrence. Such an array, known as a *partial duration series* (or just *partial series*), is not a true distribution series since the flood event is defined in terms of its magnitude rather than of its occurrence. An objection is frequently raised to the partial series on the grounds that any decision as to the relative independence of consecutive events, such as flood peaks, must be arbitrary. If two consecutive events are judged to be independent, both are listed in the series; otherwise, only the higher is considered.

The two types of series provide quite different distributions, particularly for the shorter return periods.[1] It can be demonstrated by theoretical analysis that the two distributions are related,[2] as shown in Table 11-1. For return periods exceeding 10 yr, there is negligible

TABLE 11-1. Corresponding Return Periods (Years) for Annual and Partial Series

Partial series	Annual series	Partial series	Annual series
0.5	1.16	5.0	5.52
1.0	1.58	10	10.5
1.45	2.00	50	50.5
2.0	2.54	100	100.5

difference between the two series. If interest is centered on the more frequent events, it is perhaps advisable to base the analysis on partial-duration data, judging the independence of consecutive events in the light of the problem at hand.

[1] *Return period* and *recurrence interval* are used interchangeably in this text to signify the average number of years within which a given event will be equaled or exceeded. The *exceedance interval*, defined as the average number of years between the occurrence of the event and a greater event, has received some recognition but its use has been avoided in the text to minimize possible confusion.

[2] W. B. Langbein, Annual Floods and the Partial Duration Flood Series, *Trans. Am. Geophys. Union.*, Vol. 30, pp. 879–881, December, 1949.

A third method of summarizing data, the *full series*, involves the use of all values of record, such as mean daily flows. The full series does not provide independent events and hence is not suitable for flood-frequency studies in the usual sense. Frequency relations derived from the full series, termed *duration curves*, are discussed later in the chapter.

11-2. Plotting positions and the significance of the N-yr event. Frequency analysis delineates the event which can be expected to occur, on an average, once every N yr, the *N-yr event*. There is no implication that such events will occur at even reasonably constant intervals of N yr. Rather, there is a 1 per cent chance that the 100-yr flood will occur within any 365-day period. The theoretical distribution of the return period is illustrated by Table 11-2. It will be seen that, over a

TABLE 11-2. Theoretical Distribution of the Return Period

Average return period, $\bar{T}_r$	Actual return period T_r exceeded various percentages of the time *PROB or THE EVENT NOT OCCURING IN THE NEXT ——YRS*						
	1%	5%	25%	50%	75%	95%	99%
2	8	5	3	1	0	0	0
5	22	14	7	3	1	0	0
10	45	28	14	7	3	0	0
30	137	89	42	21	8	2	0
100	459	300	139	69	29	5	1
1,000	4,620	3,000	1,400	693	288	51	10
10,000	46,200	30,000	14,000	6932	2880	513	100

long period of years, 25 per cent of the intervals between floods equal to or greater than the 100-yr flood will be less than 29 yr while an equal number will be in excess of 139 yr. In other words, for 75 per cent assurance that the capacity of a structure will not be exceeded by a flood within the next 29 yr, it must be designed for the 100-yr (average return period) flood.

After either the partial or annual series is compiled, the items are customarily arranged in descending order of magnitude and assigned an order number m. There is no general agreement as to the proper return period to be assigned to any item of the series.[1] The California method assigns a return period of n to the maximum observed flood in n yr of

[1] Flow in California Streams, *Calif. Dept. Public Works Bull.* 5, 1923.
A. Hazen, "Flood Flow," Wiley, New York, 1930.
C. S. Jarvis and others, Floods in the United States, *U.S. Geol. Survey Water-supply Paper* 771, 1936.
E. J. Gumbel, On the Plotting of Flood Discharges, *Trans. Am. Geophys. Union*, Vol. 24, Part 2, pp. 699–719, 1943.

record, whereas Hazen assigned a return period of $2n$. The plotting
formula now commonly used is

$$T_r = \frac{n+1}{m} \qquad (11\text{-}1)$$

where T_r is the return period, or recurrence interval, in years; n, the
number of years of record; and m, the rank of the event ($m = 1$ for maximum and $m = n$ for minimum event[1]). This procedure is applicable to
either the annual or partial series and is in conformance with modern
theories.

Table 11-3 is included to illustrate the reliability of return periods
derived from relatively short periods of record. For example, the table

TABLE 11-3. Average Return Periods for Various Levels of Probability

Rank from top, m	Number of years of record, n	Probability *prob that the indicated event has a true Tr of less than ___ years*				
		0.01	0.25	0.50	0.75	0.99
1	2	1.11	2.00	3.41	7.46	200
	5	1.66	4.13	7.73	17.9	498
	10	2.71	7.73	14.9	35.3	996
	20	4.86	14.9	29.4	70.0	1990
	60	13.5	43.8	87.0	209.0	5970
2	3	1.06	1.48	2.00	3.06	17.0
	6	1.42	2.57	3.78	6.20	37.4
	11	2.13	4.41	6.76	11.4	71.1
	21	3.61	8.12	12.7	21.8	138
	61	9.62	23.0	36.6	63.4	408
3	4	1.05	1.32	1.63	2.19	7.10
	7	1.31	2.06	2.75	3.95	14.1
	12	1.86	3.32	4.62	6.86	25.6
	22	3.03	5.86	8.35	12.6	48.6
	62	7.76	16.1	23.3	35.8	140
4	5	1.03	1.24	1.46	1.83	4.50
	8	1.25	1.80	2.27	3.04	8.26
	13	1.70	2.77	3.63	5.02	14.4
	23	2.67	4.72	6.36	8.98	26.6
	63	6.63	12.5	17.2	24.8	75.2

shows that there is a 1 per cent chance that the true average return period
of the maximum event occurring in a 10-yr record is as low as 2.71 yr

---

[1] In the partial duration series there may be either more or fewer items than the
number of years of record, depending on the base value selected.   Except when return
periods of less than one year are of interest, it is customary to limit the partial series
to the largest n events.

and that there is almost a 1 per cent chance that the 1000-yr flood will occur in a particular 10-yr period of observations.

11-3. Derivation of the frequency distribution function. The accumulative frequency relation for a partial or annual series can be graphically developed by plotting computed return periods vs. the magnitude of the respective events $(X_1, X_2, \ldots, X_n)$ and fitting a smooth curve. This procedure (Fig. 11-1) is quite acceptable if one is interested in only the shorter return periods, say $T_r \leq n/5$. Fitting a curve by eye to the higher events places unjustified reliance on computed plotting positions which are of doubtful accuracy. The desire to increase

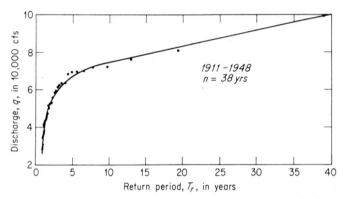

FIG. 11-1. Annual floods of the Clearwater River at Kamiah, Idaho.

the reliability of estimated frequency values has spurred many investigators[1] to develop methods which use the entire data series as a basis for fitting a curve. This requires the assumption of a theoretical frequency distribution. A lengthy discussion of the subject is well beyond the scope of this text. Only one of the more widely accepted approaches is presented here.

Gumbel,[2] following the work of Fisher and Tippett,[3] makes use of the *distribution of extreme values.* If $X_1, X_2, \ldots, X_n$ are the extreme

[1] E. J. Gumbel, On the Plotting of Flood Discharges, *Trans. Am. Geophys. Union,* Vol. 24, Part 2, pp. 669–719, 1943.

H. A. Foster, Theoretical Frequency Curves, *Trans. ASCE,* Vol. 87, pp. 142–173, 1924.

J. J. Slade, An Asymmetric Probability Function, *Trans. ASCE,* Vol. 101, pp. 35–104, 1936.

[2] E. J. Gumbel, Statistical Theory of Extreme Values and Some Practical Applications, *Natl. Bur. Standards (U.S.) Appl. Math. Ser.* 33, February, 1954.

[3] R. A. Fisher and L. H. C. Tippett, Limiting Forms of the Frequency Distribution of the Largest or Smallest Member of a Sample, *Proc. Cambridge Phil. Soc.,* Vol. 24, pp. 180–190, 1928.

values observed in n samples of equal size N and if X is an unlimited, exponentially distributed variable, then the theory of extreme values states that, as n and N approach infinity, the cumulative probability P that any of the n extremes will be less than X approaches the expression (Appendix B)

$$P = e^{-e^{-y}} \tag{11-2}$$

where e is the base of Napierian logarithms and y, termed the *reduced variate*, is given by

$$y = a(X - X_f) \tag{11-3}$$

For an infinitely large sample, it can be shown by the theory of extreme values that the mode of the distribution X_f and the dispersion parameter a are functions of the arithmetic mean $\bar{X}$ and the standard deviation σ_x,

$$X_f = \bar{X} - 0.45005\sigma_x \tag{11-4}$$

and

$$a = \frac{1.28255}{\sigma_x} \tag{11-5}$$

Equation (11-2) is an expression of probability of nonoccurrence. The return period can be computed from

$$T_r = \frac{1}{1 - P} \tag{11-6}$$

In practice, the engineer is required to estimate return periods from limited samples and, therefore, Eqs. (11-4) and (11-5) are not strictly applicable. There are several possible approaches[1] for determining values of the parameters a and X_f from the annual series. That advocated by Gumbel is based on least-squares analysis of Eq. (11-3). This equation can be represented by a straight line (X vs. y) on cartesian coordinates (Fig. 11-5), and Gumbel's solution minimizes the squares of the deviations measured perpendicular to the derived line of expected extremes. The resulting equations are

$$X_f = \bar{X} - \sigma_x \frac{\bar{y}_n}{\sigma_n} \tag{11-7}$$

$$a = \frac{\sigma_n}{\sigma_x} \tag{11-8}$$

The theoretical quantities $\bar{y}_n$ and σ_n are functions only of the sample size (Table 11-4).

[1] J. Lieblein, A New Method of Analyzing Extreme-value Data, *Natl. Advisory Comm. Aeronaut. Tech. Note* 3053, January, 1954.

TABLE 11-4. Expected Means and Standard Deviations of Reduced Extremes
(After Gumbel)

n	$\bar{y}_n$	σ_n	n	$\bar{y}_n$	σ_n
20	0.52	1.06	80	0.56	1.19
30	0.54	1.11	90	0.56	1.20
40	0.54	1.14	100	0.56	1.21
50	0.55	1.16	150	0.56	1.23
60	0.55	1.17	200	0.57	1.24
70	0.55	1.19	∞	0.57	1.28

Combining Eqs. (11-3), (11-7), and (11-8), we have

$$X = \bar{X} + \frac{\sigma_x}{\sigma_n}(y - \bar{y}_n) \tag{11-9}$$

Chow[1] has shown that most frequency functions applicable for hydrologic analysis can be resolved to the generalized form

$$X = \bar{X} + K\sigma_x \tag{11-10}$$

where the "frequency factor" K takes various forms depending upon which approach one uses. From Eq. (11-9), it will be seen that for the Gumbel method

$$K = \frac{y - \bar{y}_n}{\sigma_n} \tag{11-11}$$

and can be expressed by a function of T_r and n. Figure 11-2 is based on the Gumbel method and permits solving[2] for $X - \bar{X}$. If σ_x falls outside the range shown on the chart, scale values of both σ_x and $X - \bar{X}$ can be multiplied by a convenient factor.

Cumulative frequency plottings on a cartesian grid display pronounced curvature, as may be seen from Fig. 11-1. Any curve can be adjusted to a straight line by appropriate warping of either the X or T_r scale. This is the procedure used in designing probability paper. The choice of a distribution function thus dictates the design of the probability paper to be used. Normal probability paper, introduced by Hazen,[3] distorts

[1] V. T. Chow, A General Formula for Hydrologic Frequency Analysis, *Trans. Am. Geophys. Union*, Vol. 32, pp. 231–237, April, 1951.

[2] L. L. Weiss, A Nomogram for Log-normal Frequency Analysis, *Trans. Am. Geophys. Union*, Vol. 38, pp. 33–37, February, 1957.

[3] A. Hazen, Storage to Be Provided in Impounding Reservoirs for Municipal Water Supply, *Trans. ASCE*, Vol. 77, pp. 1539–1669, 1914.

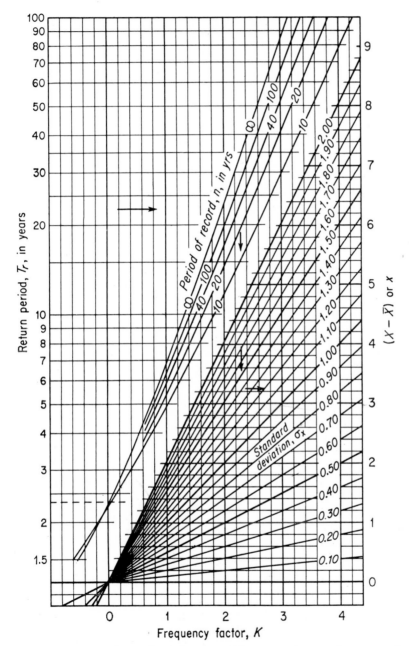

FIG. 11-2. Coaxial chart for the Gumbel method of fitting annual series of extreme values. (After Weiss.)

TABLE 11-5. Frequency Analysis for the Clearwater River at Kamiah, Idaho
(Drainage area = 4850 sq mi)
(After U.S. Geological Survey)

Year	Month	Day	Discharge, cfs	Annual floods		Partial duration series	
				Order, m	Return period, yr	Order, m	Return period, yr
1911	May	6	34,600	...	.....	83	0.47
		17	29,400	...	.....	110	0.35
	June	4	35,900	...	.....	75	0.52
		13	39,500	29	1.35	58	0.67
1912	May	21	55,200	...	.....	27	1.44
		20	61,900	13	3.00	20	1.95
	June	21	38,000	...	.....	62	0.63
1913	April	20	29,400	...	.....	111	0.35
		27	30,700	...	.....	101	0.39
	May	11	45,800	...	.....	40	0.98
		26	76,600	3	13.0	4	9.75
1914	May	18	42,200	27	1.44	53	0.74
		23	41,500	...	.....	55	0.71
	June	3	30,700	...	.....	102	0.38
1915	May	19	28,200	38	1.03	120	0.32
1916	April	28	30,000	...	.....	104	0.37
	May	7	44,400	...	.....	43	0.91
	June	5, 9	36,600	...	.....	69	0.57
		19	56,000	16	2.44	26	1.50
		29	36,600	...	.....	70	0.56
1917	May	15	63,600	...	.....	15	2.60
		30	69,700	...	.....	10	3.90
	June	9	56,800	...	.....	25	1.56
		17	70,500	6	6.50	8	4.88
	Dec.	29, 30	37,300	...	.....	65	0.60
1918	May	5	52,800	17	2.29	28	1.39
		15	35,200	...	.....	80	0.49
	June	10	52,800	...	.....	29	1.35
1919	April	29	30,700	...	.....	103	0.38
	May	23	52,000	20	1.95	33	1.18
1920	May	18	43,600	26	1.50	47	0.83
	June	16	42,900	...	.....	52	0.75
1921	April	23	35,200	...	.....	81	0.48
	May	20	69,700	8	4.88	11	3.55
1922	May	19	60,600	...	.....	22	1.77
		26	52,100	...	.....	32	1.22
	June	6	62,400	12	3.25	18	2.17
1923	May	8–10	38,800	...	.....	60	0.65
		26	49,600	21	1.86	36	1.08
	June	12	43,200	...	.....	49	0.80
1924	May	4	45,600	...	.....	41	0.95
		13	58,900	15	2.60	24	1.62

TABLE 11-5. Frequency Analysis for the Clearwater River at Kamiah, Idaho (Continued)

Year	Month	Day	Discharge, cfs	Annual floods		Partial duration series	
				Order, m	Return period, yr	Order, m	Return period, yr
1925	April	17	41,800	...	.....	54	0.72
	May	7	44,800	...	.....	42	0.93
		20	59,800	14	2.79	23	1.70
1926	April	19	35,900	33	1.18	76	0.51
	May	1	35,900	...	.....	77	0.51
		21	32,400	...	.....	95	0.41
1927	April	28	46,400	...	.....	37	1.05
	May	17	64,200	...	.....	14	2.79
	June	8	68,600	9	4.33	12	3.25
	Nov.	5	43,900	...	.....	46	0.85
		26	29,200	...	.....	113	0.35
1928	May	9	65,700	...	.....	13	3.00
		26	72,100	4	9.75	5	7.80
1929	May	24	52,700	18	2.17	30	1.30
	June	1	28,500	...	.....	117	0.33
		9	35,800	...	.....	78	0.50
1930	April	25	31,000	36	1.08	100	0.39
1931	May	7	40,800	28	1.39	56	0.70
		14, 16	36,500	...	.....	72	0.54
1932	April	14	28,500	...	.....	118	0.33
	May	14	72,100	5	7.80	6	6.50
		21	62,200	...	.....	19	2.05
	June	13–15	35,100	...	.....	82	0.48
1933	April	27	35,800	...	.....	79	0.49
	June	4	71,200	...	.....	7	5.57
		10	81,400	2	19.5	3	13.0
	Dec.	23	43,600	...	.....	48	0.81
1934	March	30	32,300	...	.....	96	0.41
	April	14	37,800	...	.....	63	0.62
		25	45,900	23	1.70	39	1.00
	May	8	34,300	...	.....	85	0.46
1935	May	24	44,000	25	1.56	45	0.87
		31	34,400	...	.....	84	0.46
	June	6	29,900	...	.....	106	0.37
1936	April	19	50,600	...	.....	34	1.15
	May	5	49,800	...	.....	35	1.11
		15	63,200	11	3.54	17	2.29
		28	34,300	...	.....	86	0.45
	June	1	32,900	...	.....	93	0.42
1937	May	19	34,300	34	1.15	87	0.45
		28	32,200	...	.....	97	0.40
1938	April	19	63,400	10	3.90	16	2.44
	May	1	39,400	...	.....	59	0.66
		17	31,500	...	.....	98	0.40
		28	60,800	...	.....	21	1.86

TABLE 11-5. Frequency Analysis for the Clearwater River at
Kamiah, Idaho (Continued)

Year	Month	Day	Discharge, cfs	Annual floods		Partial duration series	
				Order, m	Return period, yr	Order, m	Return period, yr
1939	May	4	46,400	22	1.77	38	1.03
		17	36,400	...	.....	73	0.53
1940	May	12	37,100	30	1.30	66	0.59
		25	29,600	...	.....	107	0.36
1941	May	13	28,900	37	1.05	114	0.34
1942	April	14	28,900	...	.....	116	0.34
		21	28,900	...	.....	115	0.34
	May	26	37,100	31	1.26	67	0.58
1943	April	20	43,200	...	.....	51	0.76
	May	1	29,600	...	.....	108	0.36
		29	52,200	19	2.05	31	1.26
	June	11	37,100	...	.....	68	0.57
		19	43,200	...	.....	50	0.78
		22	40,100	...	.....	57	0.68
1944	May	16	34,200	35	1.11	88	0.44
1945	May	6	44,400	24	1.63	44	0.89
		31	38,400	...	.....	61	0.64
1946	April	20	33,300	...	.....	92	0.42
		26	33,700	...	.....	91	0.43
	May	6	36,600	32	1.22	71	0.55
		19	30,000	...	.....	106	0.37
		28	36,100	...	.....	74	0.53
	June	4	28,300	...	.....	119	0.33
	Dec.	15	33,900	...	.....	89	0.44
1947	May	8	69,900	7	5.57	9	4.33
		27	37,600	...	.....	64	0.61
	June	9	31,200	...	.....	99	0.39
1948	April	18	29,400	...	.....	112	0.35
		22	32,600	...	.....	94	0.42
	May	8	33,800	...	.....	90	0.43
		22	86,500	...	.....	2	19.5
		29	99,000	1	39.0	1	39.0
	June	22	29,600	...	.....	109	0.36

Period: 1911–1948   53,020 = mean of annual floods
                         16,470 = standard deviation of annual floods

the frequency scale so that a normal distribution plots as a straight line.[1] Whipple[2] introduced log-normal paper for fitting those distributions in which the logarithms of the variate are normally distributed. Examination of Eq. (11-3) will show that a plot of X vs. the reduced variate y is linear on a cartesian grid, and this equation forms the basis of Gumbel probability paper (Fig. 11-5) introduced by Powell.[3] The nature of the distribution is such that the arithmetic average of the annual series has a return period which approaches 2.33 yr for large values of n, and lines fitted by eye on the probability paper are usually constructed so as to pass through this point.

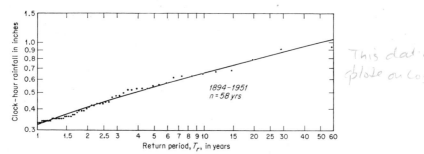

This data plate on log log

FIG. 11-3. Clock-hour rainfalls in excess of 0.32 in. at Salt Lake City, Utah.

It should be emphasized that the Gumbel distribution does not provide a satisfactory fit of partial-duration flood or rainfall data, as may be surmised from Table 11-1. The partial rainfall series (Fig. 11-3) usually approximates a straight line on log-log paper while the partial flood series (Fig. 11-4) generally approximates a straight line on semilogarithmic paper (discharge on arithmetic axis).

The Clearwater River at Kamiah, Idaho, has been selected for illustrative purposes. Both annual- and partial-series data were compiled (Table 11-5) from published records[4] of the U.S. Geological Survey. Return periods shown in the table were computed from Eq. (11-1).

---

[1] The mode, median, and arithmetic mean are coincident in the symmetrical, normal distribution and plot at a return period corresponding to 50 per cent probability. Moreover, the line of best fit passes through the points $1 - P = 0.500 \pm 0.341$ and $X = \bar{X} \pm \sigma_x$.

[2] G. C. Whipple, The Element of Chance in Sanitation, *J. Franklin Inst.*, Vol. 182, pp. 37–59, 205–227, 1916.

[3] R. W. Powell, A Simple Method of Estimating Flood Frequency, *Civil Eng.*, Vol. 13, pp. 105–107 (Discussions by W. E. Howland and E. J. Gumbel, pp. 185 and 438, respectively), 1943.

[4] Annual extremes are readily obtainable from the *Water-supply Papers* which are issued annually for the several sections of the country, but the lesser flood peaks were not included until recent years. Some summarized data do appear in special papers as, for example, *U.S. Geol. Survey Water-supply Papers* 771 (1936) and 1080 (1949).

The standard deviation of the annual series (adjusted for sample size) is

$$\sigma_x = \sqrt{\frac{\Sigma(X - \bar{X})^2}{n - 1}} = \sqrt{\frac{\Sigma X^2 - \bar{X}\Sigma X}{n - 1}} \qquad (11\text{-}12)$$

The partial-series data are plotted in Fig. 11-4, and the curve shown was fitted by eye. The curve shown for the annual data (Fig. 11-5) was determined from Fig. 11-2.

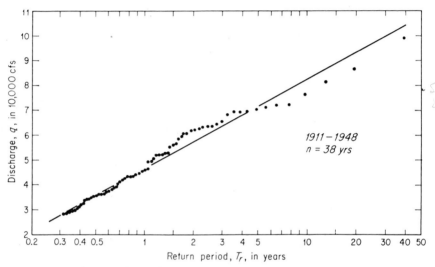

FIG. 11-4. Floods above 28,000 cfs on Clearwater River at Kamiah, Idaho.

11-4. Selection of design frequency. The return period established by frequency analysis as just described indicates only the average interval between events equal to or greater than a given magnitude, or the probability that such an event will occur in any one year. Tables 11-2 and 11-3 both indicate that there is a distinct possibility that actual return periods may be substantially less than the average for a given event. Thus if it is desired to select a design flow which is not likely to occur during the life of the structure, it is necessary to use a return period greater than the estimated useful life. If the probability of nonoccurrence of an event in any year is P, the probability J of the event occurring in any n-yr period is

$$J = 1 - P^n \qquad (11\text{-}13)$$

which is the basis of Tables 11-2 and 11-3.

Table 11-6, also computed from Eq. (11-13), shows, for example, that there is a 10 per cent chance that a flood with an average return period of

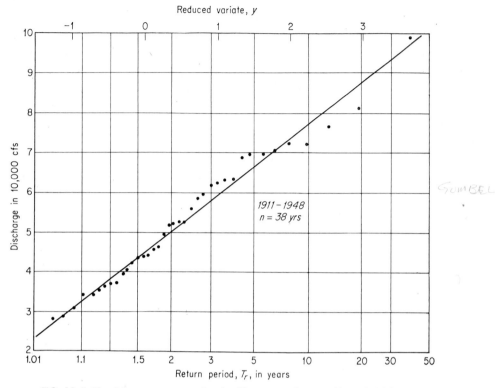

FIG. 11-5. Flood-frequency curve for the Clearwater River at Kamiah, Idaho.

460 yr will occur within the next 50 yr. Note that it is assumed that the true value of P is known. If P is only approximate, then an even longer return period is necessary for a given risk.

TABLE 11-6. Return Periods Required for Specified Risk of Occurrence within Project Life

Permissible risk of failure	Expected life of project, yr				
	1	10	25	50	100
0.01	100	910	2440	5260	9100
0.10	10	95	238	460	940
0.25	4	35	87	175	345
0.50	2	15	37	72	145
0.75	1.3	8	18	37	72
0.99	1.01	2.7	6	11	22

GENERALIZATION OF FREQUENCY DATA

There has always been considerable demand for generalized frequency data, in the form of charts or maps, for estimates at locations having no record. This expressed need has led to numerous studies covering a variety of approaches as evidenced in the references cited in the following sections. In addition to providing estimates of frequency data, generalization can actually enhance the stability and reliability of the results.

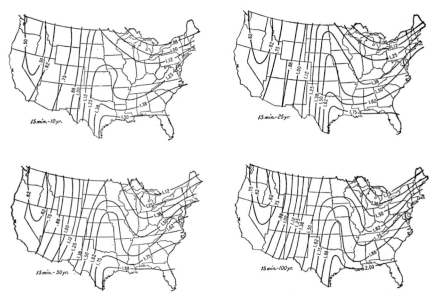

FIG. 11-6. Fifteen-minute rainfalls to be expected, on an average, once in 10, 25, 50, and 100 yr. (After Yarnell.)

Through utilization of all available data, an areal analysis can, in effect, increase the size of the sample beyond the length of record at a single station. No attempt is made to present a detailed description of the various techniques for generalization. Most approaches fall into one of four categories, with limited overlap, and each category is discussed briefly.

11-5. Areal interpolation of point-rainfall frequencies. Given sufficiently long records for a dense network of precipitation stations, the preparation of isopluvial maps that show the maximum point rainfall for selected durations and return periods is a straightforward process. Methods described in the previous section are applicable, and one need only tabulate the required series for selected durations, fit the frequency functions by an appropriate method, plot maps of rainfall for selected return periods and durations, and construct the isolines. This is essentially the procedure followed by Yarnell[1] in developing a set of maps of the type shown in Figs. 11-6 and 11-7. Yarnell's analysis, conducted in the early 1930's, covered only the shorter durations and was, of necessity, limited to the data available from the first-order Weather Bureau stations equipped with recording gages (about 200 stations with average record lengths of about 30 yr).

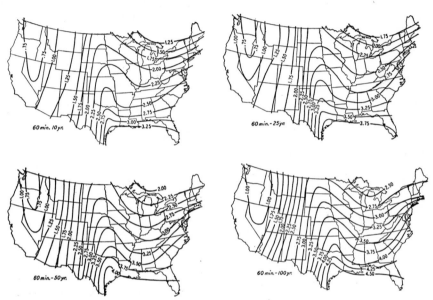

FIG. 11-7. One-hour rainfalls to be expected, on an average, once in 10, 25, 50, and 100 yr. (*After Yarnell.*)

A U.S. Weather Bureau report[2] presents maps of the 2-yr, 1-hr rainfall and relationships for converting these values to other return periods and durations. A detailed analysis of rainfall-frequency data from about 200 U.S. Weather Bureau offices is also available.[3] The inadequate density of recording gages in regions of rugged terrain has led to studies of the relation between rainfall frequencies and physiographic features.[4]

In an attempt to overcome deficient record length, the Miami Con-

[1] D. L. Yarnell, Rainfall Intensity-Frequency Data, *U.S. Dept. Agr. Misc. Publ.* 204, 1935.

[2] Rainfall Intensities for Local Drainage Design in Western United States, *U.S. Weather Bur. Tech. Paper* 28, 1956.

[3] Rainfall Intensity-Duration-Frequency Curves, *U.S. Weather Bur. Tech. Paper* 25, 1955.

[4] R. K. Linsley, Relations between Rainfall Intensity and Topography in Northern California, *Stanford Univ. Dept. Civil Eng. Research Rept.* 1, 1955.

servancy District[1] used what has been termed the "station-year" method[2] to derive maps of maximum expected 1- to 6-day point rainfalls for return periods of 15 to 100 yr (examples shown in Figs. 11-8 and 11-9). The method assumes that records from several stations in a limited area can be combined and treated as a single series with length equivalent to the sum of the individual record lengths. For rigorous application, the selected stations must all lie within an area of meteorological homogeneity and yet must be far enough apart that no two gages provide

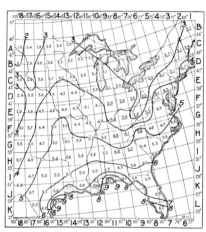

FIG. 11-8. One-day rainfalls to be expected, on an average, once in 15 yr. (*Miami Conservancy District.*)

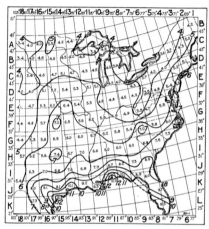

FIG. 11-9. One-day rainfalls to be expected, on an average, once in 50 yr. (*Miami Conservancy District.*)

values for the same storm in the derived series. In practice, these two criteria tend to be mutually exclusive—one must be tempered at the expense of the other—and the homogeneity qualification renders the method wholly inadequate in mountainous areas.

The reliability of station-year analysis is usually limited by the interdependence of the selected stations. The maximum rainfall observed by any of 10 grouped stations in 10 yr of record is assigned a return period of 101 yr and the tenth highest amount, a return period of 10.1 yr. If the 10 stations are so close as to measure essentially identical amounts storm by storm, the 10 highest amounts would be equal and this value should represent a return period of 11 yr. Under these circumstances the station-year method tends to underestimate the expected rainfall.

[1] Storm Rainfall in the Eastern United States, rev. ed., pp. 43–93, *Tech. Rept.* 5, Miami Conservancy District, Dayton, Ohio, 1936.

[2] K. C. Hafstad, Reliability of Station-year Rainfall Frequency Determinations, *Trans. ASCE*, Vol. 107, pp. 633–683, 1942.

Practically, high-intensity, short-duration rainfall is usually the result of intense, small-area thunderstorms, and dependence between stations 30 or more miles apart is not great. Even if conditions of homogeneity and independence could be satisfied, many critics still question the assumption that simultaneous observations at numerous points can be considered to represent the observations at a single station over a long period of time. The basis of this criticism becomes evident if one considers an observation period of 1 or 2 yr which may happen to be either abnormally wet or dry.

The station-year method is not to be confused with averaging techniques which are restricted only by meteorological homogeneity. Whether or not selected stations are independent, averaging the precipitation values ($m = 1$, $m = 2$, etc., respectively) for several stations with equivalent record length provides a rainfall amount which can be assigned a return period corresponding to m and the record length. In other words, the resulting averages may be treated as a series derived from a single station. This procedure tends to increase the reliability over single-station analysis but does not provide data on long return periods, the attractive advantage claimed for the station-year method. Averaging data for several stations improves area sampling and provides better definition of the frequency curve within the time range of the data. It can improve the estimated values of rare occurrence only to the extent that an assumed frequency distribution is better fitted.

11-6. Areal interpolation of flow frequencies. Studies directed toward generalization of flow frequencies usually follow a two-step procedure. All flow data over a reasonably homogeneous area are first combined on a nondimensional, comparable basis to develop a regional frequency relation which can be used to estimate the return period of any flow for those points for which discharge records are available. Application of the regional frequency curve to ungaged points requires the development of a relation involving physiographic factors.

In the procedure now employed by the U.S. Geological Survey,[1] each flood at each station is divided by the mean of the annual floods for the station. The same base period is used in computing means and dimensionless flood ratios for all stations. The base period is usually made as long as possible by estimating missing values from floods at nearby stations. This procedure assures comparability of the annual means and permits assigning order numbers to all observed peaks. The estimated peaks are not used directly in deriving the regional

[1] Floods in Youghiogheny and Kiskiminetas River Basins, Pennsylvania and Maryland, *U.S. Geol. Survey Circ.* 204, 1952.

Tate Dalrymple, Regional Flood Frequency, *Highway Research Board Research Rept.* 11-B, pp. 4–20, 1950.

frequency curve, since this would only give added weight to the station used in making the estimate.

For illustration, assume that one has assembled the annual-flood series for each of a group of stations and has estimated any missing peaks for the selected standard period and that tests have shown the records to meet homogeneity requirements (see Dalrymple).   Analysis would then proceed as follows:

1. Assign order numbers to floods for each station and compute the return periods from Eq. (11-1).

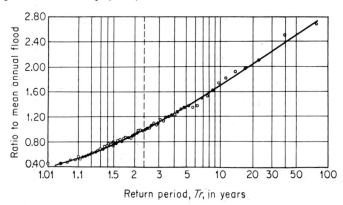

FIG. 11-10. Composite flood-frequency curve for selected stations in the Youghiogheny and Kiskiminetas River Basins, Pennsylvania and Maryland. (*After U.S. Geological Survey.*)

2. Plot discharge vs. return period (station by station) on extreme probability paper and fit the curve by eye to obtain the 2.33-yr flood. The graphical mean annual flood, determined in this way, tends to be more stable than the arithmetic mean since it is little affected by the chance inclusion or exclusion of a major flood.

3. Compute the ratio of annual flood to mean (2.33-yr) flood for each year and station and tabulate by order number.   Use estimated data in assigning order numbers, but omit entry of the corresponding flood ratio.

4. Determine the median flood ratio for each order number.

5. Plot median flood ratio vs. return period on extreme probability paper and fit a smooth curve of composite frequency (Fig. 11-10).

6. Correlate mean annual floods with basin characteristics (Fig. 11-11). This relation provides a basis for estimating return periods for ungaged areas.

To illustrate the use of relations derived by the foregoing procedure, assume that the 25-yr flood is required for an ungaged site with a drainage area of 100 sq mi and within the region of applicability.   Entering

Fig. 11-11 with 100 sq mi yields an estimated mean annual flood of 4200 cfs. From Fig. 11-10 it is seen that the 25-yr flood is 2.16 times the mean annual flood, or 9070 cfs. The complete frequency curve can be derived by plotting discharges for several return periods.

11-7. Rainfall-runoff relations and unit hydrographs in esti-mating flood frequency. One cannot hope to have a long streamflow record applicable to each possible project site. There will, also, continue to be major projects for which the design flood is not adequately

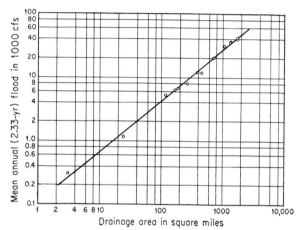

FIG. 11-11. Variation of mean annual flood with drainage area, Youghiogheny and Kiskiminetas River Basins, Pennsylvania and Maryland. (*After U.S. Geological Survey.*)

defined by available discharge records. It is therefore necessary to use all available data and hydrologic skill to achieve the most efficient design. Since precipitation records are generally longer than those of streamflow and since the data are usually more readily transposable, the technique discussed in this section possesses great potentiality.

Experience has shown that rainfall-runoff relations of the type shown in Fig. 8-8 or 8-9 can be developed from only a few years of record and that flow data for a number of basins can often be combined for correlation purposes. In other words, a single relation may be applicable over a considerable area. When used in conjunction with a unit hydrograph or other procedure for distributing runoff volume, the rainfall-runoff relation provides a means of extrapolating streamflow records.[1] With a synthetic unit hydrograph, it is even feasible to compute an extended flood history for an ungaged point. For flood-frequency

[1] R. F. Kresge and T. J. Nordenson, Flood Frequencies Derived from River Forecasting Procedures, *Proc. ASCE*, Vol. 81, Separate 630, February, 1955.

analysis, one need only compute peak flow for enough storms each year
to be certain that the maximum annual value is determined.

Studies[1] have shown that the rainfall network need not be located in
the problem basin, provided that both have similar precipitation-fre-
quency characteristics.   Thus, a set of rainfall data can be applied for
flood-frequency determination within a considerable area and, if data are
available for several networks of differing areal extent, one is in a position
to select the network most nearly approaching in size the study basin.

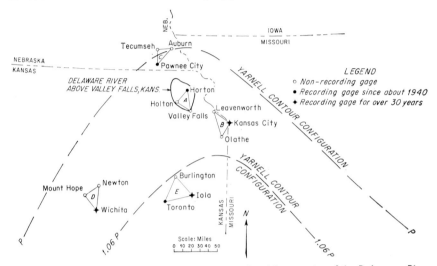

FIG. 11-12. Precipitation networks used to compute flood frequencies of the Delaware River
at Valley Falls, Kansas (see Fig. 11-13).   (U.S. Weather Bureau.)

Figure 11-13 shows frequency curves for the Delaware River at Valley
Falls, Kansas, as derived from several different networks located as
shown in Fig. 11-12.   Greater consistency was found among curves
derived from the several networks than among the curves for 10-yr
segments of the observed streamflow record.

11-8. Empirical formulas.   Before extensive collection of hydrologic data began, the practicing engineer was forced to use empirical
formulas in solution of design problems.   Most of the formulas were
simple in form, considered only one or two of the many causal factors,
and were usually derived from limited data over a restricted region.
Although better techniques are now available, many of these formulas
are still used blindly.   With the possible exception of the so-called
"rational" formula, these generalized equations (Sec. 9-10) have become
somewhat obsolete.

[1] J. L. H. Paulhus and J. F. Miller, Flood Frequencies Derived from Rainfall Data,
J. Hydraulics Div. ASCE, December, 1957.

Many studies have been directed to the development of empirical relations for estimating rainfall intensity as required in applying the rational formula and other similar equations. The resulting relations

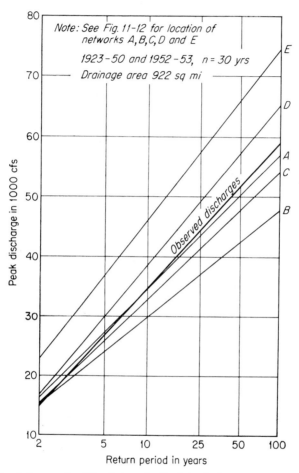

FIG. 11-13. Flood frequencies (Gumbel method) of the Delaware River at Valley Falls, Kansas, as observed and as derived from precipitation networks in and near the basin. (*U.S. Weather Bureau.*)

are usually of the form

$$i = \frac{kT_r^x}{t^b} \tag{11-14}$$

where i is the rainfall intensity in inches per hour; T_r, the return period; t, the rainfall duration in minutes; and k, x, and b are regional constants.

Using data from Yarnell's charts, Bernard[1] derived maps depicting values of k, x, and b over eastern United States. The relative consistency in rainfall-frequency formulas is to be expected since they need not include elusive indices of basin shape, slope, etc. One may assume that the rainfall-intensity frequency formulas are generally more reliable than corresponding formulas for flood flows. Nevertheless, since the physical significance of the coefficients employed is vague, there is no reason to believe that better results can be obtained by selecting coefficients from a map than by determining the desired rainfall intensity from a map.

RELATED STUDIES

Preceding sections have been restricted to consideration of discharge and point-rainfall frequencies. Many similar problems are encountered in hydrology. There is frequent need for rainfall expectancies over areas too large to be represented by a single station. The engineer may be interested in the frequency of droughts as well as floods. Design studies sometimes involve joint-frequency determination, e.g., the occurrence of heavy runoff on a tributary coincident with a major flood on the main stream. An important phase in the design of power and water-supply projects is the determination of the rate or volume of flow which will be available for use.

11-9. Frequency of areal rainfall. Point rainfall of a given frequency is not representative of areas in excess of a few square miles. Moreover, the average of point-rainfall values of a given frequency does not give an areal average of corresponding frequency. An analysis[2] for seven dense networks (mostly east of the Mississippi River) indicates the existence of a rather stable relation between storm rainfall of specified frequency and duration at a point and that for areas as large as several hundred square miles. The resulting curves (Fig. 11-14) are not to be confused with depth-area curves for a specific storm (Fig. 3-11) which tend to be much steeper. To illustrate the use of Fig. 11-14, assume that one wishes to obtain the 10-yr, 3-hr rainfall for a 200-sq mi basin in a locality where the corresponding average point rainfall is 3.0 in. Entering the chart with an area of 200 sq mi and a duration of 3 hr yields a reduction factor of 80 per cent. Applying this factor to the 3.0-in. point value gives 2.4 in. for the basin as a whole. Attention is directed to the fact that the relation of Fig. 11-14 is based on limited data for the eastern half of the United States, and caution should be exercised in its application to other climatic regions.

[1] M. Bernard, Formulas for Rainfall Intensities of Long Duration, *Trans. ASCE*, Vol. 96, pp. 592–624, 1932.

[2] Rainfall Intensity-Frequency Regime, Part I: Ohio Valley, Part II: Southeastern United States, *U.S. Weather Bur. Tech. Paper* 29, 1957, 1958.

11-10. Drought studies. A sustained period of time with deficient rainfall is called a *drought*. Because of the variety of needs for water, it is not practicable to define a drought in specific terms without drastically limiting its applicability. A period of only a few weeks without precipitation may be a serious matter to the farmer, if it is abnormal for the season of the year. The type of crop under production must be considered in defining a drought. Some irrigation projects are designed to operate successfully during periods of deficient rainfall lasting several years.

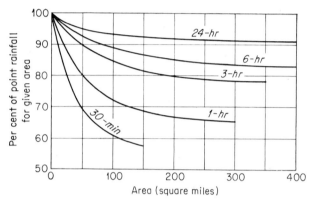

FIG. 11-14. Reduction of point-rainfall-frequency values for application to basins of specific size. (*U.S. Weather Bureau.*)

Agriculturally speaking, an index of moisture deficiency such as the antecedent-precipitation index discussed in Chap. 8 is equally applicable as an index of drought severity, provided that precipitation is the sole source of water supply for plant growth. Normal antecedent-precipitation-index values vary widely from region to region and season to season. Drought for a particular crop in a specified locality can be defined as a threshold index value which varies with time of year.

The hydrologist is more directly interested in drought as it affects streamflow and groundwater. In fact, he commonly defines drought in terms of streamflow. Extreme floods can occur several times in one year, whereas several years of deficient runoff may be required to develop serious drought conditions for irrigation projects having large volumes of storage. Under such circumstances our records of drought are effectively much shorter than records of floods, and much can be gained by study of long-term precipitation data. Such studies may take either of two courses. Annual, seasonal, or monthly precipitation-runoff relations may be developed and used to extrapolate the streamflow record, in which case the frequency analysis would be made in terms of flow volumes. As an alternative, the frequency of precipitation deficiencies may be derived and the design precipitation converted to corresponding streamflow.

The latter approach was used in a study of the Missouri Basin[1] to determine the relative need to design for the severe drought experienced in the 1930's. The derived frequency relation for the area above Sioux City, Iowa, is shown in Fig. 11-15. Based on these curves, estimated return periods of the minimum observed 1-, 2-, 3-, and 5-yr precipitation

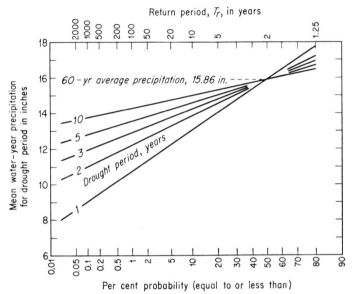

FIG. 11-15. Frequency of 1-, 2-, 3-, 5-, and 10-yr precipitation for the Missouri River above Sioux City, Iowa. (U.S. Weather Bureau.)

during the period 1930 to 1940 are 560, 170, 2000, and 1100 yr, respectively. As might be expected, however, the estimated frequencies are subject to rather large errors; there is roughly a 5 per cent chance that the true average return period is as short as 30 yr for each. Deficient streamflow for periods as short as a few days may be critical for water-supply or sewage-disposal problems. Conventional frequency analysis of low-flow data for various durations can be used to obtain curves such as those of Fig. 11-16.

11-11. Duration curves. An accumulative frequency curve of a continuous time series, such as mean daily discharges, displays the relative duration of various magnitudes and is known as a *duration curve.* Flow-duration curves for the Sacandaga River are shown in

---

[1] "Adequacy of Flows in the Missouri River," Report by Missouri Basin Inter-Agency Committee, pp. 23–34, April, 1951.

Fig. 11-17. The resulting curve is highly dependent on the observation period used in the analysis, mean daily data yielding a much steeper curve than annual data, and this must be borne in mind when applying

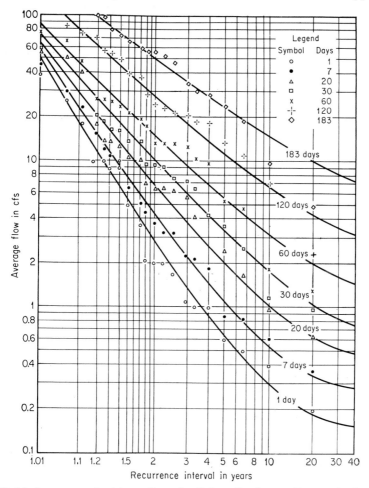

FIG. 11-16. Frequency of minimum flows for Yellow Creek near Hammondsville, Ohio (1915–1935). (*From W. P. Cross and E. E. Webber, Ohio Stream-flow Characteristics, Ohio Dept. Natural Resources Bull. 13, Part 2, Table 1, December, 1950.*)

a duration curve. The use of daily data is recommended for most problems.

The flow-duration curve is most frequently used for the purpose of determining water-supply potential, particularly for run-of-river power projects. The amount of flow available for any selected per cent of time (assuming no added storage facilities) can be read directly from

the curve.   In 1920 U.S. Geological Survey adopted the flows available
50 and 90 per cent of the time as the standards of flow for water-power
statistics.   The higher figure is a measure of the prime power potential,
and the lower value is an index of the power potential with adequate

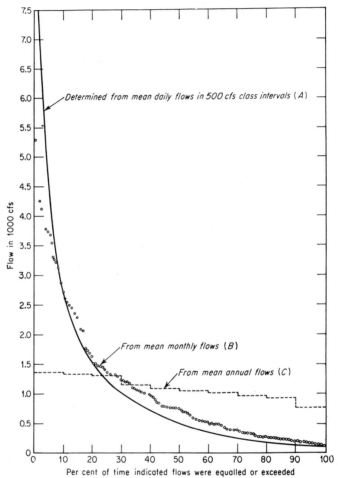

FIG. 11-17. Flow-duration curves for the Sacandaga River near Hope, New York (1936–
1945).

storage facilities.   The chronological sequence of events is completely
masked in a duration curve, and this deficiency greatly restricts its use.
Thus, it is not generally applicable to flood studies nor can it serve to
provide a reliable estimate of the storage required to assure any selected
flow.

11-12. Hydrometeorological studies. For major water-control and utilization structures the designer needs to know much more than can be obtained from frequency analyses of observed or synthesized streamflow data. Major dams, for example, may be designed for a flood with a recurrence interval of several hundred years. If the dam is to be located immediately upstream from a large city where its failure could result in large loss of life or property, its design may even be based on the probable maximum flood.

Frequency analyses of streamflow data are not satisfactory in such cases because (1) they are of necessity based on relatively short records, and the curves must be extrapolated considerably to estimate flood magnitudes for large recurrence intervals and (2) they do not indicate whether the flood magnitudes estimated in this fashion are meteorologically or hydrologically possible. For these reasons the design of major structures is often based on *hydrometeorological studies*, which analyze the basic factors of major floods, i.e., storm rainfall and snowmelt; maximize them to their upper physical limits consistent with current accepted meteorological and hydrologic knowledge and experience; and then reassemble them into more critical but meteorologically and hydrologically acceptable combinations or chronological sequences to provide the probable maximum flood.

The probable maximum precipitation is derived[1] by (1) taking the results of depth-area-duration analyses (Sec. 3-9) of precipitation in major storms that have or could have occurred in the area of interest, (2) adjusting them for maximum moisture charge and rate of moisture inflow, and (3) enveloping the adjusted values for all storms to obtain the depth-area-duration curves of probable maximum precipitation. The use of storms outside the area of interest is called *storm transposition* and involves modification for differences in factors affecting rainfall such as elevation, latitude, and distance from moisture source. Changes in shape and orientation of isohyetal patterns are also considered. Storm transposition is not used in mountainous regions because it is not possible to accurately adjust rainfall for the orographic influences.

In many areas snowmelt is an important, and sometimes predominant, factor in major floods. In such cases the probable maximum flood requires determination of optimum snow cover, maximum melting rates, and the probable maximum precipitation consistent with the optimum

[1] J. L. H. Paulhus and C. S. Gilman, Evaluation of Probable Maximum Precipitation, *Trans. Am. Geophys. Union*, Vol. 34, pp. 701–708, October, 1953.

R. D. Fletcher, Hydrometeorology in the United States, in T. F. Malone (ed.), "Compendium of Meteorology," pp. 1033–1047, American Meteorological Society, Boston, 1951.

A. K. Showalter and S. B. Solot, Computation of Maximum Possible Precipitation, *Trans. Am. Geophys. Union*, Vol. 23, Part 2, pp. 258–274, 1942.

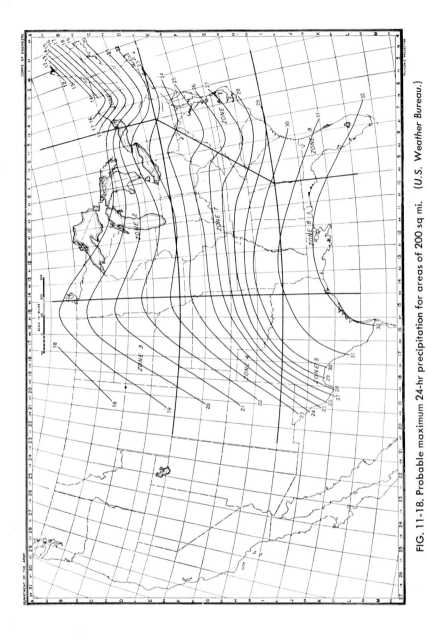

FIG. 11-18. Probable maximum 24-hr precipitation for areas of 200 sq mi. (U.S. Weather Bureau.)

snowmelt conditions. This requires that the seasonal variation of the probable maximum precipitation be determined so that the magnitudes of possible floods, with and without snowmelt, can be estimated for various times of the year and compared.

TABLE 11-7. Depth-Area-Duration Relationships of Probable Maximum Precipitation

(Percentage values to be applied to 200-sq mi 24-hr values of Fig. 11-18)

Area, sq mi	Duration, hr	Zone 1	Zone 2	Zone 3	Zone 4	Zone 5	Zone 6	Zone 7	Zone 8–9
10	6	111	117	102	112	101	113	102	96
	12	123	127	121	124	121	123	120	108
	24	133	141	134	132	130	132	130	123
	48	142	151	155	141	144	143	140	137
20	6	103	108	98	105	95	106	95	90
	12	115	118	115	117	114	116	113	103
	24	126	131	126	124	124	125	122	118
	48	134	141	146	134	138	137	133	132
50	6	92	97	92	96	85	97	86	83
	12	105	106	107	108	104	106	104	96
	24	116	118	117	114	115	116	114	111
	48	123	129	133	125	129	128	124	125
100	6	83	88	87	89	78	90	79	78
	12	97	98	100	100	96	98	96	91
	24	108	109	108	107	108	108	106	105
	48	114	119	124	118	123	122	118	119
200	6	74	80	81	82	70	82	73	72
	12	89	90	93	93	88	90	89	86
	24	100	100	100	100	100	100	100	100
	48	105	110	115	111	116	115	111	114
500	6	62	70	72	74	60	72	64	64
	12	77	79	83	84	77	79	80	78
	24	88	88	90	91	91	89	91	92
	48	94	98	104	102	107	104	102	107
1000	6	52	63	64	68	52	64	58	58
	12	67	72	74	76	68	70	73	74
	24	78	80	82	85	84	79	84	86
	48	85	88	95	96	100	94	96	102

Detailed hydrometeorological studies involve a tremendous amount of work, and the cost may not be justified when only preliminary estimates of the design flood are required. For this reason generalized charts of probable maximum precipitation and its seasonal variation have been prepared[1] for eastern and central United States by transposing and adjusting all major storms of record to all points within their respective transposition limits. Figure 11-18 shows the enveloping values of probable maximum precipitation for 200 sq mi and 24 hr. Values for areas from 10 to 1000 sq mi and for durations from 6 to 48 hr may be obtained by applying the depth-area-duration percentage values of Table 11-7. Generalized estimates have also been prepared[2] for the Sierra slopes of the Central Valley of California.

BIBLIOGRAPHY

Bailey, S. M., and G. R. Richards: The Maximum Probable Flood and Its Relation to Spillway Capacity, *Civil Eng.*, Vol. 9, pp. 32–35, 1939.

Bernard, M.: The Role of Hydrometeorology in Planning the Water Economy of the West, *Trans. Am. Geophys. Union*, Vol. 30, pp. 263–271, April, 1949.

Bernard, M.: The Primary Role of Meteorology in Flood Flow Estimating, *Trans. ASCE*, Vol. 109, pp. 311–382, 1944.

Chow, V. T.: A General Formula for Hydrologic Frequency Analysis, *Trans. Am. Geophys. Union*, Vol. 32, pp. 231–237, April, 1951.

Foster, E. E.: "Rainfall and Runoff," Macmillan, New York, 1948.

Hazen, A.: "Flood Flows," Wiley, New York, 1930.

Hydrology Handbook, *ASCE Manual* 28, 1949.

Jarvis, C. S., and others: Floods in the United States, *U.S. Geol. Survey Water-supply Paper* 771, 1936.

Landsberg, H. E.: "Advances in Geophysics," Vol. 1, Academic Press, Inc., New York, 1952.

Linsley, R. K., and J. B. Franzini: "Elements of Hydraulic Engineering," McGraw-Hill, New York, 1955.

McClendon, E. W.: The Role of Meteorology in Projects of the Corps of Engineers in the Missouri River Basin, *Bull. Am. Meteorol. Soc.*, Vol. 31, pp. 238–243, September, 1950.

PROBLEMS

11-1. Using the data given in Table 11-1 and the frequency curve of Fig. 11-5, construct a partial-duration frequency curve. Plot the frequency curve of Fig. 11-4 on the same chart for comparative purposes. Are the two curves of the same functional form? Are the differences between the two curves significant in view of possible sampling errors?

11-2. Assuming the curve of Fig. 11-5 to represent the true average return period, for what discharge would you design to provide 50 per cent assurance that failure would not occur within the next 20 yr?

11-3. Using the data in Table 11-5 and Fig. 11-2, compute the frequency distributions for the four 10-yr periods beginning with 1911, 1921, 1930, and 1939. Plot the four curves so derived on a single sheet of extreme probability paper for comparative purposes. What is the extreme error at the 40-yr return period, assuming the curve of Fig. 11-5 to yield the true average return period?

[1] Seasonal Variation of the Probable Maximum Precipitation East of the 105th Meridian for Areas from 10 to 1000 Square Miles and Durations of 6, 12, 24, and 48 Hours, *U.S. Weather Bur. Hydrometeorol. Rept.* 33, 1956.

[2] Probable Maximum Precipitation on Sierra Slopes of the Central Valley of California, *U.S. Weather Bur. Coop. Studies Rept.* 12, 1954.

11-4. Obtain annual and partial-duration flood data for a selected gaging station (from *Water-supply Paper* 771 or other source) and plot the two series on extreme probability paper and semilogarithmic paper, respectively. Fit a curve to each by eye, and also compute the frequency curve for annual data, using Fig. 11-2. How does the curve fitted by eye compare with the Gumbel curve; what is the percentage error at return periods of 10 and 100 yr? How do the annual and partial-duration return periods compare relative to those given in Table 11-1?

11-5. Obtain excessive-precipitation data for a selected first-order Weather Bureau station (from *Bulletin W* or other source) and derive intensity-frequency curves for durations of 5, 15, 30, 60, and 120 min. Compare your results for the 15- and 60-min durations with Yarnell's maps (Figs. 11-6 and 11-7).

11-6. Equation (11-14) involves three constants which can be derived by selecting three points from the chart developed in Prob. 11-5. Solve for k, x, and b for each of several combinations of three points. Are the values of the constants so derived reasonably consistent? Would you conclude that Eq. (11-14) is suitable in form for the data used in Prob. 11-5?

11-7. Compile an annual series of minimum flow for a selected gaging station and plot on extreme probability paper. Fit curves to the plotted data by eye and then by using Fig. 11-2. Do the data appear to follow the theory of extreme values?

11-8. Using about three or four years of mean daily flow data, develop the duration curve for a selected gaging station. Develop also the duration curve of monthly flows for the same period of record. Explain the differences in the derived curves. (NOTE TO INSTRUCTOR: If each student is assigned a different period of record, summarized data derived by the group can be used to develop a long-record curve for comparative purposes. The magnitude of sampling errors in a short record can be demonstrated in this manner.)

11-9. Using Fig. 11-18 and Table 11-7, construct depth-area-duration curves of probable maximum precipitation for a basin centered at lat. 31° N., long. 91° W. and for one centered at lat. 45° N., long. 69° W. (Suggest plotting on semilogarithmic paper, using the ordinate logarithmic scale for area and the abscissa linear scale for depth, and labeling the curves with duration.)

12

SEDIMENTATION

Several billion tons of soil is removed annually from the United States by water erosion. Soil loss from agricultural land is in itself a serious economic loss. This sediment is subsequently deposited in stream channels, lakes, reservoirs, and harbors, requiring costly remedial measures. Erosion has been proceeding throughout geologic history, and whole mountain systems have disappeared as a result of erosion. Man cannot materially alter the course of natural erosion but he can avoid accelerating it by his activities.

Because water is the primary agent of erosion and the principal vehicle for the transport of the eroded material, sedimentation studies may be viewed as a special field of hydrology. This chapter presents only a general introduction to the subject which has become a very broad field in itself.

12-1. The erosion process. The process of erosion consists of the *detachment* of soil particles from their position in the soil mass and their *movement* to a channel in which they may be *transported* for the balance of their journey. *Gully erosion* occurs where a small rivulet forms during storms. Turbulence in the flow creates local forces capable of dislodging soil particles from the bed and banks of the channel. As the gully deepens, the profile (Fig. 12-1) is steepest at the head. Since erosion is most rapid in this region of maximum slope, the gully grows headward.

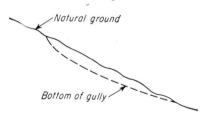

FIG. 12-1. Profile of a typical gully.

Sheet erosion is the removal of a relatively uniform layer of soil from the ground surface. No definable channels are formed, and sheet erosion is difficult to observe except as the ground level is below old soil marks on fence posts, tree roots are exposed, or small pillars of soil capped by stones remain.[1] Since overland flow is predominantly laminar, the moving water cannot detach soil particles firmly attached to the soil mass. However, sheet flow may pick up loose or dusty material from the ground and thus aid in erosion. On very steep slopes, *creep*, or the gravity flow of moist soil, may be a factor in sheet erosion.

Ellison[2] has shown that the energy of falling raindrops may be a significant factor in erosion. Raindrops vary in diameter d from about 0.02 to 0.25 in. (Sec. 3-2), and terminal velocities v vary with the diameter from about 12 to 25 fps. Since kinetic energy is proportional to d^3v^2, the erosive power of the drops varies widely with size, high-intensity rains with large drops being several thousand times more erosive than light drizzle. Assuming a 4-in. rain with mean drop diameter of 0.1 in. and terminal velocity of 23 fps, the kinetic energy delivered to the soil is sufficient to raise the top 4 in. of soil to a height of 6 ft.

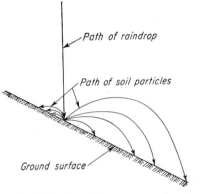

In the absence of wind and on level ground, splash carries particles uniformly in all directions. On sloping ground the net movement of soil by splash is downhill because of the

FIG. 12-2. Downhill transport of soil particles by splash.

longer trajectory in that direction (Fig. 12-2). As the particles fall to the ground they enter the sheet of overland flow and receive a further impetus downhill before they settle to the soil surface.

Because of the importance of raindrop impact in erosion, a vegetal cover is one of the best protections against erosion. Generally, vegetation absorbs much of the energy of the drops. Chapman[3] has shown, however, that drops falling from the branches of a pine tree may impart more energy to the soil than light natural rain. Terracing, contour plowing, and other practices which reduce surface runoff and land slope are also important erosion-control measures since the overland flow is important in moving the loosened soil material to channels. Plot measurements suggest[4] that erosion E is related to physical features of the

[1] C. H. Gleason, Indicators of Erosion on Watershed Lands in California, *Trans. Am. Geophys. Union*, Vol. 34, pp. 419–426, June, 1953.

[2] W. D. Ellison, Studies of Raindrop Erosion, *Agr. Eng.*, Vol. 25, pp. 131–136, 181–182, 1944.

[3] G. Chapman, Size of Raindrops and Their Striking Force at the Soil Surface in a Red-pine Plantation, *Trans. Am. Geophys. Union*, Vol. 29, pp. 664–670, October, 1948.

[4] G. W. Musgrave, The Quantitative Evaluation of Factors in Water Erosion—A First Approximation, *J. Soil and Water Conservation*, Vol. 2, pp. 133–138, July, 1947.

land by

$$E = ks^{1.35}L^{0.35}P^{1.75} \qquad (12\text{-}1)$$

where s is land slope in per cent; L, length of slope in feet; and P, maximum annual 30-min. rainfall in inches.

Equation (12-1) represents the results of small test plots; additional information would be required for estimates of the sediment yield of natural watersheds. As has already been intimated, the type of vegetal cover and land use in the basin are factors. It has also been shown that the relative density of incised channels in the basin is significant.[1] Unless channels which are competent to transport sediment exist, there can be no large movement of sediment out of the basin. Broad shallow swales may carry water but they will transport little sediment. The physical characteristics of the soil are also significant in determining the rate of splash erosion. Tightly cemented soils resist erosion more readily than loose soils. Much research is aimed at relating measurable soil characteristics with relative erosibility. Splash erosion increases with the percentage of sand in the soil and decreases with increasing percentages of water-stable aggregates.[2] A better measure of the rainfall characteristics is also required. Attempts have been made to develop an index to the erosive power of rains by exposing pans of standard sand and noting the soil loss after each rain. Such an index of erosive power obtained on a regular basis and combined with data on the relative erosibility of soils should greatly improve estimates of sediment production.[3]

12-2. Suspended-sediment transport. Sediment moves in streams as *suspended sediment* in the flowing water and as *bed load* along the channel bottom. The two processes are not wholly independent, for material which travels as bed load at one section may subsequently become suspended load, and vice versa. A third process, *saltation*, is sometimes defined as the movement of particles by bouncing along the bed. It is thus a transitional case between bed and suspended load.

Material suspended in still water tends to settle at a rate approximately in accordance with Stokes' law.[4] In turbulent flow this gravitational

[1] Personal communication from W. C. Ackermann, Director of the Illinois State Water Survey.

[2] R. Woodburn and J. Kozachyn, A Study of the Relative Erodibility of a Group of Mississippi Gully Soils, *Trans. Am. Geophys. Union*, Vol. 37, pp. 749–753, December, 1956.

[3] G. W. Eley and C. H. Lloyd, Graphic Solution of Probable Soil Loss Formula, *U.S. Soil Conservation Service Misc. Publ.* 204, January, 1952.

[4] Stokes' law states that the settling velocity v_s is

$$v_s = \frac{2(\rho_g - \rho)gr^2}{9\mu}$$

where ρ_g and ρ are densities of the particle and liquid, respectively, r is the radius of settling is counteracted by upward movement in eddies. Because the gravitational settling results in an increasing sediment concentration with depth, upward-moving eddies carry more sediment than downward-moving eddies. The system is said to be in equilibrium if the gravity movement and turbulent transport are in balance.

In a discussion of the principles of sediment movement Brown[1] states:

The movement of sediment in alluvial streams is so complex a problem that it may never be completely subject to rational solution. It represents, in fact, the most extreme degree of unsteady, non-uniform flow, since the stream bed as well as the water surface may be continually changing in form. With the present state of knowledge, an approximate understanding of the general transport mechanism can be obtained only by isolating particular details or by so simplifying the boundary conditions that only the most significant variables need be considered.

In the light of this comment, discussion of the theory of sediment movement is held to a minimum. Analysis of suspended-sediment transport usually begins with the basic equation[2]

$$c_s v_s = -\epsilon \frac{dc_s}{dy} \tag{12-2}$$

where c_s is the average concentration of sediment with settling velocity v_s at depth y and ϵ is a mixing coefficient which is assumed to be the same for sediment and momentum. Assuming[3] that ϵ is constant with depth and equal to its mean value $D \sqrt{gDs}/15$, where D is depth and $s =$ slope, integration of Eq. (12-2) leads to

$$\frac{c_s}{c_{sa}} = e^{-15\chi(y-a)/D} \tag{12-3}$$

where c_{sa} is the concentration of sediment at depth a and $\chi = v_s/\sqrt{gDs}$ for wide streams. Total suspended load M_i per unit time per unit width is equal to $\int_0^D vc_s \, dy$. Combining the Prandtl-von Kármán equation for

---

the particle, and μ is the absolute viscosity of the liquid. The equation assumes (1) that the particles are large compared with the molecules of the liquid but that viscosity is the only source of resistance to their fall; (2) that the particles are rigid, smooth, and spherical; and (3) that their fall is not impeded by adjacent particles. Stokes' law is generally considered applicable to particles from 0.0002 to 0.2 mm in diameter.

[1] See Bibliography ("Engineering Hydraulics").

[2] M. P. O'Brien, Review of the Theory of Turbulent Flow and Its Relation to Sediment Transportation, *Trans. Am. Geophys. Union*, Vol. 34, pp. 487–491, 1933.

[3] E. W. Lane and A. A. Kalinske, Engineering Calculations of Suspended Sediment, *Trans. Am. Geophys. Union*, Vol. 22, pp. 603–607, 1941.

velocity distribution with Eq. (12-3) gives

$$M_i = qc_{sa}\xi e^{15\chi a/D} \tag{12-4}$$

where ξ is the ratio of the average concentration to that at the bottom and is a function of χ and relative roughness $n/D^{1/6}$ (Fig. 12-3). Equation (12-4) applies only to particles having a common fall velocity, and its use requires integration through the range of particle sizes in the suspension.

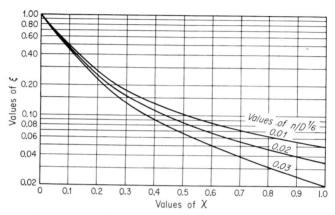

FIG. 12-3. The relation between ξ and χ in Eq. (12-4) for various values of relative roughness. (After Lane and Kalinske.)

Nonequilibrium transport of sediment is far more common in nature than are equilibrium conditions, since velocity and depth of flow usually vary along any channel. In nonequilibrium conditions the sediment load changes with distance along the stream. The general equation is

$$v\frac{\partial c_s}{\partial x} = v_s\frac{\partial c_s}{\partial y} + \frac{\partial \epsilon_x}{\partial x}\frac{\partial c_s}{\partial x} + \frac{\partial \epsilon_y}{\partial y}\frac{\partial c_s}{\partial y} + \epsilon_x\frac{\partial^2 c_s}{\partial x^2} + \epsilon_y\frac{\partial^2 c_s}{\partial y^2} \tag{12-5}$$

This equation has not been solved without qualifying assumptions which render the solutions of little value in natural streams.

12-3. Bed-load transport. For many years analysis of bed-load transport has been based on the classical equation of du Boys[1]

$$G_i = \Upsilon\frac{\tau_0}{w}(\tau_0 - \tau_c) \tag{12-6}$$

where G_i is the rate of bed-load transport per unit width of stream, Υ is an empirical coefficient depending on the size and shape of the sediment

[1] P. du Boys, Le Rhone et les rivières a lit affouillable, *Ann. ponts et chaussées, Ser.* 5, Vol. 18, pp. 141–145, 1879.

particles, w is the specific weight of water, τ_0 is the shear at the stream bed, and τ_c is the magnitude of shear at which transport begins. Numerous variations on the original du Boys formula have been proposed,[1] all using the concept of a critical tractive force to initiate motion. This approach ignores the modern concepts of turbulence and the boundary layer as they affect entrainment of bed particles. The successful application of Eq. (12-6) lies in the proper selection of the coefficient Υ. Most available values are determinations from studies with small flumes. Table 12-1 summarizes values given by Straub.[2]

TABLE 12-1. Factors in Eq. (12-6) for Bed-load Movement

Particle diameter, mm........	$\frac{1}{8}$	$\frac{1}{4}$	$\frac{1}{2}$	1	2	4
Υ, ft^6/lb^2-sec...............	0.81	0.48	0.29	0.17	0.10	0.06
τ_c, lb/sq ft................	0.016	0.017	0.022	0.032	0.051	0.09

Recent work on the bed-load problem has stressed attempts to apply basic concepts of turbulent flow, including the statistical variation of fluid forces at a point. These more rigorous analyses lead to extremely involved solutions suggestive of the possibility that no simple bed-load equation exists. Kalinske[3] assumed that the rate of sediment movement G_i (in lb/sec/unit width) must equal the product of particle volume $\pi d^3/6$, mean particle velocity $\bar{v}_g$, average number of particles per unit of bed area $4j/\pi d^2$, and specific weight w_g, or

$$G_i = \frac{\pi d^3}{6}\,\bar{v}_g\,\frac{4j}{\pi d^2}\,w_g = \frac{2}{3}\,\bar{v}_g j d w_g \qquad (12\text{-}7)$$

where j is the portion of the bed taking shear. Rearranging and dividing by the time average of fluid velocity $\bar{v}$,

$$\frac{G_i}{j\bar{v}dw_g} = \frac{2}{3}\frac{\bar{v}_g}{\bar{v}} \qquad (12\text{-}8)$$

Assuming that time variations in v follow the normal-error law, it can be shown that $\bar{v}_g/\bar{v}$ is a function of τ_c/τ_0 and the intensity of turbulence $\sigma/\bar{v}$, where σ is the standard deviation of the time variations in v (Fig. 12-4). From boundary theory, $\bar{v} = 11\sqrt{\tau_0/\rho}$; hence

$$\frac{G_i}{w_g j d \sqrt{\tau_0/\rho}} = f\left(\frac{\tau_c}{\tau_0}\right) \qquad (12\text{-}9)$$

[1] See Linsley and Brown (1950) in Bibliography.

[2] L. G. Straub, H. R. Doc. No. 238, 73d Cong., 2d Sess., p. 1135, 1935.

[3] A. A. Kalinske, Movement of Sediment as Bed Load in Rivers, *Trans. Am. Geophys. Union*, Vol. 28, pp. 615–620, August, 1947.

From experimental work by White,[1] $j = 0.35$ and $\sigma/\bar{v} = 0.25$. Figure 12-5 is a comparison of Eq. (12-9) with experimental data. Equation (12-9) gives the rate of transport for particles of diameter d. The total

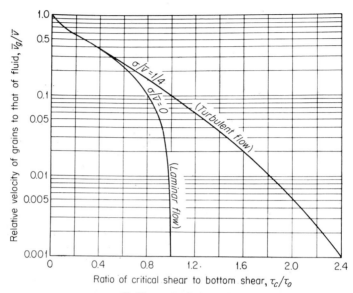

FIG. 12-4. The relation between $(\bar{v}_g/\bar{v})$ and (τ_c/τ_0) for laminar and turbulent flow.   (*After Kalinske.*)

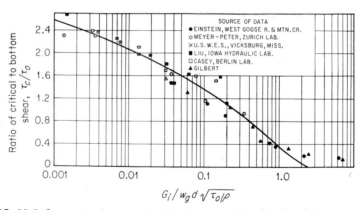

FIG. 12-5. Comparison between bed-load data and Eq. (12-9).   (*After Kalinske.*)

transport must be integrated through the range of grain sizes. A single computation using the median diameter seems to yield a reasonable approximation.

[1] C. M. White, Equilibrium of Grains on the Bed of a Stream, *Proc. Roy. Soc. (London): A,* Vol. 174, pp. 322–334, 1940.

Much more detailed discussions of bed-load movement will be found in some of the references in the bibliography.

12-4. Sediment measurement. Since the total sediment transport in a stream cannot be accurately computed, good field measurement becomes extremely important.   Early suspended-sediment observations were made with open bottles or complex grab samplers which failed to provide adequate data, for a number of reasons.   A good sampler must

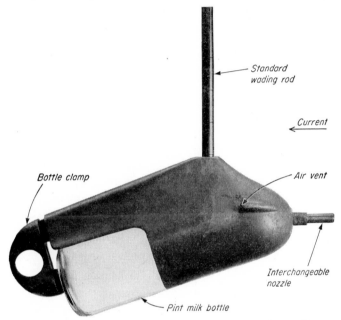

FIG. 12-6. A U.S. DH-48 depth-integrating hand sampler for small streams.

cause minimum disturbance of streamflow, avoid errors from short-period fluctuations in sediment concentration, and give results which can be related to velocity measurements.   These requirements are met in a series of samplers[1] designed at the Iowa Hydraulic Laboratory under the sponsorship of several Federal agencies.   The samplers (Fig. 12-6) consist of a streamlined shield enclosing a standard milk bottle as a sample container.   A vent permits escape of air as water enters the bottle and controls the inlet velocity so that it is approximately equal to the local stream velocity.   Nozzle tips of various sizes are available to control the rate of filling of the bottle.   The large models have the bottle fully enclosed and are fitted with tail vanes to keep the sampler headed into the current when cable-supported.

[1] A Study of Methods Used in Measurement and Analysis of Sediment Loads in Streams, *U.S. Govt. and Iowa Inst. Hydraulic Research Repts.* 3, 6, and 8.

The sampler is lowered through the stream at constant vertical speed until the bottom is reached and is then raised to the surface at constant speed. The result is an integrated sample with the relative quantity collected at any depth in proportion to the velocity (or discharge) at that depth. The duration of the traverse is determined by the time required to nearly fill the sample bottle and can be computed from the filling-rate curves for the particular nozzle when the stream velocity is known. A number of traverses are made at intervals across the section to determine the total suspended-sediment load for the section. Thus there is no problem of whether a point sample is representative of sediment load in the section. Point samplers are used only where it is impossible to use the depth-integrating type because of great depths or high velocity, or for studies of sediment distribution in streams. Because of the shape of the sampler, the nozzle cannot be lowered to the stream bed, and consequently a few inches of the depth near the bed is not sampled. This may represent a large error[1] in shallow streams.

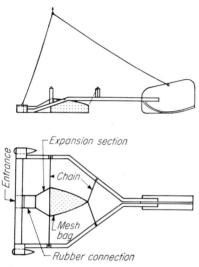

FIG. 12-7. Pressure-difference type of bed-load sampler as developed by the Netherlands government.

The collected samples are usually filtered and the sediment dried. The ratio of dry weight of sediment to total weight of the sample is the sediment concentration, usually expressed in parts per million. Other analyses which may be performed include determination of grain-size distribution, fall velocity, and, occasionally, heavy-mineral or chemical analysis. The latter tests may be useful in tracing the original source of the sediment.

There is as yet no wholly satisfactory bed-load sampler. Portable samplers consist of a container lowered to the stream bed. The most successful is the pressure-difference sampler (Fig. 12-7). The expansion section causes a pressure drop which encourages inflow at the same rate as the prevailing flow while at the same time the reduced exit velocity encourages deposition of sediment in the mesh bag. Fine sediment particles can escape through the mesh, and a calibration in a flume is desirable. The difficulty of designing a sampler which does not disturb

[1] B. R. Colby, Relationship of Unmeasured Discharge to Mean Velocity, *Trans. Am. Geophys. Union*, Vol. 38, pp. 708–717, October, 1957.

the flow and at the same time effectively traps all sizes of bed load should be apparent.

One type of permanent bed-load trap for research purposes on small streams consists of a grated opening in the stream bed into which the bed material falls. The trapped material is later excavated or sluiced out and measured. Turbulence-producing weirs have also been designed which throw the bed load into suspension locally so that it can be sampled with a suspended-sediment sampler. Comparison of the samples thus

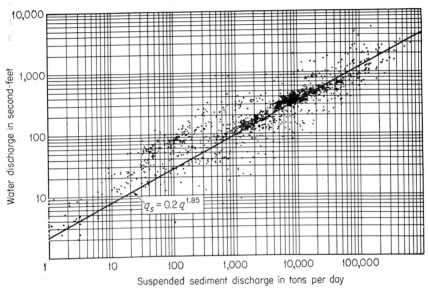

FIG. 12-8. Sediment-rating curve for the Powder River at Arvada, Wyoming. (*Leopold and Maddock.*)

obtained with those from a section upstream of the weir indicates the quantity of bed load. This method is suitable only when the bed material is relatively fine.

12-5. Annual sediment transport. Most sediment-sampling methods give only spot measurements of sediment load and must be interpolated to determine total annual transport. This is commonly done by use of sediment-rating curves (Fig. 12-8) in which sediment is considered as a function of flow. The figure clearly shows that the relation leaves much to be desired. Actually, there is little reason to expect a simple relation between streamflow and sediment load. A given flow rate may result from melting snow, moderate rain, or intense rain. A different sediment load would result in each case. Some portions of the basin may be more prolific sediment sources than others. In this case, areal distribution of runoff is a significant factor.

Currently, no better method of interpolating sediment measurements is available. Rating curves should be used with caution and applied where possible to small, relatively homogeneous basins. If used only for estimating mean annual sediment production, the results should be reasonably satisfactory. A completely satisfactory approach must await accumulation of considerably more factual data. Where sediment is of major concern, daily measurements may be advisable.

12-6. Reservoir sedimentation. The relatively quiescent waters of a reservoir encourage the deposition of sediment transported in the inflowing water. The rate at which the capacity of a reservoir is reduced by sedimentation depends on (1) the quantity of sediment inflow, (2) the percentage of this inflow which is trapped in the reservoir, and (3) the density of the deposited sediment.

TABLE 12-2. Selected Data on Rates of Sediment Production

Location	Drainage area, sq mi	Annual sediment production	
		Acre-ft/sq mi	Tons/sq mi
Bayview Reservoir, Ala...............	72	1.34	1769
San Carlos Reservoir, Ariz.............	12,900	0.26	389
Morena Reservoir, Calif...............	112	2.56	3340
Black Canyon Reservoir, Idaho........	2,540	0.13	172
Pittsfield Reservoir, Ill.................	1.8	3.54	3090
Mission Lake, Kans...................	11.4	2.00	2705
High Point Reservoir, N.C..............	63	0.50	544
Tygart Reservoir, W. Va..............	1,182	0.05	51

For reservoir sedimentation studies, sediment inflow is usually expressed in acre-feet or tons per year. If sediment measurements are available near the reservoir site, the inflow may be estimated by the methods described in Sec. 12-5. Since suspended-sediment measurements are most common and do not include bed load, an arbitrary increase of 10 to 20 per cent is customarily included to allow for bed load. There are relatively few sediment-sampling stations, and for most small projects (and many large ones) sediment yield of a basin is estimated on a basis of drainage area. There are formulas for estimating sediment production (Sec. 12-1), but these are generally applicable to a specific area since the general relationships are not yet thoroughly understood. Table 12-2 presents selected data on rates of sediment production in various parts of the United States. These data are commonly obtained from surveys of the sediment accumulation in existing reservoirs.[1]

[1] L. C. Gottschalk, Measurement of Sedimentation in Small Reservoirs, *Trans. ASCE*, Vol. 117, pp. 59–71, 1952.

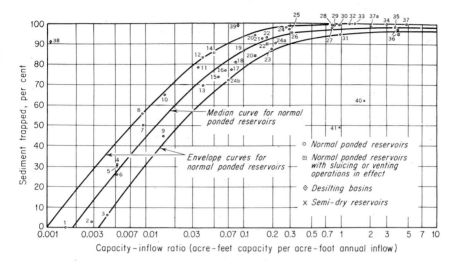

FIG. 12-9. Reservoir trap efficiency as a function of the capacity-inflow ratio. (*Brune.*)

LEGEND

1 Williams Reservoir	23 T. and P. Reservoir
2 Lake Halbert (Rock Reservoir No. 1)	24 Hiwassee Reservoir
3 Lake Halbert (Rock Reservoir No. 3)	24a Imperial Dam Reservoir (1938–1942)
4 Hales Bar Reservoir (1935 and 1936)	24b Imperial Dam Reservoir (1943–1947)
5 Hales Bar Reservoir (1938)	25 Lake of the Ozarks
6 Hales Bar Reservoir (1937)	26 Pardee Reservoir
7 Keokuk Reservoir	27 Possum Kingdom Lake
8 Lake Taneycomo	28 White Rock Reservoir
9 Wilson Lake	29 Buchanan Lake
10 Lake Marinuka	30 Norris Reservoir
11 Lake Decatur	31 Senecaville Reservoir (1939–1943)
12 Bullard's Bar Reservoir	32 H. Lage Pond
13 Lake Halbert (Earth Reservoir No. 1)	33 Denison Reservoir
14 Lake Rockwell	34 Lake Mead
15 Corpus Christi Reservoir (1942–1943)	35 San Carlos Reservoir
16 Corpus Christi Reservoir (1934–1942)	36 Conchas Reservoir
17 Lexington Reservoir	37 Fort Peck Reservoir
18 Lloyd Shoals Reservoir	37a Elephant Butte Reservoir
19 Lake Michie	38 All American Canal Desilting Basin
20 Lake Issaqueena	39 Hadley Creek New Desilting Basin
21 Guernsey Reservoir	40 John Martin Reservoir
22 Arrowrock Reservoir	41 Senecaville Reservoir (1936–1939)

When data from reservoir sediment surveys can be compared with measured sediment inflow it is possible to determine the sediment-trapping efficiency of the reservoir. From such information Brune[1] derived Fig. 12-9 which relates trap efficiency (sediment retained divided by sediment inflow) and the ratio of reservoir capacity to mean annual water inflow. If the reservoir capacity is much less than the annual inflow, water is retained in the reservoir for a relatively short time and some of the suspended sediment may pass the dam without being deposited. On the other hand, if the reservoir capacity is much greater than the annual inflow, water is retained for long periods, and practically all the suspended sediment has a chance to settle to the bottom. Reservoirs operated deliberately to trap debris show a marked deviation from the curve, as do the semidry reservoirs in which water is retained only as needed for flood control.

The specific weight of the accumulated sediment depends on the character of the soil materials of which it is formed and the amount of superimposed load to which it is subjected. Lane and Koelzer[2] found that the ultimate dry specific weight w_m at time t can be found from

$$w_m = [(w_1 + K_1)X_1 + (w_2 + K_2)X_2 + (w_3 + K_3)X_3] \log_{10} t \quad (12\text{-}10)$$

where the subscripts 1, 2, and 3 refer to sand, silt, and clay, respectively; w is specific weight; K is a compaction coefficient; X is the fraction of each soil class in the sediment; and t is time in years. Values of w and K for various reservoir operating conditions are given in Table 12-3.

TABLE 12-3. Constants in Eq. (12-10) for the Specific Weight of Sediment

Reservoir condition	Sand		Silt		Clay	
	w_1	K_1	w_2	K_2	w_3	K_3
Sediment always submerged..................	93	0	65	5.7	30	16.0
Moderate reservoir drawdown...............	93	0	74	2.7	46	10.7
Considerable reservoir drawdown...........	93	0	79	1.0	60	6.0
Reservoir normally empty....................	93	0	82	0.0	78	0.0

Equation (12-10) and Table 12-3 lead to values of specific weight ranging from about 46 to 93 lb/cu ft at the end of 10 yr for reasonably extreme assumptions as to the sediment composition. Data from sediment

[1] G. M. Brune, Trap Efficiency of Reservoirs, *Trans. Am. Geophys. Union*, Vol. 34, pp. 407–418, June, 1953.

[2] E. W. Lane and V. A. Koelzer, Density of Sediments Deposited in Reservoirs, *St. Paul Dist., U.S. Corps of Engineers Rept. 9*, 1943.

surveys[1] show dry specific weights ranging from about 40 to 110 lb/cu ft with an average of about 60 lb/cu ft for new sediments and 80 lb/cu ft for old deposits.

BIBLIOGRAPHY

Brown, C. B.: The Control of Reservoir Silting, *U.S. Dept. Agr. Misc. Publ.* 521, 1943.

Brown, C. B.: Sediment Transportation, Chap. XII, in Hunter Rouse (ed.), "Engineering Hydraulics," Wiley, New York, 1950.

Einstein, H. A.: The Bed-load Function for Sediment Transportation in Open Channel Flows, *U.S. Dept. Agr. Tech. Bull.* 1026, September, 1950.

Linsley, R. K., M. A. Kohler, and J. L. H. Paulhus: "Applied Hydrology," Chap. 13, McGraw-Hill, New York, 1949.

Trask, P. D.: "Applied Sedimentation," Wiley, New York, 1950.

U.S. Bur. Reclamation Manual, Vol. VII, Part 9, Sedimentation, 1948.

DATA SOURCES

Sediment data are collected by numerous agencies, but because of the variety of measurement methods and types of data no organized publication is available. For data, contact U.S. Bureau of Reclamation, U.S. Geological Survey, U.S. Corps of Engineers, U.S. Soil Conservation Service, and state departments of water resources.

PROBLEMS

12-1. Find the equation of a sediment rating passing through the points $q = 10$, $q_s = 4$ and $q = 1000$, $q_s = 8000$ in Fig. 12-8.

12-2. (a) Find the equation applicable to the graph of Fig. 12-8 with sediment load expressed in acre-feet per day. Assume an in-place density of 100 lb/cu ft. (b) The drainage area of the Powder River at Arvada is 6050 sq mi. Write the equation in terms of average depth of erosion in inches. (c) What is the approximate extreme departure (error) of the plotted points from the line in per cent?

12-3. A proposed reservoir has a capacity of 3000 acre-ft and a tributary area of 50 sq mi. If the annual streamflow averages 5 in. of runoff and the sediment production is 0.69 acre-ft per sq mi, what is the probable life of the reservoir before its capacity is reduced to 500 acre-ft? Use the median curve from Fig. 12-9. Repeat the computations using the two envelope curves.

12-4. A reservoir has a capacity of 50,000 acre-ft, and the annual inflow averages 78,000 acre-ft. The estimated sediment production of the area is 950 tons/sq mi, and the drainage area is 1120 sq mi. Sediment samples indicate that the grain-size distribution is sand, 24 per cent; silt, 33 per cent; clay, 43 per cent. (a) When will 80 per cent of the reservoir capacity be filled with sediment? Use line 3 of Table 12-3 and assume minimum w_m of 40 lb/cu ft. (b) Discuss the form of Eq. (12-10) and its limitations.

[1] D. C. Bondurant, Sedimentation Studies at Conchas Reservoir in New Mexico, *Trans. ASCE*, Vol. 116, pp. 1283–1295, 1951.

13

APPLICATION OF HYDROLOGIC TECHNIQUES

The main purpose of engineering hydrology is to derive the factual information on quantities and rates of flow on which the design of engineering projects can be based. The discussions of specific methods in the previous chapters have necessarily treated individual steps in the over-all picture. It is the purpose of this chapter to illustrate how these techniques are combined to solve a complete problem. The usual hydrologic problem utilizes large quantities of data and extensive computations which cannot be reproduced completely. Hence, the examples are schematic in some respects.

It should not be inferred from these examples that there is only one possible method of solution for a particular type of problem. On the contrary, almost every hydrologic problem is unique in some way. The examples which follow illustrate possible solutions adapted to the assumed conditions of the problem. A change in these conditions, especially in the availability of data, would necessitate a change in procedure.

13-1. Storage-reservoir design. The hydrologic problems associated with the design of storage reservoirs include determination of the available flow, estimation of probable demand for water, and selection of reservoir capacity appropriate to the demand and available water. The details of design depend to some extent on the relative size of the reservoir. A very small reservoir might conceivably be overtaxed by a drought of a few weeks' duration. In this case daily data are required for the analysis, and the capacity can be selected for any desired frequency of drought by using the methods of Sec. 11-10. At the other extreme are reservoirs with a capacity several times the annual inflow (e.g., Lake Mead, Nevada-Arizona) where water is carried over in storage for years and the critical drought period is measured in years. In such cases annual data may be sufficient, although for important projects detailed statistical treatment may be employed.[1] Most reservoirs operate on an annual cycle, with each year's inflow generally adequate for the year's water requirements. The critical dry period in such a case will ordinarily cover 1 or 2 yr, and monthly data are needed for a thorough analysis. The example which follows deals with this latter case but is, in principle, applicable to the other cases as well.

The available flow is the actual streamflow at the head of the reservoir corrected for precipitation on the reservoir, evaporation loss, and water reserved for other uses.[2] If there is a record of actual flow at or near the proposed dam site, it is often too short to include a critical period of dry years. If so, a relationship between monthly precipitation and monthly streamflow may be used to estimate the streamflow for years when no record is available. If the gaging station is not at the dam site, the record must be adjusted for the inflow between the station and this point. This adjustment is usually based on a ratio of drainage areas, with allowance for differences in precipitation.

Estimates of monthly evaporation should be prepared by the most appropriate method for the data available (Chap. 5). Precipitation on the reservoir is determined from the best records available for the vicinity of the site. The reservation of water for other purposes is usually fixed by legal considerations or plans for other projects in the basin.

The method for estimating the expected demand for water depends on the projected uses. Water requirements for municipal, industrial, recreational, or power uses are usually determined by combining population projections with per capita requirements and are largely independent of hydrologic considerations. The requirements for irrigation are usually determined by combining estimates of potentially irrigable land area with estimates of probable consumptive use per unit area (Chap. 5).

When the estimates of available water and the various items of water use and water loss are assembled, the reservoir capacity is usually determined by an *operation study*. This is a simulation of the reservoir operation which would have taken place during the critical period if specified operating rules were followed. Such a study is illustrated in Table 13-1. The known or estimated data on which the study is based—precipitation, evaporation, inflow, and demand—are listed in Cols. 2 to 5. A monthly release for downstream use (Col. 8) of 40 acre-ft or the natural inflow, whichever is less, is required. The reservoir is assumed to be empty on Dec. 1, 1931. For this study a reservoir capacity of 9500 acre-ft

[1] H. E. Hurst, Long-term Storage Capacity of Reservoirs, *Trans. ASCE*, Vol. 116, pp. 770–808, 1951.

[2] If the flow record is at the dam site, adjustment should be made for the difference between reservoir evaporation and natural evapotranspiration from the reservoir area.

TABLE 13-1. Operation Study for a Storage Reservoir

Month and year	Precipi- tation, ft	Evapo- ration, ft	Flow, acre-ft	De- mand, acre-ft	Precipi- tation, acre-ft	Evapo- ration, acre-ft	Re- lease, acre-ft	Stor- age change, acre-ft	Stor- age, acre-ft	Area, acres
(1)	(2)	(3)	(4)	(5)	(6)	(7)	(8)	(9)	(10)	(11)
1931										
Dec....	1.062	0.060	3440	100	88	5	40	3383	3383	165
1932										
Jan.....	0.379	0.079	2030	100	72	15	40	1947	5330	215
Feb....	0.390	0.111	4470	130	103	29	40*	4170	9500	315
Mar....	0.042	0.199	96	140	13	62	40	−133	9367	312
Apr....	0.062	0.294	11	250	19	91	11	−322	9045	308
May....	0.018	0.411	11	440	5	125	11	−560	8485	298
June....	0	0.482	0	440	0	140	0	−580	7905	282
July....	0	0.500	0	440	0	138	0	−578	7327	270
Aug....	0	0.450	0	400	0	118	0	−518	6809	256
Sept....	0	0.385	0	370	0	96	0	−466	6343	243
Oct....	0.034	0.252	0	250	8	60	0	−302	6041	235
Nov....	0.066	0.137	0	130	15	32	0	−147	5894	230
Dec....	0.381	0.074	6	100	87	17	6	− 30	5864	229
1933										
Jan.....	0.745	0.083	1090	100	182	20	40	1112	6976	260
Feb....	0.100	0.102	33	130	26	26	33	−130	6846	257
Mar....	0.280	0.210	347	140	73	55	40	185	7031	263
Apr....	0.021	0.274	12	250	5	71	12	−316	6715	253
May....	0.155	0.398	11	440	38	98	11	−500	6215	241
June....	0	0.499	3	440	0	116	3	−556	5659	224
July....	0	0.547	0	440	0	119	0	−559	5100	210
Aug....	0	0.465	0	400	0	95	0	−495	4605	198
Sept....	0	0.384	0	370	0	74	0	−444	4161	186
Oct....	0.158	0.240	0	250	29	44	0	−265	3896	179
Nov....	0	0.140	0	130	0	25	0	−155	3741	175
Dec....	0.577	0.079	3	100	101	14	3	− 13	3728	174
1934										
Jan.....	0.110	0.080	66	100	19	14	40	− 69	3659	173
Feb....	0.455	0.098	332	130	80	17	40	225	3884	178
Mar....	0	0.214	14	140	0	38	14	−178	3706	175
Apr....	0.056	0.266	8	250	10	46	8	−286	3420	168
May....	0.054	0.392	5	440	9	63	6	−495	2925	153
June....	0.046	0.480	0	440	7	70	0	−503	2422	139
July....	0	0.507	0	440	0	68	0	−508	1914	128
Aug....	0	0.450	0	400	0	52	0	−452	1462	103
Sept....	0.079	0.370	0	370	7	34	0	−397	1065	81
Oct....	0.084	0.250	0	250	6	19	0	−263	802	71
Nov....	0.434	0.126	0	130	30	9	0	−109	693	65
Dec....	0.304	0.079	1	100	19	5	1	− 86	607	63
1935										
Jan.....	0.755	0.068	1820	100	75	7	40	1748	2355	137
Feb....	0.108	0.088	18	130	15	12	18	−127	2228	135
Mar....	0.491	0.213	1620	140	76	33	40	1483	3711	175
Apr....	0.486	0.258	3680	250	107	57	40	3440	7151	266

TABLE 13-1. Operation Study for a Storage Reservoir (Continued)

Month and year	Precipitation, ft	Evaporation, ft	Flow, acre-ft	Demand, acre-ft	Precipitation, acre-ft	Evaporation, acre-ft	Release, acre-ft	Storage change, acre-ft	Storage, acre-ft	Area, acres
(1)	(2)	(3)	(4)	(5)	(6)	(7)	(8)	(9)	(10)	(11)
1935										
May....	0	0.390	23	440	0	100	23	−540	6611	250
June....	0	0.494	8	440	0	120	8	−560	6051	235
July....	0	0.515	1	440	0	117	1	−557	5494	221
Aug....	0.025	0.447	0	400	5	96	0	−491	5003	208
Sept....	0.019	0.360	0	370	4	73	0	−439	4564	197
Oct....	0.065	0.244	0	250	13	47	0	−284	4280	190
Nov....	0.037	0.140	0	130	7	26	0	−149	4131	186
Dec....	0.288	0.068	8	100	53	13	8	− 60	4071	184
1936										
Jan.....	0.228	0.074	533	100	43	14	40	422	4493	194
Feb....	0.515	0.080	8970	130	131	20	40 †	5007	9500	315

* Plus 204 acre-ft over spillway.
† Plus 3904 acre-ft over spillway.

is assumed. It is further assumed that as long as there is water in the reservoir the demand will be met in full.

The computations are nothing more than an application of the storage equation. Precipitation and evaporation in acre-feet are computed by multiplying the data of Cols. 2 and 3 by the average reservoir area for the month. This requires an estimate of the area at the end of the month, which can usually be obtained with sufficient accuracy by a trial solution of the flow balance for the month. Area values are obtained from a curve of storage vs. reservoir area (Fig. 13-1). The storage change (Col. 9) is the sum of Cols. 4 and 6 less Cols. 5, 7, and 8. The storage at the end of the month (Col. 10) is the storage at the end of the preceding month plus the storage change during the month.

This study shows that the reservoir could supply the estimated demand and still have a reserve of 607 acre-ft at the lowest point (Dec. 31, 1934). If this reserve were utilized during the 3 yr when the reservoir was constantly below full capacity, the annual yield could be increased by about 202 acre-ft. If the reservoir capacity were increased to 9700 acre-ft an additional 200 acre-ft could have been conserved from the spill during February, 1932. Since the study was based on an annual demand of 3190 acre-ft, it appears that the maximum possible yield during this period (with 9700 acre-ft capacity) is about $3190 + 202 + 67 = 3459$ acre-ft/yr. Practically speaking a figure of 3400 acre-ft/yr is probably more consistent with the accuracy of the data.

The period analyzed in Table 13-1 represents the most severe dry spell in approximately 50 yr.   Hence the reservoir yield in most other years would be larger than could be obtained in the study period.   Occasional deficiencies in water supply for irrigation projects are permissible, and a study such as that illustrated by Table 13-1 should be extended over other

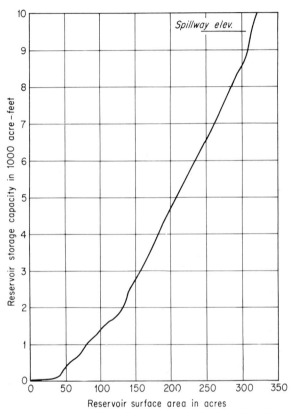

FIG. 13-1. Example of relation between reservoir capacity and water-surface area.

years to establish a reasonable yield value.   For the project under discussion one might estimate such a yield to be about 3400/0.8 = 4250 acre-ft/yr if a 20 per cent deficiency is tolerable in an unusually dry period. Note that the possibility of a drought more severe than any shown in the record always exists.   In the absence of any better data, the most critical period of the record is commonly accepted as the basis of design. Deficiencies resulting from the very infrequent droughts have little influence on the economic analysis of a project.

Operation studies involve considerable arithmetic and may have to be repeated several times.   Card-operated digital computers are finding more frequent use for such purposes. Allowance for loss of storage capacity through sedimentation, progressive growth of demand, and many other variables should be included in the analysis of major projects.

13-2. Spillway design. The flood hydrograph or peak discharge finally adopted as the basis for design is called the *design flood.* Some projects may require several design floods. For example, the spillway

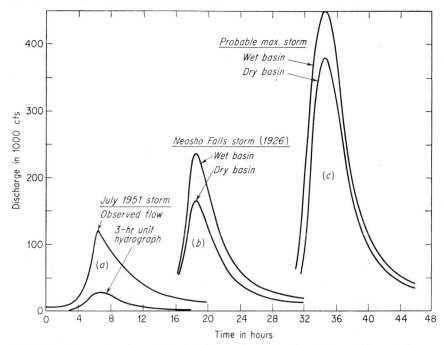

FIG. 13-2. Observed and synthesized hydrographs for the Neosho River at Council Grove, Kansas.

design flood may be a far rarer event than the reservoir design flood (Sec. 13-3). A design flood is based on analysis of the hydrologic potentialities of the basin in the light of economic and other practical considerations.

To illustrate the hydrologic aspects of spillway design, let us assume that a major flood-control reservoir is to be constructed on the Neosho River just upstream of Council Grove, Kansas. For simplicity it is assumed that the discharge record at Council Grove (250 sq mi) is applicable to the dam site. Possible loss of life in case of a dam failure dictates a spillway design flood well beyond that obtainable through frequency analysis (Chap. 11).

The discharge record at Council Grove began in 1939, and the maximum observed discharge prior to July, 1951, was 69,500 cfs (October,

1941). Flood marks indicate that the 1903 flood reached a stage of 37.3 ft, or about 0.2 ft higher than the 1941 flood. A peak of 121,000 cfs occurred at 8:30 A.M., July 11, 1951, and just 24 hr later a second distinct peak of 71,100 cfs occurred.[1] The first of these two floods and the 3-hr unit hydrograph derived therefrom are shown in Fig. 13-2a. The derived unit hydrograph fits the July 12 flood reasonably well, but it is more peaked than one derived from lesser storms of record (Sec. 9-2).

The July, 1951, storm which produced the maximum observed discharge at Council Grove was not nearly as severe as the maximum observed storm in that region. On Sept. 12, 1926, a storm centered at Neosho Falls, 60 mi to the southeast, deposited an average of 11.4 in. of rain over 200 sq mi in 6 hr. The depth-area-duration data for this storm and the one at Council Grove in July, 1951, are given[2] in Table 13-2. The 9-hr, 250-sq mi rain for the 1926 storm is about 11.2 in., and

TABLE 13-2. Depth-Area-Duration Data for Major Storms Centered at Neosho Falls (September, 1926) and Council Grove, Kansas (July, 1951)
(From U.S. Corps of Engineers)

Area, sq mi	Rainfall depth, in.					
	Neosho Falls, Sept., 1926			Council Grove, July, 1951		
	6 hr	12 hr	18 hr	6 hr	12 hr	18 hr
Point	13.6	13.8	14.0	5.8	7.5	8.2
10	13.4	13.7	13.9	5.3	7.0	7.9
100	12.2	12.5	12.7	4.7	6.4	7.4
200	11.4	11.7	11.9	4.6	6.2	7.2
500	9.5	10.0	10.2	4.3	5.8	6.7

the time distribution of the storm was such that 3-hr increments of 1.5, 9.5, and 0.2 in. appear reasonable. From a runoff relation (similar to Fig. 8-8), this rainfall would yield runoff increments of 0.4, 8.5, and 0.2 in. if the basin were initially very wet and 0.2, 6.0, and 0.0 in. if the basin were initially very dry. Application of the unit hydrograph derived from the 1951 storm to these runoff increments results in the synthesized hydrograph shown in Fig. 13-2b.

From a meteorological viewpoint, there is every reason to expect that the 1926 storm is far short of the maximum which can occur over the

---

[1] Kansas-Missouri Floods of July 1951, *U.S. Geol. Survey Water-supply Paper* 1139, p. 180, 1952.

[2] Storm Rainfall in the United States, *U.S. Corps of Engineers* (processed).

problem basin (Sec. 11-12). From Fig. 11-18 the probable maximum 24-hr, 200-sq mi rainfall is about 24.5 in. Interpolation from Table 11-7 gives 250-sq mi values of 19.5, 22.0, and 24.0 in. for durations of 6, 12, and 24 hr, respectively. From the depth-duration curve defined by these three values it is estimated that the probable maximum rainfall for the problem basin is 17.0, 19.5, and 21.0 in. for durations of 3, 6, and 9 hr, respectively. Assuming that successive differences of these three values constitute reasonable 3-hr increments and that the largest is most apt to occur during the second period gives a chronological sequence of 2.5, 17.0, and 1.5 in. Storms approaching this magnitude can occur from June through September.[1] From an applicable runoff relation it is found that such a storm occurring on an initially wet basin in June or July would generate runoff increments of 1.5, 16.0, and 1.2. in. Should it occur in August or September with the basin initially dry, the corresponding runoff increments would be 0.2, 14.0, and 1.1 in. Applying the unit hydrograph provides the two flood hydrographs shown in Fig. 13-2c.

The observed and synthesized hydrographs are indicative of flow potentialities under natural conditions. If the reservoir capacity and plan of operation are such that the water could be stored at time of peak discharge, the hydrograph should be modified by routing (Sec. 10-5). Any anticipated flow through sluiceways should also be subtracted from the spillway flow.

Having determined the hydrologic potentialities of the problem basin, the designer must evaluate the economic and practical aspects of several assumed design values. If the consequences of failure are sufficiently severe, he may be justified in designing for the probable maximum flood (450,000 cfs in this case). If a lesser spillway design flood is adopted, it must be done with the full realization that some risk is being accepted. Just what degree of risk is involved cannot be determined for such extreme events as the Neosho Falls storm. Even the July, 1951, flood is well beyond the limits of reliable frequency analysis. Although quite meaningless, straight-line extrapolation of a regional frequency relation[2] to 1000 yr yields a flow of only 40,000 cfs, a value which has been exceeded on four occasions since the turn of the century. The 1000-yr flood may be well above the indicated 40,000 cfs and could be as great as the 1951 flood, but the 235,000-cfs flow computed from the Neosho Falls storm is an extremely remote event and is perhaps less

[1] Seasonal Variation of the Probable Maximum Precipitation East of the 105th Meridian for Areas from 10 to 1000 Square Miles and Durations of 6, 12, 24, and 48 Hours, *U.S. Weather Bur. Hydrometeorol. Rept.* 33, 1956.

[2] Tate Dalrymple, Flood-Frequency, Kansas-Missouri Floods of July 1951, *U.S. Geol. Survey Water-supply Paper* 1139, pp. 225–229, 1952.

likely to occur than other types of catastrophe facing the populace of the area. If the cost of providing spillway capacity for the largest flood is about the same as for lesser floods, the decision is simplified. In some cases a portion of the flood flow may be assumed to pass over the top of the dam with negligible damage. While called a spillway design flood, the basic criterion is that this flow safely pass the dam by any feasible means, emergency or otherwise.

13-3. Flood-control-reservoir design. The primary purpose of a flood-control reservoir is to reduce downstream flood flows to a level which will not cause damage. For major projects the *project design flood* is usually about equal to the worst flood known to have occurred in the general region of the project. For small projects the design flood may be selected on the basis of frequency analysis. In either case, economic and social factors control the final decision.[1]

After the design flood has been selected and the permissible flow in the reach to be protected has been determined, the safe release is equal to the desired controlled flow less any local inflow between the dam and the protected area. If the local inflow is small, the computation is quite simple. In Fig. 13-3 the Neosho Falls storm, using wet antecedent conditions, is taken as the project design flood (Fig. 13-2b). The minimum safe reservoir capacity is the difference in volume between the design inflow and the permissible outflow (area ABC). If the local inflow is large, the flows must be routed to the protected area, using several possible plans of control until the most satisfactory plan is determined.

The operation illustrated in Fig. 13-3 assumes that a full knowledge of the forthcoming flood is available to the reservoir operator, for only with a precise knowledge of the inflow could the operation shown be performed successfully. In practice, then, an additional storage volume must be allowed as a safety factor. It is possible also that a second flood could occur while the reservoir is filled from the first flood (Sec. 13-2). Hence, additional capacity must be kept in reserve against this contingency. In determining the necessary reserve, the design flood may be assumed to consist of two events in series based on some case of record, or meteorological considerations may be used to determine the probable interval between floods and the magnitude of the second event. In an analysis of three floods at Chattanooga, Tennessee, Rutter[2] concluded that the TVA reservoirs were only about 50 per cent effective.

After a tentative design of the reservoir has been selected, its over-all

---

[1] R. K. Linsley and J. B. Franzini, "Elements of Hydraulic Engineering," pp. 336–338, 442–445, 525–527, McGraw-Hill, New York, 1955.

[2] E. J. Rutter, Flood-control Operations of Tennessee Valley Authority Reservoirs, *Trans. ASCE*, Vol. 116, pp. 671–707, 1951.

effect on the flood regime of the basin must be calculated to establish the economic benefits of the project.   Basically, this requires that the frequency curves of flood stages with and without the reservoir be established.   If the damage resulting from various stages is known, the average annual damage can be calculated by multiplying the damage resulting from a given stage by the probability of the stage occurring in any year (Chap. 11).   The difference in annual damage before and after the

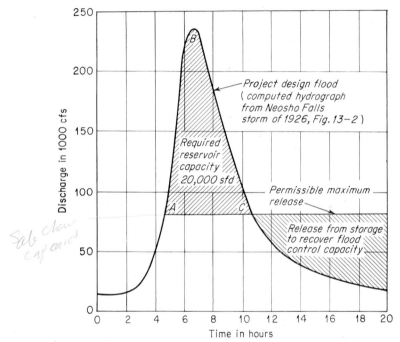

FIG. 13-3. Ideal operating plan for flood control, Neosho River at Council Grove, Kansas.

project represents the flood-control benefits.   Presumably the frequency curve of stages before the project can be determined by conventional frequency analysis of actual records.   The frequency curve which may be expected after project construction is usually determined by routing several of the major floods of record through the reservoir in accordance with the accepted operating plan.   The stages (or flows) thus computed provide the data for plotting a second frequency curve showing the effect of the reservoir (Fig. 13-4).[1]

Flood-control reservoirs are commonly constructed in conjunction with other works such as channel improvement and levees.   The optimum combination of methods (including zoning and flood forecasting) is

[1] Note that Fig. 13-4 is for a hypothetical reservoir and does not represent conditions at Council Grove.

that for which the ratio of benefits to costs is the greatest.[1]   The methods of reservoir design in such combination solutions are no different from those for the isolated reservoir, but numerous trials must be made of the possible combinations to determine the optimum plan.

13-4. Storm-drain design.   No completely satisfactory method of storm-drain design has been demonstrated as yet.   Actual observations of storm flows within a city provide the best basis for design of additional

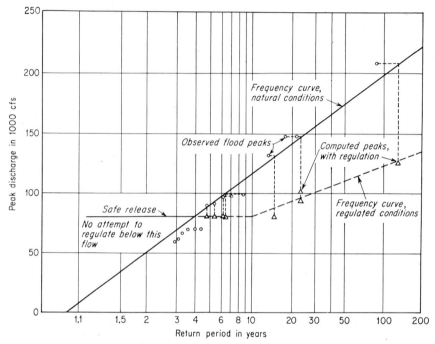

FIG. 13-4. Effect of a flood-control reservoir on flood frequency.

elements of the storm-drain system or for new systems in nearby locations. Unfortunately, such data are generally available only for the major cities.   The method which follows is felt to be reasonably sound from a hydrologic viewpoint but has not been clearly demonstrated on observed data.

Because of the lack of runoff data from small watersheds and urban areas, design of a storm-drain system must usually begin with an analysis of rainfall frequency.[2]   Using the nearest rainfall-intensity record, a conventional frequency analysis of maximum rainfalls is made by the

[1] R. K. Linsley and J. B. Franzini, "Elements of Hydraulic Engineering," Chap. 20, McGraw-Hill, New York, 1955.
[2] Rainfall Intensities for Local Drainage Design in the United States, *U.S. Weather Bur. Tech. Paper* 24, 1953.

methods outlined in Chap. 11. The resulting relations are then usually transformed to curves showing the relation between average intensity for various durations and frequencies (Fig. 13-5). Equation (11-14) is helpful in fitting the curves, especially if the intensity record is short. The most readily available data are the hourly rainfall amounts published by the U.S. Weather Bureau. The maximum clock-hour value published

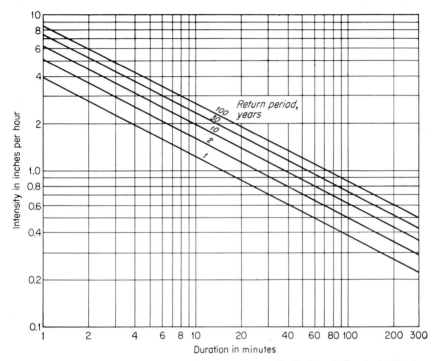

FIG. 13-5. Rainfall-intensity–duration–frequency curves for Redwood Creek, California.

may not be the maximum 60 min during the storm. On an average, the maximum 60 min is about 14 per cent greater than the maximum clock hour. If the area under study is small, the point-rainfall values established as described above are adequate, but for large areas the values should be reduced (Fig. 11-14).

Because of the great influence of surface detention on the runoff from small areas, t_e as defined by Eq. (9-18) seems to be a good definition of the critical duration of rainfall. Combining Eqs. (9-18), (9-19), (9-21), and (9-22), ignoring the intensity term in Eq. (9-22), and expressing the supply rate as Ci, where C is the runoff coefficient (ratio of total runoff to total rainfall) for the area,

$$t_e = \frac{41cL_o^{1/3}}{s_o^{1/3}(Ci)^{2/3}} \tag{13-1}$$

where c is the retardance coefficient (Table 9-2), L_o is the distance of overland flow in feet, s_o is the average ground slope, and i is the rainfall intensity in inches per hour. This equation can be solved by trial for a combination of i and t which conform to the curves of Fig. 13-5 for the design frequency. If Eq. (11-14) is applicable, Eq. (13-1) can be further modified by substituting for i

$$t_R = \left(\frac{41cL_o^{1/3}}{s_o^{1/3}a^{2/3}}\right)^{\frac{1}{1-2b/3}}
\tag{13-2}$$

where $a = CkT_r^x$, the product of the numerator of Eq. (11-14) and the runoff coefficient for the area, and b is the exponent of duration in the denominator of Eq. (11-14).

Using mean values of s_o and L_o for the basin, and appropriate values of c, a, and b, a value of t_R and the corresponding rainfall intensity i can be determined. If equilibrium conditions were attained throughout the entire basin simultaneously and continued until all parts of the basin were contributing to outflow, the peak flow would be given by the rational formula $q_p = CiA$ [Eq. (9-26)]. However, Eq. (13-2) only provides time for each individual portion of the area to attain equilibrium, and an allowance for travel time and storage en route to the outlet must be included. It is convenient to use a lag-and-route procedure in which the various subareas of the basin are lagged to the outlet and then routed through a hypothetical reservoir at the outlet to simulate basin storage. The determination of the proper values of lag time and storage is the uncertain step in the procedure. It seems reasonable to assume that the lag time is the flow time from the subarea to the outlet as computed from the velocity in the channels. Use of the Muskingum method for routing with $K = $ lag and $x = 0$ appears to be a conservative assumption.

The procedure is illustrated by the following example. Figure 13-6 shows a portion of the drainage area of Redwood Creek, including some of the residential area through which it flows. The probable 30-yr flood peaks at Stations 1, 2, and 3 are needed for the design of the channel and channel crossings. Random sampling on a topographic map gives average values of L_o and s_o above Station 1 as 200 ft and 0.1, respectively. For a 30-yr return period, the equation of the rainfall-intensity–duration relation (Fig. 13-5) is $i = 7.33/t^{1/2}$, where t is the duration in minutes. A runoff coefficient $C = 0.4$ and a retardance coefficient $c = 0.05$ are assumed. Hence $a = 0.4 \times 7.33 = 2.93$ and $b = 0.5$. Introducing these values in Eq. (13-2) gives

$$t_R = \left(\frac{41 \times 0.05 \times 200^{1/3}}{0.1^{1/3} \times 2.93^{2/3}}\right)^{3/2} = 44 \text{ min}$$

For convenience, a duration of 45 min is used for which the rainfall intensity is 1.1 in./hr.

Using Manning's formula and cross sections and slopes of the channel, the flow time from the extreme headwaters of the area to Station 1 is computed as 40 min. The base of the lagged rainfall hydrograph will

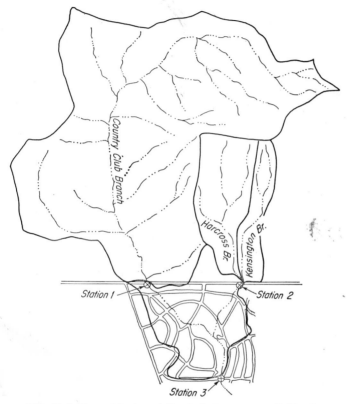

FIG. 13-6. Map of Redwood Creek drainage area, California.

therefore be 45 + 40 = 85 min. It is assumed that the lagged hydrograph will be an isosceles triangle if the travel time is greater than t or a trapezoid if the lag is less than t. Hence, in this case the lagged hydrograph is a trapezoid with a base of 85 min and a top width of 5 min. The total volume of flow (from 1220 acres) is

$$Q = 0.4 \times 1.1 \times {}^{45}\!/_{60} \times 1220 = 402 \text{ acre-in.}$$

It is convenient to use this flow in second-foot-minutes so that the peak flow is in cubic feet per second. Thus

$$Q = 402 \times 0.5 \times \frac{1}{12} \times 1440 = 24{,}150 \text{ sfm}$$

The height of the trapezoid is therefore computed from

$$24,150 = \frac{85 + 5}{2} q_p$$

from which $q_p = 537$ cfs. The lagged rainfall hydrograph is tabulated at 5-min intervals in Col. 2 of Table 13-3. Columns 3, 4, and 5 are the routing computations using $K = 40$ min. The computed hydrograph for Station 1 is given in Col. 6. The hydrograph at Station 2 computed in the same manner is shown in Col. 7. Columns 8 to 12 contain the computations for routing the sum of flows at Stations 1 and 2 to Station 3 by the Muskingum method, using $K = 6$ min, $x = 0$.

TABLE 13-3. Hydrograph Computations for Redwood Creek

Time, min (1)	I (2)	$0.06I_2$ (3)	$0.06I_1$ (4)	$0.88O_1$ (5)	Sta. 1 (6)	Sta. 2 (7)	Sum 1+2 (8)	$0.29I_2$ (9)	$0.29I_1$ (10)	$0.42O_1$ (11)	O (12)	I (13)	$0.26I_2$ (14)	$0.26I_1$ (15)	$0.48O_1$ (16)	O (17)	Total flow (18)
0	0	0	0	0	0	0	0	0	0	0	0	0	0	0	0	0	0
5	67	4	0	0	4	0	4	1	0	0	1	86	22	0	0	22	23
10	134	8	4	4	16	1	17	5	1	0	6	120	31	22	11	64	70
15	201	12	8	14	34	6	40	12	5	3	20	120	31	31	31	93	113
20	268	16	12	30	58	16	74	21	12	8	41	120	31	31	45	107	148
25	335	20	16	51	87	32	119	35	21	17	73	120	31	31	51	113	186
30	402	24	20	77	121	50	171	50	35	31	116	120	31	31	54	116	232
35	470	28	24	106	158	67	225	65	50	49	164	120	31	31	56	118	282
40	537	32	28	139	199	86	285	83	65	69	217	120	31	31	57	119	336
45	537	32	32	175	239	100	339	98	83	91	272	120	31	31	57	119	391
50	470	28	32	210	270	99	369	107	98	114	319	86	22	31	57	110	429
55	402	24	28	238	290	86	376	109	107	134	350	0	0	22	53	75	425
60	335	20	24	255	299	66	365	106	109	147	362	0	0	0	36	36	398
65	268	16	20	263	299	50	349	101	106	152	359	0	0	0	17	17	376
70	201	12	16	263	291	38	329	95	101	151	347	0	0	0	8	8	355
75	134	8	12	256	276	24	300	87	95	146	328	0	0	0	4	4	332
80	67	4	8	243	255	19	274	79	87	137	303	0	0	0	2	2	305
85	0	0	4	224	228	15	243	70	79	127	276	0	0	0	1	1	277
90	0	0	0	201	201	11	212	61	70	116	247	0	0	0	0	0	247

The urban area below Stations 1 and 2 is 240 acres. The flow time through the street drains is computed from street lengths, slopes, and gutter dimensions as 4 min. Travel time in the main channel from Stations 1 and 2 to Station 3 is taken as 6 min. The lag is the sum of the 4-min time in the gutters and one-half the time in the channel, or $4 + 3 = 7$. Thus the trapezoidal inflow graph has a base length of 52 min and a peak of 120 cfs. The routing of this flow is shown in Cols. 13 to 17. The total flow at Station 3 (Col. 18) is the sum of Cols. 12 and 17.

13-5. River forecasting. The previous sections of this chapter treat problems of hydrologic design. Equally important, and in many respects more tangible, is the role of hydrology in the operation of water-control projects. In design, the hydrologist is most often required to estimate the magnitude of extreme events, whereas operation is often dependent on reliable estimates of flow for an ensuing period of hours, days, or possibly longer. The time sequence of flow is an important aspect of the forecast. Each forecast should attempt to extrapolate the hydrograph as far in advance as operational planning requires, and provision must be made for revision during rapidly changing meterological conditions.

In addition to the role of forecasts in planning water-control operations, flood forecasts constitute a direct means for the reduction of flood damage and loss of life. Advance warning of an approaching flood permits evacuation of people, livestock, and equipment with no loss except for the cost of removal. The relatively low ratio of cost to benefit for a flood forecast and warning service makes it an ideal flood-protection measure in many areas where physical means cannot be economically justified. The soundest approach to the flood problem lies in a planned combination of water-control structures, flood-plain zoning, adequate forecasting, and possibly insurance.

The formulation of a river forecast requires reliable information on current hydrologic conditions over the drainage basin, augmented by weather reports and forecasts. The necessary data—precipitation, river stage, water equivalent of snow pack, reservoir storage, temperature, depth of frost, etc.—are assembled by telephone, telegraph, and/or radio from an organized network of stations reporting to the forecast office on a regular or occasional basis in accordance with specific instructions. In this connection increasing use is being made of radar for evaluating areal rainfall.[1] Imminent modifications in present-day radar will greatly increase its utility for this purpose.

The tools of the river forecaster are the same as those used in design: runoff relations, unit hydrographs, routing relations, gage relations, etc. Because of the need to formulate the forecast in a minimum of time, however, far more effort must be expended in the development phase to streamline the procedures. The technique used in a particular case

[1] S. G. Bigler and R. D. Tarble, Applications of Radar Weather Observations to Hydrology, *Final Rept. under Weather Bur. Contract Cwb*-9090, Texas A & M College, College Station, Tex., November, 1957.

H. W. Hiser, L. F. Conover, and H. V. Senn, Investigation of Rainfall Measurements by Radar, *Final Rept. under Weather Bur. Contract Cwb*-9012, University of Miami, Miami, Fla., June, 1957.

G. E. Stout and F. A. Huff, Research Study on Intensity of Surface Precipitation Using Radar Instrumentation, *Final Rept. under Contract DA*-36-039 *sc*-42446, Illinois State Water Survey, Urbana, Ill., July, 1955.

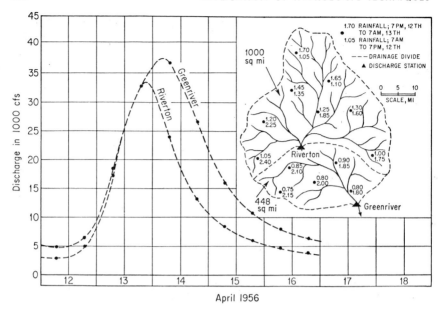

FIG. 13-7. Storm rainfall map and predicted consequent hydrographs.

depends to a large extent on the forecasts needed and the hydrologic characteristics of the basin. A forecast of crest height and time of occurrence will usually suffice as a warning in small, headwater areas. The rapid rate of rise and fall makes the duration above flood stage so short that there is little value in forecasting the entire hydrograph. In the lower reaches of large rivers where rates of rise are slow, it is important to forecast the time when various critical stages will be reached during the rise and fall. Efficient operation of flood-control reservoirs requires forecasts of the complete hydrograph.

TABLE 13-4. Computation of Storm Runoff for Rainfall Data Plotted in Fig. 13-7, Using the Runoff Relation of Fig. 8-8

Tabular entry	Above Riverton		Riverton to Greenriver	
	7 P.M., Apr. 12	7 A.M., Apr. 13	7 P.M., Apr. 12	7 A.M., Apr. 13
Antecedent-precipitation index..	1.05	1.05	0.95	0.95
Week number................	15	15	15	15
Storm duration, hr............	12	24	12	24
Storm rainfall, in.............	1.32	3.00	1.98	2.78
Storm runoff, in..............	0.55	1.60	0.85	1.40
Previous runoff, in...........	0	0.55	0	0.85
Runoff increment, in..........	0.55	1.05	0.85	0.55

To illustrate the manner in which forecasts of a hydrograph are formulated for a series of points over a river basin, let us assume that the area mapped in Fig. 13-7 represents the upper reaches of one of several tributary areas. The forecasts are to be prepared as of 7:00 A.M.,

TABLE 13-5. Runoff Distribution and Routing Computations

River station or area	Tabular entry		Discharge in 1000 cfs									
			Apr. 12		Apr. 13		Apr. 14		Apr. 15		Apr. 16	
			7 A.M.	7 P.M.	7 A.M.	7 P.M.	7 A.M.	7 P.M.	7 A.M.	7 P.M.	7 A.M.	7 P.M.
Riverton	12-hr unit hydrograph.		...	0	4.8	20.5	16.0	7.5	3.5	1.6	0.5	0
	12-hr storm runoff (1.05 in.).........		...	0	5.0	21.5	16.8	7.9	3.7	1.7	0.5	0
	12-hr groundwater runoff...........		...	...	....	0	0.2	0.4	0.6	0.8	1.0	1.2
	Previous forecast (7 P.M., Apr. 12)....		2.8	5.0	12.3	11.3	7.1	5.0	4.2	3.6	3.2	2.6
	Total..........		2.8	5.0	17.3	32.8	24.1	13.3	8.5	6.1	4.7	3.8
Local to Greenriver	12-hr unit hydrograph.		...	0	2.0	9.8	6.8	3.6	1.3	0.3	0	0
	12-hr storm runoff (0.55 in.)...............		...	0	1.1	5.4	3.7	2.0	0.7	0.2	0	0
	12-hr groundwater runoff...........		...	...	....	0	0.1	0.2	0.3	0.4	0.5	0.4
	Previous forecast (7 P.M., Apr. 12)....		1.5	3.0	9.0	7.0	4.5	2.8	2.0	1.7	1.5	1.3
	Total..........		1.5	3.0	10.1	12.4	8.3	5.0	3.0	2.3	2.0	1.7
Greenriver	Riverton	$0.285I_2$	...	1.4	4.9	9.3	6.9	3.8	2.4	1.7	1.3	1.1
	routing	$0.572I_1$	...	1.6	2.9	9.9	18.8	13.8	7.6	4.9	3.5	2.7
	$K = 10$ hr	$0.143O_1$	...	0.5	0.5	1.2	2.9	4.1	3.1	1.9	1.2	0.9
	$x = 0.2$	O_2	3.3	3.5	8.3	20.4	28.6	21.7	13.1	8.5	6.0	4.7
	Local runoff.........		1.5	3.0	10.1	12.4	8.3	5.0	3.0	2.3	2.0	1.7
	Total............		4.8	6.5	18.4	32.8	36.9	25.7	16.1	10.8	8.0	6.4

April 13, following a 24-hr storm with precipitation as shown. Although it is assumed that a forecast had been made at 7:00 P.M. on April 12, the runoff computations for both 12-hr periods are shown in Table 13-4. In this illustration, average runoff over each of the areas has been computed by entering Fig. 8-8 with areal average precipitation, but it is more common to compute the runoff at each rainfall station and average these values over the area. Unit-hydrograph and routing computations are shown in Table 13-5, and the predicted hydrographs are plotted in Fig.

13-7. The computations have been based on the assumption that the groundwater flow peaks at the cessation of storm runoff. The magnitude of the groundwater peak is estimated subjectively. Adding the groundwater flow and direct runoff to the previous forecast provides the required forecast for Riverton.

Local inflow from the area between Riverton and Greenriver is computed in a similar fashion. The Greenriver forecast hydrograph is obtained by routing the Riverton hydrograph (Muskingum method, $K = 10$ hr, $x = 0.2$) and adding the expected flow from the local area. In practice, stages to 7:00 A.M. of April 13 would be available, and the forecast hydrograph would be smoothed into the observed data. For flood-warning purposes the computed flows would be converted to stages by application of stage-discharge relations.

Although simplified, the example shows how forecasts may be prepared from rainfall reports for numerous points over a river basin. The forecasts are made in sequence proceeding downstream, point by point, routing upstream flows and adding predicted local inflow. While this compounding of forecasts might seem insecure, the dampening effect of storage, error compensation, and the curvature of the stage-discharge relation all combine to produce downstream stage forecasts that are generally more accurate than the headwater forecasts from which they are derived.

BIBLIOGRAPHY

Davis, C. V. (ed.): "Handbook of Applied Hydraulics," 2d ed., Sec. 7, McGraw-Hill, New York, 1952.

Hathaway, G. A.: Design of Drainage Facilities, *Trans. ASCE*, Vol. 110, pp. 697–848, 1945.

Jens, Stifel W.: Drainage of Airport Surfaces—Some Basic Design Considerations, *Trans. ASCE*, Vol. 113, pp. 785–836, 1948.

King, R. E.: Stage Predictions for Flood Control Operations, *Trans. ASCE*, Vol. 117, pp. 690–704, 1952.

Linsley, R. K., and J. B. Franzini: "Elements of Hydraulic Engineering," Chaps. 14 to 21, McGraw-Hill, New York, 1955.

Linsley, R. K., M. A. Kohler, and J. L. H. Paulhus: "Applied Hydrology," Chaps. 21 and 22, McGraw-Hill, New York, 1949.

Riesbol, H. S.: Snow Hydrology for Multiple-purpose Reservoirs, *Trans. ASCE*, Vol. 119, pp. 595–627, 1954.

Turner, Robert E.: Operation of the Conowingo Hydroelectric Plant, *Trans. ASCE*, Vol. 114, pp. 79–110, 1949.

Williams, G. R.: Hydrology, Chap. IV, in Hunter Rouse (ed.) "Engineering Hydraulics," Wiley, New York, 1950.

PROBLEMS

Instead of text problems, it is suggested that the instructor assign a typical design problem requiring the student to refer to the original data sources to obtain his data and carry through an analysis following one of the cases described in this chapter.

APPENDIX A

GRAPHICAL CORRELATION

Hydrology is largely an empirical science, and a preponderance of the problems confronting the hydrologist involves correlation analysis or the application of a relation derived through such analysis. While the student may be acquainted with the least-squares technique[1] of curve fitting, it is believed unlikely that he has received instruction in the graphical methods now so widely used in hydrology. For this reason the following brief discussion of graphical correlation has been incorporated into the text.

A-1. Two-variable correlation. If a linear relation is to be used, the line of best fit must pass through the point defined by the means ($\bar{X}$ and $\bar{Y}$) of the observed values of the two variables X and Y. This is true not only for graphical correlation but also for the least-squares line. With one point ($\bar{X}, \bar{Y}$) on the line determined, the proper slope can be estimated by first plotting the data (Fig. A-1) and then determining average coordinates for groups of points. The selected groups should comprise all points falling within specified values of the independent variable (X) irrespective of the value of Y, the factor to be estimated. If the total number of points be divided into two groups of approximately equal size, then the line connecting their means will pass through the mean of all points, and this is the best line that can be readily determined graphically. The relation determined by *group averages* usually has a slightly steeper slope (dy/dx) than that determined by least squares. As the degree of correlation increases, the difference between the two lines diminishes, and for perfect correlation they are coincident. The relation of averages tends to minimize the absolute sum of the deviations, while the least-squares relation minimizes the sum of the squares of the deviations.

The group averages can be estimated graphically by first estimating successive two-point averages (halfway between the plotted points).

[1] M. Ezekiel, "Methods of Correlation Analysis," 2d ed., Wiley, New York, 1941.
G. W. Snedecor, "Statistical Methods," 4th ed., Iowa State College Press, Ames, Iowa, 1946.

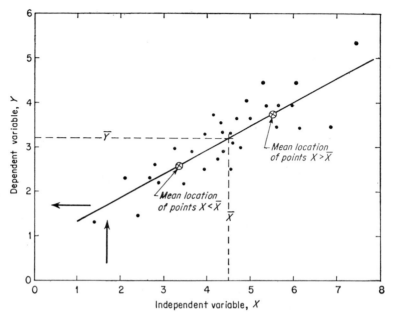

FIG. A-1. Two-variable linear correlation by graphical method.

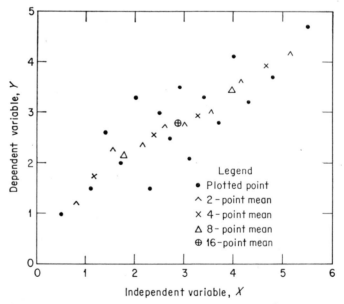

FIG. A-2. Graphical determination of group means of points classified with respect to the independent factor X.

The four-point averages are then halfway between the two-point averages, etc. (Fig. A-2). The points should be grouped with respect to values of the independent variable. Unless the correlation is perfect, a different line will result if points are grouped according to the dependent variable, with the difference increasing as the correlation decreases.

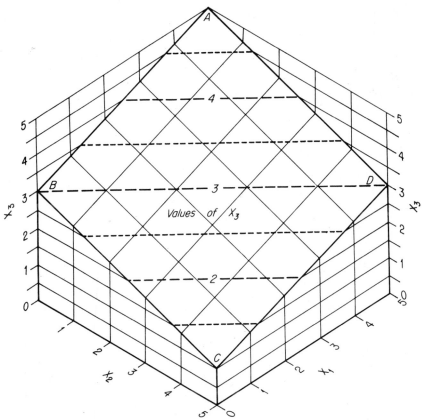

FIG. A-3. Three-dimensional figure for solution of the equation $X_1 = X_2 + 2.5X_3 - 7.5$.

If, upon examination of the group averages (two-point, four-point, etc.), it is decided that the relation is curvilinear in form, then a curve can be fitted to the mean points with the aid of a drafting curve. A curve does not necessarily pass through the mean of all the data.

A-2. Three-variable correlation. Perhaps the most logical method of presenting a three-variable relation is by means of a three-dimensional sketch (Fig. A-3). It will be noted that the *contours* of X_3 (i.e., curves connecting equal values of X_3) are parallel straight lines and are equally spaced for equal increments of X_3. This is true of any plane surface.

Given the values of any two of the variables, the third can be estimated from the chart of Fig. A-3. A close examination of the figure will disclose the fact that, once the three families of lines have been constructed on the surface $ABCD$ represented by the equation, all remaining portions of the sketch become superfluous. In practice, the surface $ABCD$ is projected onto one of the coordinate planes and shown by a family of curves on cross-section paper.

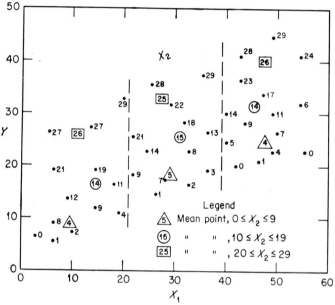

FIG. A-4. Graphical determination of group means of points classified with respect to two independent variables (X_1 and X_2).

A chart similar to $ABCD$ of Fig. A-3 can be developed from a series of simultaneous observations of three related variables. By plotting values of Y vs. X_1 and labeling the points with corresponding values of X_2, contours of X_2 can be fitted in much the same manner as elevation contours are drawn in the preparation of a topographic map. In correlation analysis, however, we are attempting to derive a logical relationship between three variables from observations subject to random error. Moreover, the true relationship frequently involves additional variables. For these reasons, no attempt is made to exactly fit each observation. If the degree of correlation displayed by the plotted data is not particularly high, averages of points grouped with respect to the independent variables (X_1 and X_2) should be determined before any attempt is made to construct X_2 contours (Fig. A-4). The location of the mean points is determined graphically, and the label is the average of the X_2 values for the group.

Sharp discontinuities, in either spacing or curvature of the lines, should not be embodied in a family of curves based on limited data unless they can be logically explained. The complexity of the derived curve family should be held to a minimum consistent with available data and a priori

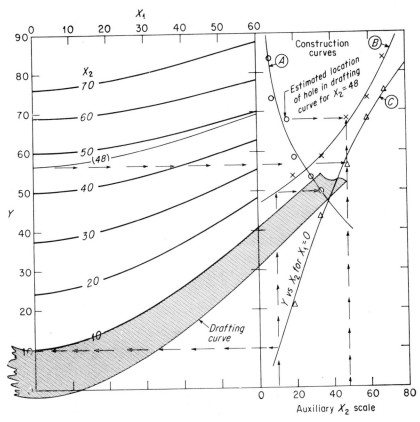

FIG. A-5. Construction of smooth curve family.

knowledge of the relationship. With the general character of the curve family decided upon, the method[1] of construction (Fig. A-5) is as follows:

1. Estimate the optimum position of the drafting curve for various X_2 curves, noting in each case the location of the hole in the drafting curve (or any other identifiable point) and the value of Y for some fixed value of X_1.

2. Fit a smooth curve (A) through the points defined by the locations of the hole in the drafting curve.

3. Replot the points used to define curve A by shifting them hori-

---

[1] M. A. Kohler, "The Use of Crest Stage Relations in Forecasting the Rise and Fall of the Flood Hydrograph," U.S. Weather Bureau, 1944 (mimeo.).

zontally to the proper value of X_2 on the auxiliary scale (for example, $X_2 = 48$ and $Y = 68$) and fit construction curve B. Curves A and B together fix the position of the hole in the drafting curve for any desired X_2 curve.

4. Plot the values of Y (for $X_1 = 0$) derived in step 1 at the corresponding values of X_2 on the auxiliary scale and fit construction curve C. This curve fixes the orientation of the drafting curve for any selected X_2 curve.

5. Construct selected X_2 curves as illustrated for $X_2 = 10$. The hole in the drafting curve is placed on curve A at a value of Y corresponding to $X_2 = 10$ on curve B. The drafting curve is then rotated so as to fit the point $X_1 = 0$ and Y corresponding to $X_2 = 10$ on curve C.

If the curve family were to consist of equally spaced straight parallel lines, construction curve C (also a straight line) would determine the spacing, and the line for $\bar{X}_2$ drawn through the point $\bar{X}_1$, $\bar{Y}$ would determine the slope. If variable spacing and/or convergence were to be incorporated into a family of straight lines, two construction curves analogous to curve C (for two selected values of X_1) would be required.

Any three-variable relation can be expressed by a chart of the type just discussed. For linear functions, the contours are equally spaced, straight, and parallel; for curvilinear functions, they may be curved, unequally spaced, or both. Contours which converge indicate a *joint function*, i.e., a function in which the effect of one independent variable is dependent upon the value of a second (for example, $Y = X_1 X_2$).

A-3. Coaxial correlation of four or more variables. The development of a runoff relation by coaxial correlation is described in Sec. 8-7. The treatment of the method in this section is general in character, but detailed plottings and tabular data are provided. Although minor duplication between the two sections is intentional, they are largely supporting and should be studied jointly. The *coaxial method of graphical correlation*[1] is based on the premise that, if any important factor is omitted from a relation, the scatter of points in a plotting of observed values of the dependent variable vs. values computed from the relation will be at least partially explained by the omitted factor. In other words, if the points on such a plotting are labeled with the corresponding values of the new factor, a family of curves can be drawn to modify the values computed from the original relation. It will be seen that a coaxial relation is in reality a series of three-variable relations arranged with common axes to facilitate plotting and computing (Figs. 8-7 and A-6).

For purposes of illustration, assume that we wish to develop a relation for predicting Y from X_1, X_2, and X_3 and that the available data have been tabulated as shown in Table A-1. The analysis proceeds as follows:

[1] M. A. Kohler, "The Use of Crest Stage Relations in Forecasting the Rise and Fall of the Flood Hydrograph," U.S. Weather Bureau, 1944 (mimeo.).

1. For the entire series of observations, plot Y against X_1 and label each point with the value of X_2, as shown in chart A of Fig. A-6. Fit a family of curves to the plotted data (Sec. A-2). In this example it appeared that straight, parallel lines would adequately fit the data; more complex functions should be used only when clearly indicated or when they can be logically explained.

TABLE A-1. Data for Coaxial-correlation Illustration (Figs. A-6 and 7)

Obser- vation No.	Y	X_1	X_2	X_3	Absolute error		Obser- vation No.	Y	X_1	X_2	X_3	Absolute error	
					First approxi- mation	Second approxi- mation						First approxi- mation	Second approxi- mation
1	88	58	58	61	1	0	27	44	45	24	53	2	1
2	32	21	26	51	3	1	28	78	68	45	62	2	2
3	74	34	53	63	0	0	29	50	27	35	64	4	2
4	73	47	62	30	1	1	30	36	39	24	44	2	0
5	86	40	82	22	1	0	31	54	16	51	41	0	0
6	29	2	28	59	4	0	32	64	66	41	47	4	4
7	35	18	27	58	4	1	33	61	33	47	56	3	3
8	21	26	15	41	1	3	34	62	41	43	56	1	1
9	30	34	10	61	0	2	35	65	11	62	39	4	1
10	68	43	40	77	4	4	36	68	31	50	60	0	0
11	57	48	30	58	2	2	37	55	40	44	36	1	1
12	67	57	60	19	2	2	38	35	28	20	62	3	1
13	87	64	66	44	3	2	39	59	53	42	43	2	3
14	49	8	29	84	0	3	40	73	61	41	54	4	3
15	65	51	31	72	1	1	41	32	10	36	31	1	3
16	70	25	48	76	2	1	42	39	48	5	76	1	0
17	15	13	3	72	5	2	43	74	54	50	49	1	1
18	52	31	44	39	0	1	44	45	19	43	48	5	4
19	80	45	61	53	2	2	45	43	21	46	27	0	0
20	26	16	29	34	2	1	46	49	37	26	67	2	0
21	37	6	30	65	3	1	47	87	52	72	40	2	2
22	11	6	27	19	3	1	48	42	34	34	35	1	2
23	23	7	24	55	7	2	49	47	57	18	54	2	1
24	59	24	49	52	1	1	50	43	12	29	69	1	2
25	57	37	51	29	1	0	Sum	...	...	...	...	101	71
26	77	57	54	48	0	0	Mean	...	...	...	...	2.0	1.4

2. Next plot observed values of Y against those computed from chart A (entering with X_1 and interpolating within the X_2 curves); label each point with the value of X_3, as shown in chart B of Fig. A-6; and again fit a family of curves.

3. Entering with X_1, X_2, and X_3 in sequence (Fig. A-6), compute the value of Y for each observation in the series and tabulate the corresponding error (Table A-1).

If additional variables were to be introduced, step 2 of the process

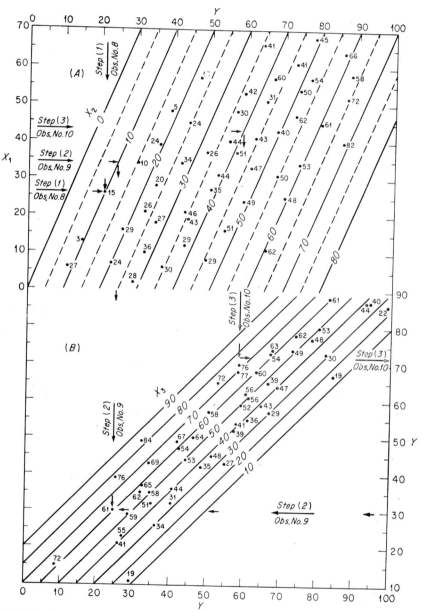

FIG. A-6. Development of first-approximation curves by coaxial method (data from Table A-1).

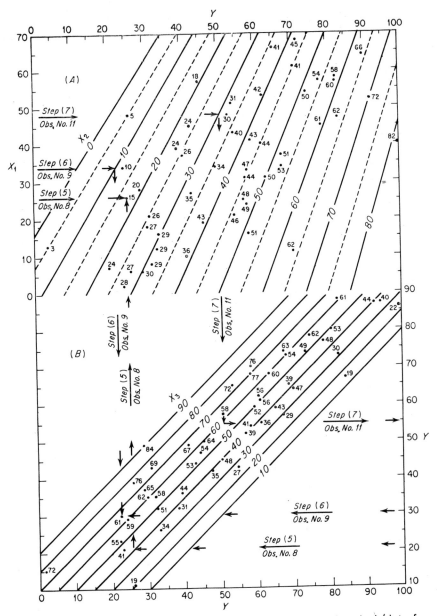

FIG. A-7. Development of second-approximation curves by coaxial method (data from Table A-1).

would be repeated in essence. In each case, Y as computed from the derived chart sequence would be plotted against observed values of Y, and the points would be labeled with values of the variable to be introduced.

Since chart A of Fig. A-6 was derived without consideration of X_3, the subsequent introduction of this factor may necessitate a revision of chart A, particularly if appreciable correlation exists between X_3 and either X_1 or X_2. In other words, the coaxial technique usually requires two or more successive approximations to achieve best results. Although several techniques are available,[1] only one method of developing second and succeeding approximations is discussed here. With this method the analysis continues as follows:

4. Reconstruct the first-approximation X_3 curves (Fig. A-6) on a second sheet of cross-section paper, as in chart B of Fig. A-7.

5. Next, in chart A of Fig. A-7, plot values of X_1 against coordinate values derived by entering chart B with observed Y (on the vertical scale) and X_3, labeling each point with X_2. Fit the second-approximation X_2 curves.

6. In chart B (Fig. A-7), plot observed values of Y against those computed from chart A in exactly the same manner as under step 2 above. Revise the X_3 curves as indicated by the plotted points. In this example it was found that the first-approximation X_3 curves were entirely satisfactory.

7. Repeat step 3 above, using the second-approximation curves of Fig. A-7, and tabulate the corresponding error (Table A-1). If any material change is made in any of the curve families, the average error of the second approximation should be appreciably smaller than that of the first approximation. To avoid possible bias in the final relation that might result from inconsistent curve fitting, the algebraic sum of the errors should be computed. If this sum is not essentially zero, one of the curve families should be shifted as required.

Third and subsequent approximations are derived by simple repetition of steps 4 to 7. If the analysis involved five or more variables, there would be three or more charts in the sequence. In any event, the second-approximation plotting for any chart is accomplished by entering the chart sequence from both ends with corresponding values of all factors (including the dependent variable). The point so determined is labeled with the value of the factor for which the chart is being developed, and a revised curve family is fitted.

This method of multiple graphical correlation usually yields good

[1] R. K. Linsley, M. A. Kohler, and J. L. H. Paulhus, "Applied Hydrology," pp. 652–655, McGraw-Hill, New York, 1949.

M. A. Kohler and R. K. Linsley, Predicting the Runoff from Storm Rainfall, *U.S. Weather Bur. Research Paper* 34, 1951.

results for many problems involving joint functions, such as rainfall-runoff and crest-stage relations, where three or more independent factors are significant. If the approximate shape and spacing of the curve families are known, the first-approximation curves for *all but one* variable can be sketched without plotting the data. The curves representing the remaining variable can then be developed by plotting in the prescribed manner. In general, it is advisable to determine the curves for the most important factor by plotting. The final position of all curve families can then be determined by the process outlined. This approach constitutes the substitution of an "estimated effect" for each variable in preference to the assumed "no effect" for those variables subsequently introduced. The number of approximations required to achieve the final solution is accordingly reduced.

PHYSICAL CONSTANTS, CONVERSION TABLES, AND EQUIVALENTS

Conversion Table for Volume

Unit	Equivalents						
	Cu in.	Gal	Imperial gal	Cu ft	Cu m	Acre-ft	Sfd
Cubic inch...........	1	0.00433	0.00361	5.79×10^{-4}	1.64×10^{-5}	1.33×10^{-8}	6.70×10^{-9}
U.S. gallon..........	231	1	0.833	0.134	0.00379	3.07×10^{-6}	1.55×10^{-6}
Imperial gallon.......	277	1.20	1	0.161	0.00455	3.68×10^{-6}	1.86×10^{-6}
Cubic foot..........	1,728	7.48	6.23	1	0.0283	2.30×10^{-5}	1.16×10^{-5}
Cubic meter..........	61,000	264	220	35.3	1	8.11×10^{-4}	4.09×10^{-4}
Acre-foot...........	7.53×10^{7}	3.26×10^{5}	2.71×10^{5}	43,560	1230	1	0.504
Second-foot-day......	1.49×10^{8}	6.46×10^{5}	5.38×10^{5}	86,400	2450	1.98	1

Conversion Table for Discharge

Unit	Equivalents						
	Gal/day	Cu ft/day	Gpm	Imperial gpm	Acre-ft/day	Cfs	Cu m/sec
U.S. gallon per day...	1	0.134	6.94×10^{-4}	5.78×10^{-4}	3.07×10^{-6}	1.55×10^{-6}	4.38×10^{-8}
Cubic foot per day...	7.48	1	5.19×10^{-3}	4.33×10^{-3}	2.30×10^{-5}	1.16×10^{-5}	3.28×10^{-7}
U.S. gallon per minute	1440	193	1	0.833	4.42×10^{-3}	2.23×10^{-3}	6.31×10^{-5}
Imperial gallon per minute............	1728	231	1.20	1	5.31×10^{-3}	2.67×10^{-3}	7.57×10^{-5}
Acre-foot per day....	3.26×10^{5}	43,560	226	188	1	0.504	0.0143
Cubic foot per second.	6.46×10^{5}	86,400	449	374	1.98	1	0.0283
Cubic meter per second	2.28×10^{7}	3.05×10^{6}	15,800	13,200	70.0	35.3	1

Miscellaneous Conversions and Physical Constants

1 second-foot-day per square mile = 0.03719 inch
1 inch of runoff per square mile = 26.9 second-foot-days
= 53.3 acre-feet
= 2,323,200 cubic feet
1 miner's inch = 0.025 cubic foot per second in Arizona, California, Montana, and Oregon
= 0.020 cubic foot per second in Idaho, Kansas, Nebraska, New Mexico, North and South Dakota, and Utah
= 0.026 cubic foot per second in Colorado
= 0.028 cubic foot per second in British Columbia
1 cubic foot per second = 0.000214 cubic mile per year
= 0.9917 acre-inch per hour
1 pound of water = 0.5507 inch over 8-inch circle
= 0.3524 inch over 10-inch circle
= 0.2448 inch over 12-inch circle
1 horsepower = 0.746 kilowatt
= 550 foot-pounds per second
e = 2.71828
$\log_{10} e$ = 0.43429
$\log_e 10$ = 2.30259

Properties of Water

Temp, °F	Specific gravity	Unit weight, lb/cu ft	Heat of vaporiza-tion, Btu/lb	Viscosity		Vapor pressure	
				Absolute, lb-sec/sq ft	Kinematic, sq ft/sec	Millibars	Psi
32	0.99987	62.416	1073	0.374×10^{-4}	1.93×10^{-5}	6.11	0.09
40	0.99999	62.423	1066	0.323	1.67	8.36	0.12
50	0.99975	62.408	1059	0.273	1.41	12.19	0.18
60	0.99907	62.366	1054	0.235	1.21	17.51	0.26
70	0.99802	62.300	1049	0.205	1.06	24.79	0.36
80	0.99669	62.217	1044	0.180	0.929	34.61	0.51
90	0.99510	62.118	1039	0.160	0.828	47.68	0.70
100	0.99318	61.998	1033	0.143	0.741	64.88	0.95
120	0.98870	61.719	1021	0.117	0.610	.....	1.69
140	0.98338	61.386	1010	0.0979	0.513	.....	2.89
160	0.97729	61.006	999	0.0835	0.440	.....	4.74
180	0.97056	60.586	988	0.0726	0.385	.....	7.51
200	0.96333	60.135	977	0.0637	0.341	.....	11.52
212	0.95865	59.843	970	0.0593	0.319	.....	14.70

Values of n for the Kutter and Manning Formulas [Eq. (4-6)]

Channel Condition	n
Plastic, glass, drawn tubing	0.009
Neat cement, smooth metal	0.010
Planed timber, asbestos pipe	0.011
Wrought iron, welded steel, canvas	0.012
Ordinary concrete, asphalted cast iron	0.013
Unplaned timber, vitrified clay, glazed brick	0.014
Cast-iron pipe, concrete pipe	0.015
Riveted steel, brick, dressed stone	0.016
Rubble masonry	0.017
Smooth earth	0.018
Firm gravel	0.020
Corrugated metal pipe and flumes	0.023
Natural channels	
Clean, straight, full stage, no pools	0.029
As above with weeds and stones	0.035
Winding, pools and shallows, clean	0.039
As above at low stages	0.047
Winding, pools and shallows, weeds and stones	0.042
As above, shallow stages, large stones	0.052
Sluggish, weedy, with deep pools	0.065
Very weedy and sluggish	0.112

NOTE. Values quoted above are averages of many determinations. Variations of as much as 20 per cent must be expected, especially in the natural channels.

Variation of Relative Humidity (Per Cent) with Temperature and Wet-bulb Depression

(Pressure = 30 in.)

Air temp, °F	\multicolumn{13}{c}{Wet-bulb depression, F°}

Air temp, °F	1	2	3	4	6	8	10	12	14	16	18	20	25	30
0	67	33	1											
5	73	46	20											
10	78	56	34	13										
15	82	64	46	29										
20	85	70	55	40	12									
25	87	74	62	49	25	1								
30	89	78	67	56	36	16								
35	91	81	72	63	45	27	10							
40	92	83	75	68	52	37	22	7						
45	93	86	78	71	57	44	31	18	6					
50	93	87	80	74	61	49	38	27	16	5				
55	94	88	82	76	65	54	43	33	23	14	5			
60	94	89	83	78	68	58	48	39	30	21	13	5		
65	95	90	85	80	70	61	52	44	35	27	20	12		
70	95	90	86	81	72	64	55	48	40	33	25	19	3	
75	96	91	86	82	74	66	58	51	44	37	30	24	9	
80	96	91	87	83	75	68	61	54	47	41	35	29	15	3
85	96	92	88	84	76	70	63	56	50	44	38	32	20	8
90	96	92	89	85	78	71	65	58	52	47	41	36	24	13
95	96	93	89	86	79	72	66	60	54	49	44	38	27	17
100	96	93	89	86	80	73	68	62	56	51	46	41	30	21

Variation of Dewpoint with Temperature and Wet-bulb Depression and of Saturation Vapor Pressure with Temperature

(Pressure = 30 in.)

Air temp, °F	Saturation vapor pressure Milli-bars	In. Hg	Wet-bulb depression, F° 1	2	3	4	6	8	10	12	14	16	18	20	25	30
0	1.29	0.038	−7	−20												
5	1.66	0.049	−1	−9	−24											
10	2.13	0.063	5	−2	−10	−27										
15	2.74	0.081	11	6	0	−9										
20	3.49	0.103	16	12	8	2	−21									
25	4.40	0.130	22	19	15	10	−3	−15								
30	5.55	0.164	27	25	21	18	8	−7								
35	6.87	0.203	33	30	28	25	17	7	−11							
40	8.36	0.247	38	35	33	30	25	18	7	−14						
45	10.09	0.298	43	41	38	36	31	25	18	7	−14					
50	12.19	0.360	48	46	44	42	37	32	26	18	8	−13				
55	14.63	0.432	53	51	50	48	43	38	33	27	20	9	−12			
60	17.51	0.517	58	57	55	53	49	45	40	35	29	21	11	−8		
65	20.86	0.616	63	62	60	59	55	51	47	42	37	31	24	14		
70	24.79	0.732	69	67	65	64	61	57	53	49	44	39	33	26	−11	
75	29.32	0.866	74	72	71	69	66	63	59	55	51	47	42	36	15	
80	34.61	1.022	79	77	76	74	72	68	65	62	58	54	50	44	28	−7
85	40.67	1.201	84	82	81	80	77	74	71	68	64	61	57	52	39	19
90	47.68	1.408	89	87	86	85	82	79	76	73	70	67	63	59	48	32
95	55.71	1.645	94	93	91	90	87	85	82	79	76	73	70	66	56	43
100	64.88	1.916	99	98	96	95	93	90	87	85	82	79	76	72	63	52

Variation of Pressure, Temperature, and Boiling Point with Elevation

(U.S. standard atmosphere *)

Elevation, ft msl	Pressure In. Hg	Millibars	Ft of water	Air temp, °F	Boiling point, °F
−1,000	31.02	1050.5	35.12	62.6	213.8
0	29.92	1013.2	33.87	59.0	212.0
1,000	28.86	977.3	32.67	55.4	210.2
2,000	27.82	942.1	31.50	51.8	208.4
3,000	26.81	907.9	30.35	48.4	206.5
4,000	25.84	875.0	29.25	44.8	204.7
5,000	24.89	842.9	28.18	41.2	202.9
6,000	23.98	812.1	27.15	37.6	201.1
7,000	23.09	781.9	26.14	34.0	199.2
8,000	22.22	752.5	25.16	30.6	197.4
9,000	21.38	724.0	24.20	27.0	195.6
10,000	20.58	696.9	23.30	23.4	193.7
11,000	19.79	670.2	22.40	19.8	191.9
12,000	19.03	644.4	21.54	16.2	190.1

* The data of this table are based on average conditions.

Map-scale Conversions

Ratio	In./mile	Miles/in.	Sq mi/sq in.
1:1,000,000	0.0634	15.7828	249.097
1:500,000	0.1267	7.8914	62.274
1:250,000	0.2534	3.9457	15.569
1:126,720	0.5000	2.0000	4.000
1:125,000	0.5069	1.9728	3.892
1:90,000	0.7040	1.4205	2.018
1:63,360	1.0000	1.0000	1.000
1:62,500	1.0138	0.9864	0.9730
1:45,000	1.4080	0.7102	0.5044
1:31,680	2.0000	0.5000	0.2500
1:30,000	2.1120	0.4735	0.2242
1:24,000	2.6400	0.3788	0.1435
1:12,000	5.2800	0.1894	0.0358
1:2,400	26.4000	0.0379	0.001435
1:1,200	52.8000	0.0189	0.000358

Values of the Reduced Variate y Corresponding to Various Values of Return Period and Probability [Eq. (11-2)]

Reduced variate y	Return period T_r	Probability P
0.000	1.58	0.368
0.367	2.00	0.500
0.579	2.33	0.571
1.500	5.00	0.800
2.250	10.0	0.900
2.970	20.0	0.950
3.902	50.0	0.980
4.600	100	0.990
5.296	200	0.995
6.000	403	0.9975

PHYSICAL CONSTANTS, CONVERSION TABLES, AND EQUIVALENTS

Values of k^t for Various Values of k and t [Eq. (8-2)]

t \ k	0.80	0.82	0.84	0.86	0.88	0.90	0.92	0.94	0.96	0.98
1	0.800	0.820	0.840	0.860	0.880	0.900	0.920	0.940	0.960	0.980
2	0.640	0.672	0.706	0.740	0.774	0.810	0.846	0.884	0.922	0.960
3	0.512	0.551	0.593	0.636	0.681	0.729	0.779	0.831	0.885	0.941
4	0.410	0.452	0.498	0.547	0.600	0.656	0.716	0.781	0.849	0.922
5	0.328	0.371	0.418	0.470	0.528	0.590	0.659	0.734	0.815	0.904
6	0.262	0.304	0.351	0.405	0.464	0.531	0.606	0.690	0.783	0.886
7	0.210	0.249	0.295	0.348	0.409	0.478	0.558	0.648	0.751	0.868
8	0.168	0.204	0.248	0.299	0.360	0.430	0.513	0.610	0.721	0.851
9	0.134	0.168	0.208	0.257	0.316	0.387	0.472	0.573	0.693	0.834
10	0.107	0.137	0.175	0.221	0.279	0.349	0.434	0.539	0.665	0.817
11	0.086	0.113	0.147	0.190	0.245	0.314	0.400	0.506	0.638	0.801
12	0.069	0.092	0.123	0.164	0.216	0.282	0.368	0.476	0.613	0.785
13	0.055	0.076	0.104	0.141	0.190	0.254	0.338	0.447	0.588	0.769
14	0.044	0.062	0.087	0.121	0.167	0.229	0.311	0.421	0.565	0.754
15	0.035	0.051	0.073	0.104	0.147	0.206	0.286	0.395	0.542	0.739
16	0.028	0.042	0.061	0.090	0.129	0.185	0.263	0.372	0.520	0.724
17	0.023	0.034	0.052	0.077	0.114	0.167	0.242	0.349	0.500	0.709
18	0.018	0.028	0.043	0.066	0.100	0.150	0.223	0.328	0.480	0.695
19	0.014	0.023	0.036	0.057	0.088	0.135	0.205	0.309	0.460	0.681
20	0.012	0.019	0.031	0.049	0.078	0.122	0.189	0.290	0.442	0.668
21	0.009	0.015	0.026	0.042	0.068	0.109	0.174	0.273	0.424	0.654
22	0.007	0.013	0.022	0.036	0.060	0.098	0.160	0.256	0.407	0.641
23	0.006	0.010	0.018	0.031	0.053	0.089	0.147	0.241	0.391	0.628
24	0.005	0.009	0.015	0.027	0.047	0.080	0.135	0.227	0.375	0.616
25	0.004	0.007	0.013	0.023	0.041	0.072	0.124	0.213	0.360	0.603
26	0.003	0.006	0.011	0.020	0.036	0.065	0.114	0.200	0.346	0.591
27	0.002	0.005	0.009	0.017	0.032	0.058	0.105	0.188	0.332	0.579
28	0.002	0.004	0.008	0.015	0.028	0.052	0.097	0.177	0.319	0.568
29	0.002	0.003	0.006	0.013	0.025	0.047	0.089	0.166	0.306	0.557
30	0.001	0.003	0.005	0.011	0.022	0.042	0.082	0.156	0.294	0.545
40	.....	.....	.....	0.002	0.006	0.015	0.036	0.084	0.195	0.446
50	.....	.....	.....	.....	.....	0.005	0.015	0.045	0.130	0.364
60	.....	.....	.....	.....	.....	.....	0.007	0.024	0.086	0.298

NAME INDEX

SUBJECT INDEX